Please remember that this is a library book,
and that it belongs only temporarily to each
person who uses it. Be considerate. Do
not write in this, or any, library book.

PRACTICAL FAMILY AND
MARRIAGE COUNSELING

By the same author:

Practical Psychotherapeutic Techniques
Practical Psychotherapy in Nonpsychiatric Specialties

PRACTICAL FAMILY AND MARRIAGE COUNSELING

By

CALVERT STEIN, M.D., LL.B.

Consulting Neuropsychiatrist
Westover A.F.B. and Springfield Hospital Medical Center
Visiting Professor of Clinical Psychiatry
Medical College of South Carolina
Visiting Associate Professor of Clinical Psychiatry
Graduate School, Springfield College
Springfield, Massachusetts

CHARLES C THOMAS · PUBLISHER
Springfield · Illinois · U.S.A.

Published and Distributed Throughout the World by
CHARLES C THOMAS • PUBLISHER
Bannerstone House
301-327 East Lawrence Avenue, Springfield, Illinois, U.S.A.
Natchez Plantation House
735 North Atlantic Boulevard, Fort Lauderdale, Florida, U.S.A.

With THOMAS BOOKS *careful attention is given to all details of
manufacturing and design. It is the Publisher's desire to present books
that are satisfactory as to their physical qualities and artistic possibilities
and appropriate for their particular use.* THOMAS BOOKS *will be true
to those laws of quality that assure a good name and good will.*

Printed in the United States of America
P-4

To
my patients and my students,
from whom I continue to learn

PREFACE

For thousands of years the function of aiding families and individuals has been taken over by a large variety of social and political institutions. These have included paternalistic feudal barons, workmen's guilds, churches, pastors, benevolent societies, sisterhoods, brotherhoods, settlement houses, clinics, social workers, charitable organizations, beneficial trusts and service clubs. Some of their activities are directed to orphans, delinquents, unwed mothers, the blind, deaf, deformed and other unfortunates. Others have tackled the great problems of alcoholism, drug addiction, disease and mental breakdown in an effort to prevent trouble before it gets underway.

Unfortunately, overspecialization in child guidance, adolescence, marriage counseling and geriatrics has sometimes produced a tendency to ignore the total situation. As with pediatrics and compulsory education, counseling and therapy often starts and stops at a particular birthday. Too often it is also restricted to the individual himself. Indeed, many therapists and counselors will not talk to any other member of the family. They will not even communicate with teachers, clinics and other agencies that have already made valuable studies and contributions to the patient's particular needs.

Furthermore, there is a long waiting list of deserving applicants in most specialized clinics, as well as in private practice. Consequently self-help and an increased enlistment of volunteer personnel with limited training is one of the current answers in an attempt to meet the insatiable need for counseling.

This book is designed to assist not only the physician and other specialists who are called upon for counseling services but also to orient and enlighten the increasing supply of paramedical, parapsychiatric and parasocial aides. These include parents and other volunteers who are seeking constructive guides towards peaceful coexistence between the older and younger generations.

No attempt is made to cover every problem in family rela-

[vii]

tions since many of the well-known psychological, psychosomatic and other emotional problems of living are presented in other publications. They even appear in the daily press, television and theatre. This book offers practical guides in the management of everyday problems in child guidance, school difficulties, the teenager and marriage. Self-evaluation and family dynamics are stressed along with suggestions for preventing conflict and anxiety.

Psychological branding by prejudiced elders and by collateral associates is shown to have profound demoralizing influences on the development of personality. Anxieties of children and the retention of unprofitable patterns of behavior in teensters and married partners are clarified through direct inquiry and short case studies. Suggestions are made for the practical management of problems in learning, speech, discipline, socialization, sexual conflicts, the unwed mother, drug dependency, delinquency, suicide and other teen-age tensions which are still treated too generally, too medically or too analytically in most available texts.

The last chapters cover unconscious selection of dates and mates; the use of role playing in short-term marriage counseling, problems of impotence, sterility, sex shoppers, homosexual disguises, parents who abdicate and abuse their children, and management of the family budget.

In brief, the book is a timely restatement of sound principles in human relations. It shows how to make the most of the first interviews and reemphasizes well-known practices of eclectic psychotherapy in family guidance and marital counseling. It is also a guide toward happier and more productive living for all specialists who counsel their patients as well as for students and clients.

C.S.

146 Chestnut Street
Springfield, Massachusetts 01103

ACKNOWLEDGMENTS

No BOOK CAN BE THE WORK OF ONLY ONE PERSON. It is therefore my privilege to acknowledge my indebtedness to those students and patients who have allowed me to publish abstracts of their reports (under assumed names); to my staff for generous assistance in preparation of the manuscript: Mrs. Everett (Helen) Daly, Mrs. Russell (Vivian) Hayner, and my wife Lucille; and also to Mrs. Betty Woodward and the staff at Charles C Thomas, Publisher, for their heroic editorial labors.

CONTENTS

PRACTICAL FAMILY AND MARRIAGE COUNSELING

Chapter 1

THE CONTEMPORARY FAMILY

COMPOSITION AND VALUES

THE COMPOSITION OF THE CONTEMPORARY FAMILY spans three generations, and sometimes four. In essence, its collective experience is the history of the twentieth century. Whether the parents and grandparents are active or retired, living in their own homes or in institutions, their influence is usually inescapable. Even when dead they are seldom far away because certain aspects of their personalities have been intimately associated with your client's earliest development. Their standards, preferences and prejudices continue to influence successive generations long after their physical departure.

Death and departure are like births and marriages—vital experiences of family life; but they are also equated with separation and desertion. Death represents a personal rejection to survivors—something that must be accepted, yet is hard to forget. During puberty and adolescence, death and desertion may be the last straw in provoking a suicide, especially when the home is already broken or unstable. In later life, the loss of a loved one, a job, or part of one's body is often followed by a reactive emotional depression and by physical illness which may be disabling and even fatal.

The family tree is important. Whether or not the family counselor's contemporary client has ever had personal contact with his forebears, he should be encouraged to learn something about them and other V.I.P.'s in his life. Appropriate inquiry can be made of surviving relatives and friends; and old letters and family albums may be scanned. When this is not feasible, much may be learned about their culture and conflicts from historic novels, libraries and schoolbooks. There is usually something or someone to be proud of in every family tree, even if one also unearths

[3]

a skeleton or two during the investigation. Incidentally one may find a skeleton in just about every family closet if one looks for it.

Surviving grandparents have their origins in the Victorian, feudalistic, rural, industrial and other cultural influences of the nineteenth century. Their times were punctuated by an industrial, social and political revolution that has not stopped yet. They have witnessed the gradual dissolution of monarchies, bolder geographic explorations and changing maps. They have lived with the evolution of industrial empires from sailing, whaling, railroads and coal to electronics, nuclear energy, new products and swifter forms of communication and transportation.

There are more people who are now past the retirement age. They have seen the passing of trolley cars and the decline of the horse drawn vehicle, the phenomenal growth of the cinema, telephone, radio, airplane, and television. Modern appliances have taken much of the drudgery out of the vast majority of homes. Modern industry permits shorter workweeks, more time for moonlighting jobs, and higher incomes. Smaller and better private homes necessitated an increase of nursing and retirement homes.

The older generations are bewildered witnesses to "necessary" luxuries and a "new" morality. They contemplate with apprehension the bolder rebellions of modern youth. Their lives are seldom dull as they try to gear themselves to the faster pace of the second half of the twentieth century. They have had to become accustomed to a smaller, more intimate and challenging world, to "impossible" miracles of organ transplants, prolonged life and exciting explorations of outer space. They have also suffered from the dearth of effective leadership in human relations, past as well as present.

Along with the younger generations most of the old-timers have made the transition fairly smoothly. They are just about convinced that almost nothing is impossible. However, as usual, the old and younger generations still disagree on the best methods of self-fulfillment and achievement. They had the same problems with their own forebears, and they continue to pay the usual price of rebellion in terms of separation, discomfort and dis-ease.

REBELLION IS AN ANCIENT DISEASE

Conflict of ideas is normal and is as old as man himself; otherwise we would still be living like Stone Age primitives. Older clients are being coerced by younger generations to abandon their former conservative standards. Challenges are constantly being hurled at previously established values and morals such as the dignity of work, pride in financial independence, abhorrence for debt, weakness, idleness, law breaking, atheism, love-ins, irresponsible motherhood, and dependency on outright charity or unearned bonuses.

With increasing apprehension and mounting anxiety many of our senior citizens are obliged to realize that some of their old habits and standards are impractical; but they have discovered no acceptable substitutes with which to indoctrinate either their children or their grandchildren. They still have no satisfactory answers for the dormant yet derogatory protests that continue to echo from their own unfulfilled childhood and restless adolescence.

Counseling issues that were formerly important seem to have faded into minor significance during the last two decades: early bedtime, spinach and vegetables in the diet, enuresis, thumbsucking, and nailbiting, music lessons and dancing school, daydreaming, truancy and low marks, masturbation and sexplorations, going steady in high school and smoking tobacco. These issues have been replaced by much more pressing problems such as the accepted use of drive-ins for making out, a sharp rise in premarital sex, venereal disease, illegitimacy, teen-age drinking, homosexuality and smoking "pot" (marijuana), school dropouts, running away from home, and demonstrations that provoke arrests, injury and death. Many of these problems are actually taken for granted in so many homes that one may as well protest topless waitresses, the burning of draft cards, picketing by policemen, strikes by nurses and doctors, unionizing or resignations and even marriages of priests and nuns as to deny that they are an established fact in 1968.

The Cost of Emancipation

The cost of emancipation from sweatshops, child labor, the

seventy-two-hour workweek, the open shop (without labor representation in management) and other impositions of the past is taking its toll in many areas. These include looser home ties, increasing abdication of parental responsibilities, and weakened emotional, moral and religious influences. There are also enhanced earnings, shorter workweeks, unwise borrowing, costly time payments, profligate spending, mounting debts and increased travel. These changes have facilitated the premature breaking up of many homes and the separations of families. They have also led to earlier sexperimentation, earlier conceptions and marriages, more unwed mothers, more abortions, more suicides, more accidents and more divorces. Since there are more people, there is also more alcoholism, crime, delinquency, venereal disease and drug addiction.* All of this means that there is much more need for effective counseling and guidance than ever before. Large families that still put in long hours of work and adhere to stricter discipline, usually have fewer problems for the guidance counselor.

Young rebels at home, on campus, or on the job eventually grow up physically; but achieving emotional stability and confident maturity is another matter. Eventually, some of them become leaders, but not necessarily because they are qualified for leadership. Aggressive leaders and paternalistic governments, both democratic and socialistic as well as authoritarian, continue to search for the Utopian state. They have repeatedly failed to improve upon ancient ethics and basic human values which they once sought to reject or destroy. Yet each generation must learn for itself that Magna Cartas, Declarations of Independence, and Monroe Doctrines must be restated and defended repeatedly, if they are to survive. Each client, family and community eventually discovers that the real price of freedom is eternal vigilance against self-indulgence and against periodic juvenile attacks of the "gimme's."

Unfortunately, the accumulating challenges often prove overwhelming. They cause even well-meaning parents to abdicate their responsibilities as youth cry for understanding.

---

* World population of 3 billion is expected to double by the 21st century.

The Cry for Understanding

The cry for understanding is an appeal for acceptance and for normal parental affection. When people are confused, challenged, cajoled, harassed and pressured their constant plea is for someone to understand, *someone to care enough to bother with them.* Beatniks, hippies, yippies and whatever the latest designations may be for the "lost generations" are no different in this respect. They are like the homosexuals who call themselves "the third sex" or like the narcotic users who rightly feel that one who has not made a "trip" with LSD has no comprehension of the intoxicated ecstasy of being "turned on."

Their plea is not for isolation and exile. On the contrary they want families and society to condone or at least to understand why they feel the need for artificial pick-me-ups and psychedelic escapism which alcohol and even sex so frequently fail to supply. They would prefer to avoid these stimulants if they were not losing out in other areas. They usually do not recognize their rationalizations for frustration and discontentment from other sources. Unfortunately, neither do most of their parents.

Disturbed Communication

It should be obvious that disturbed communication between parents and their rebellious offspring is at the root of many of the major problems. For instance it is true that abstainers have limited empathy with the addict who has taken a "trip"; but one does not have to be a woman in order to become a competent obstetrician; nor a cow to recognize when milk has soured; nor does everyone have to travel in covered wagons and rough it for a year or two in order to appreciate modern conveniences.

The counselor represents the mediator between the older and younger generation. Yet every generation goes through its own hardships, makes it own mistakes and adjustments, arrives at its own values, and plans its own destiny within the limitations of the society in which it lives. The younger generation of today scoffs at Victorian morals, but girls are resuming older styles, hair ringlets and costume jewelry including rings for pierced ears. Their male dates, not to be outdone, are adopting the beards, moustaches and vests of their grandfathers and even the ruffles and hairdo of the days of Ben Franklin. Some of them are also remembering a few of Ben's other practices, if not all of his virtues. As their colonial aristocratic forebears trafficked in slaves, molasses and rum, so do many of our teenagers traffic in "grass," (marijuana), "speed" (benzedrine), "acid" (LSD) and sex. On the whole they are neither better nor worse than their predecessors.

As for thrift, foresight and long-range planning, we elders have much to explain in terms of the mounting national debt, the shaky dollar, frequent wars, droughts, pollution of water and air, discrimination and quite a few other shortcomings.

In giving advice or censuring his clients, therefore, the counselor may be like the occupant of the glass house who thought twice before throwing stones at his neighbor.

Counselors are not headshrinkers, but they are vulnerable. Counselors too are exposed to changing values; and they themselves may feel threatened by them. This is especially liable to occur when parents openly abdicate their social and moral responsibilities and try to place the entire responsibility in the counselor's lap. In some cases the counselor can afford to carry the load until the family becomes stronger. Most of the time, however, the responsibility for developing insight and changing one's behavior belongs to the entire family. It should therefore be placed there as soon as possible. Disturbed communication between one generation and the next suggests an abdication of parental responsibility. This is a commandment that was written *after* the Decalogue.

THE SIN OF ABDICATION

Abdication of parental responsibility is a major cause of the breakdown of social and moral values in the twentieth century. Abdicating responsibility is not new in history, but it certainly shook the British Empire in 1936 when England's uncrowned King Edward VIII (now known as David Windsor) chose this method to escape what he felt were overwhelming responsibilities. In the United States many people felt similarly let down when President Lyndon Baines Johnson announced that he would not run for reelection in 1968.

It is not only the young teensters who try to avoid the inevitable consequences of their sexperiments and other indulgences. Older parents, including those who started married life without major handicaps are often remiss in their duties to chasten, correct and train their children. Like many of their forebears in previous generations, they are still preoccupied with projects for their own status and self-fulfillment including schooling and extra jobs. They often make time for socials, bridge, sports, night life and travel; and they incline more and more to leave their children with relatives, baby-sitters, the television or other devices of their own making.

Farming families find that work for all members is both therapeutic and prophylactic as well as economical; but when children reach puberty, the modern young parent may suddenly discover that estrangement and disturbed communication have already become firmly established. For instance when parents of different religions allow their children to grow up with no religious training, they usually rationalize their inability to reconcile their personal differences with their own families. They delude themselves into believing that the child will be perfectly free to choose for himself; but it is no accident that the stronger and more devoted parent finds more of his offspring on his side than the undemonstrative or indifferent parent. The child's choice is usually made during his earliest years; and a good mother usually wins out, whatever her religious beliefs may be.

Estrangement and disturbed communication between children and parents who abdicate is usually a repetition of a previous pattern that has been learned from undemonstrative and unbending forebears. It can also be a direct reaction to current situational stresses such as a physical handicap or sudden illness. Other causes include unavoidable exposure to undesirable companions, competitive schoolmates, unbending teachers, and unfriendly neighbors. In any case the net result is similar. Since the early decades of this century, when the specialty of child guidance began to come into popular use, the abdicating parent continues to represent a serious challenge in the daily work of the conscientious counselor.

Common signs of abdication by parents include the following: *playing favorites,* habitually *overindulging* children with *unearned privileges or material rewards;* obstinately *withholding praise* and demonstrative *affection;* failing to remember and attend events that are important to the child such as birthdays, athletics, art or science exhibitions, school plays, and other creative efforts; *belittling* the child's attempts to assist in family projects; withholding credit for routine chores; taking a child to a clinic or sending him to a counselor (usually after many idle threats) but *failing* to inquire or to cooperate or to *secure personal help for themselves.*

Another common sign of parental abdication is the tendency to go to the opposite extreme by being overpossessive, controlling, stifling and demanding. This takes the form of overprotection to the extent of sissifying the boys and tomboying the girls. Such parents may also keep the girls as juvenile dependents by overloading them with domestic chores, restricting their freedom, preventing normal social circulation and retarding the development of self-confidence. In either case, the child learns that praise and acceptance comes only from doing things the way their parents would approve. For them, there is safety only in conformity; and independence is impossible.

CULTURAL FACTORS

Whites are a global minority. They represent only 15 per cent of the world population, and they are no strangers to discrimination. Few people are aware that 85 per cent of the people of the world have skins that are pigmented brown, yellow, black or red. However, in the United States close to 90 per cent of the populace is white; and the 10 or 11 per cent that are "colored" certainly have no monopoly on hardship, poverty or rejection. Infant mortality has always been high among the underprivileged where malnutrition and disease are close neighbors.

Many whites, Puerto Ricans, American Indians, Orientals and other cultural and religious minorities also suffer. They may have a car and even color television, yet substandard living is common in many parts of the United States as well as all over the globe. Their way of life often includes outdoor plumbing, overcrowded living, restricted education, malnutrition, neglected health, chronic indebtedness and unconventional values in terms of morals, credit, initiative, ambition and pride in the inherent dignity of productive work.

Many of them actually refuse to use available toilet facilities. They prefer hallways and basements. They also dump garbage down elevator shafts of new project apartment buildings and behave very much like defective, rebellious or delinquent children. Respect for law, persons and property are often minimal, as was shown in riots and uprisings of the last few years. Causes include prejudice, neglect, inadequate training and pay.

On the whole, socio-cultural barriers are melting; but history is not a popular subject with the vast majority of clients. For instance, it has been estimated that ten million Africans were kidnapped and sold into slavery all over the world and that at least three million of them perished in transit during the few centuries prior to our own Civil War.

About six million Jews were annihilated in Hitler's campaign of extermination; but at least another four million non-Jews fared no better. In this twentieth century alone there are few races and nations that have not suffered: Armenians, Serbians, Poles, Austrians, Czechs, Hungarians, Mexicans, Puerto Ricans, Africans, Indians, Chinese, Japanese, Russians, Finns, Catholics, Quakers, Mormons and scores of other groups with equal needs and rights, yet similarly unequal privileges.

All of these and many more cultural and socioeconomic problems in varying degrees are liable to affect the emotional and psychological status of the contemporary family. They will also influence the nature and effectiveness of counselor's recommendations.

The Time Factor

The time factor is no longer the reliable constant in human relations. Moonlighting fathers and working mothers are no novelty. Twelve- to eighteen-hour workdays still apply in some parts of the world and for many contemporary housewives.

Longer and more frequent holidays and vacations have eroded former values. However, as the demand for two or more cars and other symbols of status and higher living standards has accelerated, so too has tension increased. Emancipated women, and men too, have been released from more and more of the drudgery of housework, kitchen, barnyard and home workshop, yet they continue to search restlessly for self-fulfillment.

For increasing numbers of women, the hairdresser has become more important than Papa's barber. She, or he, is visited much more frequently than the family pediatrician or child guidance clinic. A closet full of last season's styles often leaves the modern girl and woman "without a thing to wear." She now attends more functions, does more shopping and makes fewer clothes. "Store-boughten" has largely replaced "homemade" as a status symbol.

Few women smoked during the first decades of the twentieth century. At that time beer was primarily a man's drink and movies were a weekly treat that offered a chance to dress and get out of the house. Today our women hold more jobs, attend more schools, develop more tensions and consume more tranquilizers.

According to some estimates 90 per cent of the American families which earn less than $5,000 a year have television sets; and there is a set for every two people. This is of course a great boon to illiterates and shut-ins and to a small clientele who support a very limited proportion of educational and documentary productions. On the other hand, it is estimated that too many children in these homes spend an average of fifty-four hours per week watching a weird assortment of dubiously valuable programs. Violence, sex and high pressure advertising are on the increase.*

Unfortunately the "idiot box" habit is contagious. Like addictions to Bingo, bridge clubs, or bowling leagues and other sports, TV can divide or unite families. It competes with other forms

---

* Money, J., *et al.*: Reported in *Lilly Psychiatric Progress*, 2:2, Sept. 1967. New education programs to reach the children of low and middle class families is planned by Carnegie Corp., Ford Foundation and the U.S. Office of Education for an "Electronic Project Headstart."

of wholesome recreation, affects vision, hearing, nutrition and discipline, competes with homework and constructive reading, and invades family privacy. It also generates tensions and anxieties, causes people to eat, drink and smoke more, and frequently interferes with normal communication, relaxation and sleep.

The Personal Factor

When counseling the conflicted parent you may safely leave the spotlight of inquiry on the child while overtly sympathizing with the distraught adult. Meanwhile your attitude, if not your words, has to carry a message such as the following:

> Even when the whole world seems to be letting your client down now, *there had to be someone who cared originally.* Someone kept herself alive in order to give birth to your client. Someone fed, bathed, and dressed him. Someone taught him to talk and walk, sent him to school and paid his bills.

In short, there had to be a V.I.P., someone whose opinion mattered; someone who might not approve of everything now; yet someone whose influence can still be tapped in order to reach the unhappy and maladjusted parent of the troubled youths of today.

Effective counseling calls for search and discovery of the important people in the lives of those whom we are trying to help. As a rule, this discovery can be made during the very first therapeutic interview. Meanwhile, the counselor may well contemplate some lessons from history and sociology.

LESSONS FROM THE PAST AND CURRENT STORM WARNINGS

From his animal forebears primitive man learned the hard lessons of survival, group living, teamwork, peaceful coexistence whenever possible, specialization into fighters, hunters, workers, artisans, counselors, healers, thinkers, and leaders.

From time to time some of the thinkers, dreamers and philosophers have believed that everyone is created equal. They closed their eyes to those individual physical, intellectual and temperamental differences which abound in nature. They really believed the Utopian philosophy, "You can do anything you want to, if you only try hard enough."

Some dreamers still believe that if all the world's resources and material goods were equally distributed today there would be no greedy or aggressive people to alter the balance; no borrowing or debt; no theft or irresponsibility; no need for armed supervision to enforce society's rules for survival; no aggression, pillaging or theft; no natural suspicion and fear of neighbors who have different beliefs, customs, speech or color; and no lack of incentive to work in order to improve one's lot, develop his resources, and contribute his fair share to global stability.

Rejecting the experience of their forebears too many youngsters leave school with the idea that the world is theirs for the taking and already owes them a reward for just hanging around. They boldly demand multiple fringe benefits which used to belong exclusively to the wealthy or privileged conqueror or to those with ambition enough to earn them.

Of late, it would appear that a few radical students in Tokyo, Paris, Dublin, New York and elsewhere have the novel idea that flowers and plants can be picked without bothering to replace them and that it is okay to eat as long as someone provides the food, money, clothes, cars and drugs. After all, if the Prodigal Son could get away with it, why not others?

They have allegedly decided that it is the faculty that should change, admit them with few restrictions, accept their licentious indulgences on campus, eliminate examinations, and graduate all who desire a degree. At this writing, one leading college for women is planning to approve the sale of alcoholic beverages to minors on campus. Some people do not realize that the old taboo of females in male dormitories and vice versa have long since vanished from many a famous campus or that over 75 per cent of college students, women as well as men, in some of this country's leading universities indulge in premarital sex. The coincident rise in alcoholism, venereal disease, dropouts, abortions and unwed mothers is also all but ignored.

So far, few faculties have had the courage to close their doors rather than lower their standards and jeopardize their hard-earned reputations. Like governors who capitulate to demands for higher pay for their employees (nurses, doctors, teachers, garbage collectors and even policemen) rather than call out the National Guard when public health and safety are endangered, the trustees of universities the world over have been capitulating more and more. The swing from abuses of labor to appeasement at almost any cost is causing a progressive breakdown of hard-won standards and values of freedom, fair play and democracy. All these are inevitably reflected in the average home.

Unlike many parents and most grandparents who have not yet become accustomed to such fringe benefits as prolonged coffee breaks, paid sick leave, vacations, health insurance and retirement annuities, our young hopefuls also demand some form of profit sharing, if not *de facto* co-ownership—all this from a workweek that is not necessarily more productive and is close to one half of the seventy-two hours that were standard at the turn of the century scarcely a lifetime and only three generations ago.

Communist countries are much more realistic. People who will not work, do not eat. Unlike draft cards, one thinks twice before destroying his food ration ticket or his work permit.

In many parts of the world, most of these gains have yet to be won. For instance, compulsory education stops at fourteen years or less in most progressive countries; yet in too many areas, formal schooling is all but negligible. Small boys and girls labor for a mere pittance, while restless youths scrimp, save, borrow or steal in order to get away to more liberal countries such as Canada, the United States, Venezuela, West Germany, Japan, Hong Kong, Australia, Switzerland, Holland or Belgium, and so on.

Even that long-established institution, the state hospital, has concluded that "if you cannot fight them, it is best to join them." For instance, on the problem of preventing illegitimate pregnancies in their feebleminded and otherwise handicapped girls, they have "solved" the problem by feeding them birth control pills. Greater socialization between male and female patients in mental hospitals has been found to hasten convalescence. It also enhances the liability to illegitimate pregnancy. According to

Wignall and Meredith the rate of such unscheduled pregnancies has been sharply lowered by use of the pill.[9]

Somewhere in between the extreme demands of today's stressful living and the unjust accompanying hardships is a happy medium which even the leading socialistic and communistic countries are beginning to discover as they gradually return to more capitalistic customs in order to speed up production and feed their growing populations. When they first take over a weaker nation, these countries follow the ancient rule that to the victor belongs the spoils, but eventually they discover that replacement and prosperity do not thrive under servitude and that the welfare of the majority takes precedence over the welfare of the individual.

Like our primitive ancestors we still protect our valuable assets: the pregnant woman and the helpless infant, children, the injured, the skilled craftsmen, the healers and the competent elders. Like our forebears we still need warriors, hunters, builders and leaders to design, govern, teach, heal and counsel.

Unlike our primitive ancestors, however, we seem to have forgotten that overpermissiveness and solicitude for the unfit members of the group was also a luxury that could endanger an entire community. Perhaps it is part of our global social sickness that we ignore the lessons of history and no longer follow the rules which still govern the animal world. Strict regulations and discipline were the inexorable order of the day. The aged, the infirm, the handicapped, and the shirkers were cast aside. Sometimes the cost of freedom of speech was banishment or the dungeon, stake or headsman's axe; but, as a rule, dissidents were free to leave unless their leader could unseat or conquer the reigning chief. Eternal vigilance was the watchword, and survival of the group took precedence over the welfare of the individual.

DISCONTENTED PEOPLE IN A TURBULENT WORLD

Nations and cultures are following an age-old pattern. In the philosophical cycle of life it is said that without hope we die. Biblical history confirms this with the long saga of the Jews at Jerusalem, Masada, Goshen, Sinai, Jericho, Golen Heights, the Jordan River and Suez. Like the victims of conquering Rome, we go from serfdom into extinction, but, like the early Christians the survivors continue with some form of rebellion as a result of necessity, hope and faith.

From rebellion we achieve freedom as a result of "blood, sweat and tears," like the British in World War II and our American Colonies in the 1770s. From freedom we enjoy affluence and power as a result of work and ambition. Here the cycle regresses.

From affluence, comfort and luxury we pass into indifference and selfishness. From luxury and selfish indifference we shift to conflict and dissension; from dissension to division and weakness; from weakness to defeat at the hands of stronger, more aggressive or more determined adversaries, as in the six-day Israeli war with Egypt and its allies; and thence from defeat back into slavery (or status as another Communist satellite).

Those who have power and property must be vigilant. They must also be capable and willing to defend their possessions and their freedom. Otherwise they will become ready prey to those who covet. There are always enough people who have unconventional standards. They have nothing to lose by fighting and stealing what they want.

The rise and fall of the great empires and civilizations of history have followed this pattern, and the impressive growth in the number of new members to the United Nations testifies to a resumption of the cycle. Yet in each family, as in each nation, the counselor may meet various stages in the cycle. He will, therefore, have to deal with similar patterns and comparable challenges.

In increasing numbers minority groups all over the world are refusing to be treated as second-class citizens. New young nations are emerging in an expanding revolution of nationalism and global protest against discrimination, intimidation, domination or neglect. It is a revolt that is being felt even in some of Russia's neighbors; and the 1968 invasion of Czechoslovakia is still fresh in our minds.

In our own country, race riots, overcrowded schools, insufficient and underpaid teachers, inadequate health measures, polluted air, waters and contaminated food, crowded roads, substandard housing and habitual racial and religious discrimination—all afford some of society's failures to remember the experiences of the past, to keep pace with fast-growing populations, and to heed the lessons of today and warnings for the future.

Lessons of today are all around us. Counselors are being bombarded with a barrage of vital statistics that open up new horizons of socioeconomic and psychological considerations. Some of these are staggering, yet they keep changing and expanding so rapidly that it is all but impossible to keep up with them. The following is a small but sobering sampling.*

The population of the United States has more than doubled since the beginning of the twentieth century. During World War I (1914-1918) nearly three fourths of the present population had not yet been born. Close to 60 per cent of today's populations were not alive during the Great Depression of the 1930s.

Approximately 40 per cent of our population are under twenty years of age. They do not share with their elders the tragic memories of Hitler's invasions, Hiroshima's atomic disaster, the revitalization of the defunct League of Nations by the birth of the United Nations in 1945, the beginnings of radio, television, commercial aviation, home refrigerators, air conditioners, computers and scores of other conveniences which so many people now take for granted.

Statisticians for Ford Motor Company have pointed out that one out of three persons in the sixteen to twenty-four age bracket buys a car every year. Twenty per cent of all high school seniors own automobiles. More than three million teensters become eligible to drive each year. Fifty per cent of teen-age girls own hair dryers. They spend three hundred million dollars a year buying half the phonograph records sold in the United States. Teen-age girls account for only 11 per cent of the population, yet they buy 22 per cent of the cosmetics and take home 20 per cent of all women's clothes that are sold. This amounted to three and one-half billion dollars worth, back in 1963. The average teen-ager spent about ten dollars a week in 1963. This was 300 per cent more than his counterpart in 1945. This also amounted to eleven

---

* The population explosion is no myth. Global inhabitants have increased from ½ billion to over 3.5 billion during the past 250 years.[10]

billion annually in 1963 and is expected to reach twenty-one billion a year by 1970.*

For timely data on current changes in population, earnings, costs of living, spending habits and so on, the reader is referred to inexpensive paperbacks, available at any bookstore.[4, 8, 10]

The statistics on rising delinquency, abortions, suicides and so forth are equally astounding. For instance, our crime rate has been increasing four times as fast as the population. The management of delinquency and crime usually requires counselors with special training and wide experience. In general these antisocial problems do not directly involve the vast majority of homes; and, fortunately, the bulk of family and marriage counseling is with people who have less disturbing problems.

Between 1960 and 1966 people spent 1 per cent less for doctors and 2½ per cent less for drugs, but 5 per cent more for hospital care.**

Rainbow Over a Patch of Green

There is a rainbow of hope for the counselor, and it extends over a very large patch of green. Anyone who has travelled has observed the global popularity of movie theatres. It may be no more than the fantail or mess hall of a plodding freighter, or a large sheet hung in a jungle clearing, or a bare wall in a thatched shack in a Central American banana plantation. The films may be old and the projectors unreliable; yet the audience attraction is constant and insatiable. They verify a simple but ancient lesson from the popular tales of mythology, from our children's fairy tales and from Disney cartoon favorites.

There are many people who are concerned about the current tendency for television and movies to ignore decency and to throw censorship to the winds; and it is certainly true that many films do give distorted values of ethics, morals and behavior. It

---

* Courtesy, Paul D. Everett, Jr., Car Merchandising Mgr., Boston District Sales, Ford Motor Company. (Unpublished data, personal communication, 1965.)

** Approximately a fourth of the 31.3 billion health care dollar is spent for doctors, 10% for dentists, 16% for drugs, and nearly 31% for hospitals. Unlike rising hospital costs, health insurance dropped from 7.2 to 6.8% of the health dollar expenditure between 1960 and 1966. (*AMA News Graphichart*, April 15, 1968, p. 1.)

is also true that on-the-spot newscasts are not always impersonal nor free from sensationalism that arouses dangerous tensions in the viewers. *Still there is one sobering consolation in the undisputed fact that the most popular scenario, the world over, is the old-fashioned Western.*

In the Western there is the universal pride and respect for property, law and order. There is a renegade or group of greedy outlaws who try to take things into their own hands. There is a hero or two who stand up against overwhelming odds and finally put the bad man where he belongs. It is an effective and reassuring capsule of an age-old dream of the common man. Romance, sex, religion, charity and other values are all secondary to the main theme: challenge, acquisition and defense of life, honor and *property*; and after that, the safety of women, children, pets, friends, the church, school, library, status, or whatever is considered important at the time.*

Behind every problem that reaches the counselor is a human being with universal need for acceptance and understanding, for correction and guidance, and even for scolding and punishment. Like any boy or girl scout, every counselor has a repeated opportunity to do at least one good turn a day; and, like a good and deserving parent, he can accomplish his objectives with dignity, with firmness, and above all with patience and the milk of human kindness.

REFERENCES AND READINGS

1. ACKERMAN, N. W.: *The Psychodynamics of Family Life.* New York, Basic Books, 1958.
2. ARDREY, R.: *African Genesis.* New York, Dell, 1961.
3. BEECHER, MARGUERITE, and BEECHER, WILLARD: *Parents on the Run.* New York, Julian, 1966.
4. *Information Please Almanac, Atlas and Yearbook.* New York, S. and S., 1968.
5. MORRIS, D.: *The Naked Ape.* New York, McGraw, 1967.
6. STEIN, C.: *Practical Psychotherapy in Non-Psychiatric Specialties.* Springfield, Thomas, 1969.

---

* Preamble to the Declaration of Independence mentions "Life, liberty and the *pursuit of happiness*"; but our Constitution protects "Life, liberty and *property*" (5th Amendment).

7. STEIN, C.: *Practical Psychotherapeutic Techniques.* Springfield, Thomas, 1968.
8. *The U.S. Book of Facts, Statistics and Information,* 87 ed. U.S. Department of Commerce, Washington, D.C., 1967.
9. WIGNALL, C. M., and MEREDITH, C. E.: Illegitimate pregnancies in state institutions. *Arch Gen Psychiat, 18*:580-583, 1968.
10. *The World Almanac and Book of Facts,* Centennial Edition, New York, Newspaper Enterprise Association, 1968.

Chapter 2

FAMILY PATTERNS AND SELF-IDENTITY

PERSONAL IDENTIFICATION

ONE INHERITS CERTAIN BIOLOGICAL TRAITS including facial and physical characteristics; but one also borrows and copies multiple psychological characteristics from the important people in his life. Boys tend to identify themselves with the important male or males in their mother's life. This may be one's own father, or mother's favorite brother, or her father or a grandfather. Girls try to be like daddy's favorite female—sister, mother, grandmother, aunt, cousin, or wife.

If the V.I.P. is dead, the time of demise could be all important. As already stated in Chapter 1 this is especially true when death takes a loved one during the preteen and early teen-age years. Yet, even when your client has never seen the revered or favored adult, he grows up with deep convictions of what is expected of him. He may consciously reject what his grandfather said or did or what his Aunt Jane would have not approved. Nevertheless, the knowledge that he has disappointed his favorite V.I.P. generates varying degrees of self-rejection and a need for self-punishment.

Conflicts of this nature are not readily apparent. They are usually subclinical. They have to be considered and sought for. However, when the client makes a gross denial of such influences, the idea is not necessarily invalid. Questioning need not be pursued at that particular time because the subject will inevitably arise through other associations later on in the counseling. One group of unconscious identifications of this nature are generally and rather loosely referred to as an unresolved Oedipus complex.

OEDIPAL STRIVINGS AND ALLIANCES

The natural dependency of a child upon its mother fosters a number of psychological and emotional attachments. These are frequently grouped under the term "Oedipus complex," although there is nothing very complicated about it. Children are expected to have emotional growing pains. Like the family pet cat or dog, they will often crawl in between parents whenever they are permitted to do so, especially when they feel insecure or unhappy. The *Oedipal state* designates a "mamma's boy," while the *Electra complex* refers to the girl who has a crush on her daddy. The theory is that each child wants to control and possess the parent of the opposite sex by getting rid of, or displacing, the parent of the same sex.

Children naturally identify themselves with the parent of the same sex for another reason. It helps to compensate for an awareness of natural resentment against their first love. In the normal mother-son adulation, the father is a competitor; but resentment against one's own father, whom one also loves, is incompatible with peace of mind. Father is supposed to be the boss. The son, therefore, compensates by identifying with father. He tries to be like him. He yearns to be big enough to fill daddy's shoes. He struts, swaggers and talks like daddy. He adopts both good and bad paternal patterns and attitudes. He dreams of sharing mother's bed—not for cohabitation but cuddled in her protecting arms as he once did during infancy and early childhood.

Similarly, when the girl discovers that she resents her mother's natural competition for her father's affection, she too feels guilty. She compensates by trying to be more like her mother. Being more like mother often earns an extra dividend. It also results in *being more liked by her mother.*

There are other complications and factors. The boy frequently patterns himself after mother if she is stronger than father, especially if she accepts the boy. He may cultivate effeminate mannerisms for several reasons: in response to her smothering his development, as a result of her efforts to keep him dependent, and also to compete with his mother as a rival for the affection of his father with whom he secretly identifies himself. Unfortunately, these effeminate mannerisms do not usually endear him either to boys or to girls and seldom to his own father or to the rest of the family.

A girl can be a tomboy and may easily attract playmates of both sexes, but she eventually teams up with a mate who is less aggressive—one whom she can dominate or control.

The whole concept of Oedipal strivings, rivalries and alliances is best understood when one reviews the legend of Thebes, from which the Oedipus complex derives its name. It is a story that is old in the mythology of many cultures, and its biological factual basis can be seen in practice in any jungle herd.

THE LEGEND OF THEBES

Oedipus was a legendary character of Thebes, Greece. When he was a baby an oracle, possibly at Delphi, prophesied that Oedipus would kill his own father. People believed in these prophesies religiously, so his parents abandoned the baby and left him with bound feet to die of exposure on the side of a mountain. (The word "Oedipus," in Greek, literally means "swollen feet.") Such infanticide was not uncommon in many parts of the world.

Baby Oedipus was rescued by a shepherd and ultimately was adopted by a king who raised and loved him as his own son. But as the boy grew older the foster father could not dissuade the youth from leaving home to seek his fortune and also to search for his real parents.

The next scene took place on a narrow mountain pass where Oedipus met a man named Laius who was old enough to be his father. Laius was a king, so he refused to step aside. Oedipus had now become an aggressive youth of about seventeen or eighteen with plenty of reason to be hostile to an older man. The youthful stranger, with equal arrogance, also refused to allow passageway. Each was determined to fight to the death for the right of way.

The older man may have noticed something familiar in the youth's features. His unconscious mind may have recognized some familial characteristics, but fear of ghosts and spirits was as strong as the implicit belief in prophesy. Moreover, the psychological defense of *denial* was nothing new. Of course this could not be his abandoned son! That baby with bound feet had to be dead from exposure on another mountain side, far away and a long time ago. And this impostor must surely die. Remember the prophesy? The oracle is infallible!

A strong denial could appease the man's conscience. Perhaps he disputed the right of way as an excuse to provoke a fight to the death. Oedipus, according to legend, knew nothing of the prophesy, but he was definitely out to seek his fortune, establish a reputation for valor, and possibly also to obtain revenge for desertion. Any adult parent figure would serve as a stand-in. Whatever their reasons, each traveler refused to step aside so they fought to the death, and youthful speed and zest, plus strength, naturally won out.

Studying both legend and history, Renault,[4] Licht[2] and Frazer[1] tell of many an ancient custom in early Greek and other kingdoms, some of which were ruled by women. Annually, or whenever challenged, the king had to defend his crown and fight for his life—which he invariably lost to a younger or stronger contender. The victor then married the widowed queen and lived in uneasy comfort, luxury and style for an average of one year or until again challenged. Then he, too had to defend his crown, and, in turn, was usually killed and replaced by a stronger and often younger contender.

Such was the situation between the widow of the slain King Laius and Oedipus. Queen Jocasta had title to the throne. After solving the riddle of the Sphinx, Oedipus married the queen and became the new King of Thebes. Not until many months later did he discover that Queen Jocasta was also the mother who had left him to die on the mountain some eighteen years earlier.*

---

* According to Licht, the real father of Oedipus, King Laius, was ambisexual; like many others of his times and ours, he found pleasure in youths as well as in maidens. Laius is alleged to have fallen in love with Chrysippus, who was the beautiful son of Pelops of Corinth. Custom permitted the boy to go voluntarily but forbade abduction or rape. Laius was impatient, so he abducted the youth. In consequence, Pelops uttered the fearful curse that, in revenge, Laius would die by his own son's hand.

The tour guide "historians" at Delphi naturally prefer not to share the credit for the famous prophesy with Pelops. They proudly point to recent archeological excavations in the famous temple of Apollo that suggest some basis of historical truth in the Oracle's role of prophesy.

As Licht reminds us, the views of ancient Greeks, on both incest and homosexual activities, were much less strict than our views in modern times. For instance in Greek mythology, Zeus (another Oedipal product and also the alleged father of gods and men) is also the husband of his own sister Hera, goddess of marriage. Dictators can still make their own rules and change them at will.

Legend and truth are not easily separated, yet their persistence requires honest inquiry, if we are to avoid traps of propaganda and half-truths.

According to legend, when Oedipus eventually discovered, some time later, the identity of the man whom he had killed—the one man for whom he had searched far and wide—and then realized whom he had married, he promptly severed the relationship. He also did penance by putting out his own eyes, while the queen, his mother and legal wife, killed herself.

But, according to glibly misquoted dogma, too many young men and boys would like to kill their fathers and go to bed with their mothers for purposes of cohabitation. Rank saw this as a symbolic reunion with the mother.[3] Since this type of incest is liable to be a repugnant thought and is also universally forbidden in almost every culture, the proposition gives a bad name to the whole concept of trying to understand the normal mind of children.

For instance, boys certainly do become annoyed with fathers who discipline them. Furthermore, little boys (and girls, too) often like to crawl into bed with their parents. Fortunately there are not too many mothers who deliberately cultivate and prolong this dependency beyond the first few years of life, but it does happen. Some mothers continue to bathe, dress and wait on their growing sons indefinitely. They make decisions for them and strive to control them as long as possible in one way or another—financially, by rejecting potential daughters-in-law, or by invalidism.

Outright despotism, as in the case of the subtle but domineering "displeased" father of Elizabeth Barrett Browning in the classic, *The Barretts of Wimpole Street,* is believed to be less common in modern times, but feudalistic autocracy continues to plague many a family and accounts for a great deal of the child's natural rebellion or Oedipal conflicts.

Few mama's boys actually indulge in genital cohabitation with their mothers, although it is not unheard of in private psychiatric practice. "After all," argued one youth, who was just back from his tour of military service in the Pacific, "they do it overseas, so why cannot we?" His mother, who had not had a few drinks and was neither convinced nor "cooperative," developed an acute anxiety reaction instead. This was the first recurrence of a similar illness for which she had been successfully treated a dozen years previously.

In view of her precarious emotional balance, as a result of other personal problems (moribund grandmother, distant and ailing mother, and an impotent husband), I did not pursue the possibility that incestuous desires can work both ways. She eventually required electroshock therapy to produce the desired amnesia and to improve the family's concern for her welfare.

On the other hand, even without sexual fantasies the normal competition and jealousy between sons and fathers as well as between daughters and their mothers, often does lead to bad feelings. As a result, stormy quarrels, painful separations and occasionally even patricide or matricide are well-known complications of family living.

As to desertion or abandonment of infants, like sexual ambivalence, this too is not rare, although it may occur less frequently than physical and emotional abuse of children by those who are entrusted with their care. Oedipus is merely a symbol of normal intrafamiliar conflicts of interests; yet, for too many people, it is still a very dirty word.

"Oedipal strivings" is probably a more acceptable concept than complex, for there is nothing complicated about it. The simple fact that two is company and three is a crowd is just as evident in animal life and in children at play. It can be seen in sororities, fraternities, among brothers and sisters, visiting relatives, political groups and even in our great religions. The ancient gods were not unique in their competition for prestige, alliances and followers. In the fine art of family living, the first gods are our parents, as we are reminded in the first of the Ten Commandments.

Some parents are more discreet and tactful in distributing their favors. This serves to prevent undue jealousy in the family. However, too many parents have been raised in insecure homes and, consequently, pass on their own immaturity and instability to their children. They left home to seek acceptance and strength as well as their fortunes, but too frequently they marry partners who have had similarly insecure backgrounds. As a result, they renew their sibling rivalries, much like feuding hillbillies or war-ring tribesmen.

Instead of directing their resentments against the parental rejectors, however, they displace their hostilities onto spouses, in-laws, neighbors, partners, associates, employers, and even their own children. This is especailly liable to happen when the child resembles or takes after some other V.I.P. in the parent's life.

And so the war of emotional instability and the search for psychological revenge, emotional maturity and relative indepen-dence goes on—not only between the sexes but also between each generation and the next.

REFERENCES AND READINGS

1. FRAZER, J. G.: *The Golden Bough.* New York, Macmillan, 1945.
2. LICHT, H.: *Sexual Life in Ancient Greece.* London, Routledge & Keegan, Paul, 1932.
3. RANK, O.: *The Trauma of Birth.* New York, Harcourt, 1929.
4. RENAULT, M.: *The King Must Die.* New York, Pocket Bks., 1959.

Chapter 3

PERSONALITY OF THE COUNSELOR

SOMEONE WHO CARES

A COUNSELOR IS SOMEONE WHO IS EXPECTED TO CARE, even though the conferences may be an ordeal for both parties. Each participant is a composite of many people, both living and dead. Wishful thinking and identification play a powerful role in transference. Dependency, fear of disapproval and rejection are mixed with hope for a miraculous relief from current tensions. Motivation is also mixed; not only in the counselor, who thinks he has already made peace with his own conflicts and conscience, but also in the client or patient who may be coming just to appease someone else.

Men are particularly reluctant to be obliged to seek help on such personal matters as dating, marriage, sex, choice of jobs, and raising their own children. Counselors, lawyers, clergymen and even psychiatrists generally have just as many family problems as businessmen or mechanics.

Women usually seek help more readily; but when they serve as counselors they too are reluctant to risk having to surrender their boyfriends (in or out of marriage) or to modify their preferences for food (obesity), alcohol, and other indulgences including captious criticism, nagging and scolding. Unlike most men they do not avoid or deny a dependency on their families, doctors or clinics.

Some people go into counseling in order to compensate for the very problems they are called upon to treat. Their credo is "Do as I say, not as I do." *

The personality of the counselor has a major influence on the effectiveness of his services. It operates both positively and negatively and may continue to affect the outcome for years to come.

---

* Fortunately most counselors are conscientious and want to help others. Their chief shortcoming consists of limited training.

Counselors come from all walks of life. They embrace various religions, ages, shapes, races and sexes. They grow up with the same variety of conflicts and complexes that trouble their clients. Their successes or failures in resolving their own difficulties may be just as challenging or glaringly obvious as with the people whom they try to guide.

There is one essential difference, however, and that is the tendency for counselors to insist that their own handicaps are under control or irrelevant. Unlike the people who come for help, counselors usually do not admit their own needs for psychotherapy. For such counselors, the client's request for help seems to imply an admission of some degree of inferiority. This automatically makes the counselor feel superior. It also gives him a daily boost to his faltering ego.[1]

WHEN THE COUNSELOR IS SUBJECTIVELY INVOLVED

The counselor is automatically involved by the mere choice of his specialty. He obviously has a need and desire to become involved with other people. He has a need to share (or vicariously reject) their troubles and, hopefully, a desire to help. When a passive aggressive and secretly hostile person does counseling he frequently adopts such telltale techniques as setting up elaborate preliminary conferences and practicing therapeutic non-involvement. He delights in a long and impressive waiting list for appointments. He allows the client to flounder about and work out his own problems by trial and error, or he may set up a difficult and expensive schedule no matter how long it takes.

The counselor's hostility may not be directed to all his clients or associates. It may be focused on one particular client, as in the following case of Von, where lack of empathy and negative countertransference are obvious.

Von, an experienced physiotherapist, asked for help in one of my groups. He was unable to obtain satisfactory cooperation from one of his elderly female patients. "She does the exercises, but only when I'm there to coax her. I know she can do better." He was invited to demonstrate his approach on a substitute patient. Then he was asked to reverse roles since only he knew the patient. He now played the role of patient while another member of the group pretended that she was the therapist.

It became evident quite quickly that Von felt threatened by the "patient." He was consistently unable to be firm. As someone in the group remarked, "Maybe you're not in any hurry to get this patient well. How come you never thought of any of these suggestions up until now? You certainly know about braces, and trapeze bars, and wheelchairs." Von, who has been "hung up" with other patients in the past, admitted that he was probably in an emotional bind and that was why he had asked for help.

We then asked him to describe the patient, whose "black hair and slender body" were promptly identified with another V.I.P. in Von's life (his wife). Von was then invited to replay the scene of his house visit to the patient, with V.H. (our regular psychodramatic auxilliary ego) as the physiotherapist, and Von himself as the patient. V.H., in the role of the therapist, took the initiative and *told* the patient (Von) what was going to be done next, instead of asking for her "approval" as the others had done. She ignored the cursing and the objections and applied the imaginary braces which she told the patient were a present and the next step toward strengthening her leg muscles. She got the patient off the couch, onto "her" feet, and walking reluctantly across the room on an imaginary walker. Then the roles were reversed.

This time, Von approached his job with alacrity and heartening success. In reverse PD, Von improved his technique by overriding all objections (even walking out on the patient when she would not cooperate); but his handling was a little rough. It was not the first time he had developed insight in our private groups; but, as every child can testify, many experiences have to be tested and relearned over and over again before they become firmly entrenched.

Other indications of subjective involvement by the counselor include the following: overspecialization which is marked by habitual rejection of all but a certain type of problem; overstrictness; overindulgence amounting to negligence such as Von above; overfamiliarity; bragging or gossiping about certain clients; recurrent tardiness by client or therapist; impatience, and a tendency to slough the client off by referring to someone else or to another agency. In the following case it was teacher. principal and mother who overreacted. Counselor was young, but experienced.

A small boy of six found a box of razor blades at home. He brought them to school and was passing them around to his first grade friends. The teacher angrily sent him to the principal who accidentally cut his own finger with one of the blades. In panic at the sight of the blood, he sent for the school nurse. He also ordered the new counselor to get rid of such a "dangerous monster" at once and kept calling for the child's mother. The counselor called in the mother who was annoyed and angry at having to leave her job. She threatened to slash the child's wrists as punishment when he got home.

The counselor calmed her down, reassured her that the child was normally curious and emphasized the mother's desire to *help* the little boy. "You love him, don't you? And you want to help him? Just take him home. Restrict some of his play privileges for a day and then listen to what he has to say. He's already been scared enough." No one did anything about the poor principal's attempt to gain attention from the nurse, counselor and mother by his mishap; or to the teacher who also panicked at the sight of the blades.

It is definitely time for a change when a therapist becomes overanxious, requires frequent reports on minor details or personal intimacies in the client's life solicits gifts or favors, and becomes personally offended whenever his authority is questioned or his recommendations ignored. Counselors who are not familiar with these common examples of countertransference need further indoctrination.[2,3]

TRAINING AND SUPERVISION

Five or six college years and two degrees are the usual minimal academic requirements. Ph.D.s with three degrees are usually best qualified because their longer training includes clinical services and experience. Teachers without a master's degree are often called upon to serve as counselors in school systems. Students and volunteers without even a bachelor's degree are also serving in various counseling situations, especially at camps and in some clinics.

In well-run agencies, counselors-in-training meet frequently with experienced supervisors to review their work and their problems. With the current emphasis and demand for volunteers and paramedical or parapsychiatric aides at all levels, too many workers will not have access to such supervision. They may affiliate with an active clinic, however, or with a private professional for several hours of weekly supervised instruction and consultative review. Most workers in the field will be obliged to work out their problems as best they can through books, lectures, refresher courses and attendance at meetings of reputable social and psychological organizations.

It may not be necessary for a counselor to be married or a parent, or to belong to a certain church or group. However, he should be prepared for rejection on these and many other levels, especially when the client is seeking an excuse for resisting his help. In general, a counselor who has been through the mill of hardship and tragedy, and knows his way around, can empathize more readily; but such counselors have been known to give erroneous directions, steer good college material into other channels and discourage original efforts simply because of their own personal prejudices.

Religion, race, age and sex of the counselor inevitably affect the counseling situation. Older counselors may be out of tune with some of the problems of the younger generation; but they also serve as parental or grandparental substitutes. Usually, this is advantageous when dealing with older clients; but it may also be disenchanting to the client until identifications are worked out.

Young counselors may be at a similar disadvantage with older clients. Nevertheless their enthusiasm and self-confidence may be just what the client needs, even when the advice is not followed to the letter. Millions of people did not like the Kennedy's, yet they cannot help being impressed with their vitality, dedication, successes, tragedies and strong family ties.

Counselors with certain religious training may be unable to give unprejudiced advice; and those with strong cultural and racial affinities may find themselves overtly strict with members of their own group just to avoid the danger of being accused of favorable prejudices.

Male counselors are supposed to favor husbands and boys in domestic problems, while female counselors are believed to lean toward the feminine point of view. This may be true in some cases, but it is not consistently so. Nevertheless a broken home in the counselor's own life cannot help leaving scars.

Threatening situations are handled differently by various

schools of therapy. For instance, when the doctrine of therapeutic noninvolvement prevents the therapist from entering into the discussion on an active level, the client may develop serious emotional complications. I have seen narcotic addicts and even paranoid patients emerge from several years of such nondirective therapy by certified psychiatrists, without ever being confronted with their true diagnosis. By that time, short-term therapy was out of the question. Similarly, in nondirective group therapy, a leader who is not comfortable when members of the group analyze his silence or attack his evasive replies to specific questions may transmit his own feelings of insecurity to other members of the group. One such evidence of his defensive feelings is retaliation. Like others in his group, and especially like his threatening client, his method for covering up may be to attack or criticize others for being too controlling, hogging the show, structuring the situation to suit their own needs, coming late, and so on.

> A beautiful German blonde was suddenly dropped by her counseling therapist, allegedly without reason. For two years he had encouraged freedom of expression in private consultation and also in his small groups. Well-known four-letter words were the least shocking of his own diction and that of their group. "Some of them described the most intimate details of their sex life; but that was not my problem."
>
> Having already suffered rejection and exile from her fatherland and the fall of their national hero Hitler, she was utterly unprepared for the abrupt and unexplained dismissal. Her young therapist later relented enough to permit her to attend a small group but by this time she had found a therapist who did not exclude her husband. Her new therapist was also old enough to be a replacement for her dead father, rather than a frustrated lover, and her new group associates are more concerned with psychodramatic acting out of conflicts than with mental masturbations through overemphasis upon four-letter words.

The temptation to play God is an ever present hazard for counselors, especially those who personally err like the devil. Direct and complete symptom removal by reconditioning or hypnotic techniques is a temptation; which may also prove hazardous, especially when no adequate replacement is available to sustain the patient's confidence. In fairness to the users of nondirective techniques and the proponents of the theory of therapeutic noninvolvement, it must be remembered that those who employ directive and authoritarian techniques are repeatedly exposed to rationalizations of their own dictatorial motives. High priests and powerful church groups have been known to prescribe exile, the headsman's axe, or burning at the stake for "witches," heretics and other nonconformists. Psychiatrists have been known to use electroshock to keep uncooperative patients in line—as punishment rather than specific therapy.

Counselors, too, may become unreasonable when their advice is not followed. Broken appointments, dropouts, school detention, suspension, expulsion and referral to juvenile courts are largely preventable through conferences and arbitrations. When challenged by a client's resistance, one needs a supervisory and dual analysis. One needs to discover not only why the client did not follow the recommendations but also why the therapist found it necessary to be so inflexible, dogmatic, controlling or even dictatorial. It may also be pertinent to learn why the counselor relied so heavily on intelligence quotients, a Rorschach, or someone else's opinion instead of his own judgment. Whenever possible, one should offer several alternatives to the client and be content with relatively minor changes from time to time.

In short, the personality of the counselor is under constant scrutiny. It therefore needs to keep on growing and adapting to changes, for it may well be the decisive factor in the success or failure of his next therapeutic mission. The real test of the counselor's efficiency is not the immediate success or failure of recommendations for resolving a current problem. The success is measured by long-range development of the client's ability to learn to make future decisions for himself, to develop a stable character, and to achieve mature dependability for future constructive undertakings.

REFERENCES AND READINGS

1. FREUD, S.: *Basic Writings.* New York, Modern Lib., 1938.
2. STEIN, C.: *Practical Psychotherapeutic Techniques.* Springfield, Thomas, 1968.
3. STEIN, C.: *Practical Psychotherapeutic Techniques in Non-Psychiatric Specialties.* Springfield, Thomas, 1969.

Chapter 4

THE FIRST INTERVIEWS

PREPARATION

In unusual circumstances the counselor may make the overtures; for instance when the client keeps breaking appointments or is in a hospital, detention home, or is otherwise restricted. Fear of learning the truth or of displeasing someone who is opposed to this kind of help can often be resolved by a single house visit. The general rule, however, is that the client should seek the help and also make his own appointment. People who tend to slough off this first major responsibility onto spouses, parents or assistants are inclined to be resistive and irresponsible concerning subsequent obligations. The direct contact permits facilitation of arrangements that are best suited to counselor as well as client. It also weakens the alibi of misunderstanding when an appointment is broken.

Preparation by the counselor requires him to familiarize himself with as much background data as possible. The counselor is not expected to be a walking encyclopedia but he is presumed to be able to apply up-to-date knowledge to the current problems and questions of those who seek his help. A review of current cultural, economic and statistical data is readily available at any bookstore in such inexpensive annuals as *The World Almanac; The U.S. Book of Facts, Statistics and Information; The New Information Please Almanac,* and the *Atlas* and *Yearbook.* They contain multiple graphs, tables, latest available data and brief commentaries on marriages, births, grounds for divorce in various states, suicide, accidents, compulsory school attendance, segregation, immigration, income, expenses, wealth, sports, current history, insurance, consumption of alcohol, tobacco and so on.

Preparation by the counselor also calls for periodic self-evaluation of his motives in devoting his major energies to helping other people. Too many counselors are eager for an audience, for approval, for opportunities to lecture, to play God or be a "Hanging Judge." The habitual abuse of power and authority is not confined to parents and teachers nor are blind spots restricted to clients.

Transference and countertransference are inevitable accompaniments to the therapeutic relationship. They begin with information on the nature of the problem or the name of the client, even before the encounter. The counselor can be expected to do a better job when his client likes and trusts him, *positive transference.* However, he must also be prepared to deal with opposite attitudes, *negative transference,* whereby the client takes out on the counselor much of his pent-up hostility to other authoritarian figures in his life. Some of these V.I.P.'s may have been long since dead or otherwise removed from immediate contact, yet many an unsatisfactory interview is the result of failure to make a few simple inquiries.

> Of whom do I remind you? When else have you been in a similar situation? How do you feel about having to come here? Whom else might blame you for your present predicament? With whom might you be compared by your V.I.P.'s?

The counselor must also be prepared to admit that he, too, will have emotional as well as intellectual reactions to his client, *countertransference,* as in the case of Von in the preceding chapter. Minor annoyances and subtle influences can arouse hostility in both client and counselor. For example, tardiness, an unpleasant voice, critical gossip of other clients or counselors, idiosyncrasies in personal appearance, hairdo, dress, speech, and even the nature of the presenting problem. The counselor's personal moral and religious training will inevitably affect his attitude towards birth control, unmarried mothers, homosexuals, chronic delinquents and experimenters with drugs. Counselors who are teetotallers usually have a less tolerant attitude towards the youth who experiments with alcohol, while those who drink are often more lenient; likewise with tobacco and intermarriage.

Similarly, counselors who have been raised in undemonstrative families are not usually inclined to offer a warm, pleasant greeting to the client; yet the first few seconds of the first encounter may determine the long-range outcome of the relationship. Physical contacts are generally out of order, but a pat on the shoulder or a warm handshake may go a long way with a newly bereaved or similarly troubled client. A kiss on the cheek for a new bride who is well known to the counselor or a token slap on the wrist for an admittedly juvenile misconduct may also be in order.

Preparation by the client can be facilitated by a variety of procedures. I frequently invite future appointees to write me a letter or a brief autobiography, or to jot down some of the topics which they feel to be most urgent. I also inform them that they do not have to show me their notes and that they can ignore spelling, grammar and diction, stating whatever comes to mind, not even bothering to reread what they have written.

> Just seal it in an envelope. Mail or bring it with you; but when you come if you then decide it's too personal to show me, you are free to destroy it. Just getting it off your chest will help you to feel better.

When a client begins to reflect on his past life and to organize his story into five-year periods (preschool, first years of schooling, prepuberty, teen dating, recreation, jobs, use of free time, dealings with family, in-laws, close friends and so on), he also begins his own therapy along with varying degrees of self-evaluation. Even when he tries to cover up and put his best foot forward, he will also be censoring his own behavior and asking relevant questions. Some of these will be pertinent to the presenting complaints. Others may seem irrelevant yet will often reveal the major underlying problems.

Some counselors find value in the family album, personal scrapbooks, a diary, collections or other hobbies which the client may have once considered important. Other counselors prefer to start the interview absolutely cold and to pick up useful leads and clues as they go along. Both methods have their advantages, but the counselor should be prepared for surprises in any case.

ENCOUNTER

The first encounter represents a combination of challenge, embarrassment, an appeal, a defiance, and often an attempt to unload the burden of responsibility onto the counselor. Counselors who follow the psychoanalytical doctrine of nondirection and therapeutic noninvolvement promptly disabuse the client of this idea. They may even put the entire burden of presenting the case history onto the client. In some cases the client goes into a psychological freeze with the result that most of the first few therapeutic hours may pass with scarcely a word being uttered on either side.

Other counselors and therapists go to the opposite extreme. They use the first session to lecture; and like most beginners, they often start to offer positive suggestions and advice long before they have heard the essential details of the client's story.

A happy medium consists of putting the client at ease as soon as possible. This may be accomplished just by pronouncing his name correctly. When in doubt, ask him how he prefers to be addressed and how he spells his name. Other overtures may include offering a cigarette, a cigar, coffee, a coke or a package of Lifesavers. Opening remarks may consist of inquiring about transportation, satisfactory parking arrangements, pressure to leave for other important commitments, whether the chair is comfortable and other comparable courtesies. A compliment on attire, choice of colors, unusual or interesting costume jewelry or accessories *may* be in order for some clients. Others will immediately question your motive and sincerity. A handshake and smile are usually invaluable, but some clients fear any form of physical touching. Their grip may be firm, hostile or indifferent. They may also consider the counselor's accompanying smile as artificial, which unfortunately, it frequently is.

Encounter, confrontation and reaction merge imperceptably. Their distinctions are more technical than practical. In general, the counselor should remember that he has two ears and only one mouth. Listening is usually more valuable than talking, but when direct questions are asked and the counselor is in doubt, he could do worse than remain silent and wait for further clarification.

> Let's think about it. What are the alternatives? Which one do you favor? What are the objections? When do you have to make a decision? What's the worst possible consequences? Let's assume that the worst has already happened. Now what can be done to live with it? But if the worst hasn't yet occurred, let's think of some ways to *prevent it*.

CONFRONTATION

Your client or patient is like a guest in the house. It should be unnecessary to remind the counselor that the visit may represent an embarrassing as well as a challenging encounter. The counselor becomes an authoritarian figure (parent, teacher, policeman, judge or referee), while the client is reduced to the unhappy role of class dummy who did not know the answer and has to stay after school or go to see the principal. Reminiscences of similar failures and confrontations with parents, teachers or employers are unavoidable. In more serious cases his visit may be a brief stopover en route to reformatory or divorce court in which case the least he can expect is temporary separations and deprivations. The worst is banishment and seemingly permanent exile. For these and many other reasons, the client's first visit may also be his last.

The following brief encounters show what can be accomplished by employing a variety of techniques, most of which have been described elsewhere in considerable detail.[3] Not all of the situations occurred on the patient's very first private visit. Some of them took place during a teaching demonstration on volunteers whom I had never seen before. Others occurred in a session of group psychotherapy the first time a particular subject came up. To the extent that they are all spontaneous and unrehearsed, however, they represent a "first" for the patient or client. They, therefore, illustrate some practical applications of diagnostic and therapeutic skills that can be applied when time is short and the matter seems urgent. With clients who have obviously brittle defenses and need to delude themselves for a while longer, the counselor may decide not to confront until later. Meanwhile, here are a few revelations to watch for.

Revelations that Should Alert the Counselor

The Identity of the Person Making the Appointment

This person may afford the first clue, especially when it is the mother of an adult, e.g., a thirty-seven-year-old "boy" who cannot hold a job, or a sister-in-law or neighbor of a teen-ager whose parents are too busy to be bothered. When a physician, attorney, clergyman, principal or other authoritarian figure makes a personal telephone call, he usually gets preferential treatment for his patient or client.

When Unconscious Motivation is Stronger Than Conscious Desire (Dream Revelation)

Dr. D's patient insisted that he wanted his teeth "put right"; yet he constantly found fault with each restoration, broke appointments, and neglected to follow instructions. One day he reported the following dream: "I was happily busy pulling out my teeth, one by one."

The dentist, one of my students in a graduate course on psychotherapy, was advised to confront his patient with his obvious though unconscious desire to become edentulous. Instead of offering to repair the remaining teeth, I suggested that he advise complete exodontia.

When so confronted, the patient promptly resorted to denial; but he was also obliged to do some reflecting on the subject of control of his aggressive instincts. With no further analysis than his own contemplations, he soon discontinued his complaints and decided to live with his remaining teeth. Cooperation thereafter was satisfactory.

The Double Negative and Other Slips of the Tongue

Verbal clues may be a dead give away to underlying conflicts. Here is one from a highly competent and reputable obstetrician, during a lecture to other specialists on the applications of hypnotic relaxation in the preparation of women for childbirth. One of the students had asked about the reactions of husbands to hypnosis for their wives; and the lecturer replied, "They're no trouble at all! In all my years of practice, *I have not had no problems with husbands.*" He was not confronted, since we already knew that he knew that his statement was wishful thinking. Later in the lecture he amplified this by describing *how to deal with problem hubbies.*

Here's another instance that occurred recently during an initial interview.

> Norma, 28. I dreamed I was a whale.
>   Dr. S. What kind of a whale—male or female?
>   A. A female male—I mean a female *whale*! Wow! That was surely a freudian slip, wasn't it?
>   Q. What does Norma's "slip" suggest to you?
>   A. Oh well, I was quite a tomboy. Mother would sit me up on a table and wash one dirty leg and call it Mrs. White. Then she'd say, "Now let's wash Mr. Black. After she'd wash the other leg, she'd say, "Now it's Mr. White." But it was always "Mrs. and Mr." for my two legs. Do you suppose I'm unhappy because I'm conflicted over my role as housewife and mother?

The question needed no answer, and she continued with her free associations.

Unusually Strong Reaction (An angry retort and slip of the tongue exposes a long-repressed hostility.)

After her first self-requested visit to a group therapy session (in which some of my students psychodramatized former conflicts with substitute "parents"), Belle, a sixty-two-year old spinster school teacher, on the verge of retirement, kept reiterating:

> I don't see how you stand it week after week. Those snips! Those clowns! Those awful snips! Raking up the past! They'll have to convince *me* it's dead and gone. *They'll have to convince me, I mean them, that it's all dead and gone.*
>
> *And* you! I hope you'll excuse me but you'll have to take some courses in teaching! You shouldn't have let them get away with it. You've got to keep them in their place. Didn't you ever take any practice teaching?

I said regretfully, that I had not, but I thanked her for her advice. As already stated elsewhere, older people do poorly in mixed groups, but well enough with their peers. I decided not to confront her with her reiterated criticism of the lack of respect shown by the "children" in the psychodrama with their tardy, harassed and obviously reluctant "baby-sitter." The "children" had been precocious, rebellious, and outspoken in their criticism —not only of the incompetent baby-sitter but also of their returning "parents." Their open rebellion was something which Belle was unable to handle, except with the old-fashioned strap.

The strategy paid off. She made one more visit to the group intending to speak her piece but was unable to do so. When invited to comment she shook her head. However, at her subsequent private sessions, she poured out all that I wanted to know. She also allowed her blood pressure to return to normal, but that was with the help of drugs.

Two months later, Belle was full of apologies:

> I just finished reading your chapter on psychodrama;[3] and now I know what you were trying to accomplish. You should have stopped me when I was so rude to you. I hope you'll forgive me. . . .

I reassured her, but she was in no hurry to return to the group. Instead, she continues to prefer private conferences from time to time.

Analysis by Free or Permissive Association

Free association is a familiar psychological procedure in which everyone indulges. It is a normal phenomenon of learning and remembering in everyday living. Occasionally, however, it requires a little help from the counselor, as in the following case of Abner.

Case of Abner

Abner was reporting for his quarterly neurological checkup. Among other things he reminded me that he had been married almost two years and had a new baby; but he insisted that there were no problems or stressful situations to aggravate his dormant neurological condition. He did, however, offer the information, "I went horseback riding last week about two o'clock in the evening." When he saw my inquiring expression, he added, "Two o'clock at night! Well, it was late anyway." When I still remained silent, he added, "It was my sister's horse." He seemed to think the incident important, so I asked, "Why do you suppose you didn't say 'two o'clock in the *morning?*' "

His verbal reply was "I don't know" but his elevated foot indicated knowledgeable tension which I pretended to ignore. Instead I asked the following questions:

Q. What does two AM mean to you?

A. Nothing much; except that I didn't feel like going to bed.

Q. Why?

A. Hard to say. I don't know. I didn't go far. [He reiterated this last statement so I naturally inquired the following.]

Q. If you *had* gone far, where *might* you have gone?

A. Oh, over to a dirt road. Maybe about an eighth of a mile from our place. [My silence prompted him to anticipate my next question.] And that (road) goes no place special.

Q. No place special?

A. Er-er- Well, I know it crosses a big highway.

Q. Where does the highway go?

A. Connecticut. [The question was repeated with the same answer; so I changed my wording.]

Q. What's in Connecticut?

A. [He repeated my question (stalling for time).]

Dr. Yes.

A. Hartford, I guess. [He cleared his throat indicating that we were right on target and getting close to the bull's eye.]

Q. What's in Hartford?

A. Oh. Insurance companies. [I waited for him to continue but he didn't. So I asked the question.]

Q. "What's the attraction?"

A. Oh, I used to work there, at— [names a prominent company].

Abner had repeatedly denied that there were any unpleasant restrictions to his present job, doing similar work in a small agency for an uncle. Now, without any prompting he said, "I couldn't possibly start in on my own now. Not with a wife and baby." [His hand covered his mouth as though he were trying to keep it from telling tales.] I continued to maintain an attentive silence, while he added, "We are rather short of cash. You see my wife wants to paper and paint the kitchen, and buy some drapes . . ." [He was wandering far afield, so I brought him back, after a minute of silence.]

Q. How did your sister feel about your riding her horse?

A. Oh, she wouldn't mind. She's only thirteen, but she's got two horses.

Q. *Two* horses?

A. Yah. My father bought them for her.

Q. No one ever bought you a horse?

A. No. I never wanted one. [I did not challenge his obvious rationalization. Instead I asked the following.]

Q. What *did* they buy you when you were thirteen?

A. Probably a fishing rod.

While not his first visit for his neurological problem, this was the first occasion on which I had been able to make any progress on the possibility of underlying psychodynamics. He had insisted on being treated only with medication. Abner's dissatisfaction with his job reflects an earlier frustration over rivalry with his younger and favored sister. Father could afford to set Abner up in his own business. Abner identifies himself with his protected and indulged sister. He takes her horse and canters off symbolically in the direction of his former and more promising job in Hartford.

He had obviously developed some insight and kept saying "very interesting." He may also be willing to pursue the analysis at some later date; but he promptly declined to return soon for further conferences, on the grounds that he could not afford it. Since I did not wish to add to his anxieties I did not insist on an earlier return than his customary quarterly visit. Some analyses are best when not pursued too zealously, especially with beginners or with people who are already vulnerable clinically to stressful situations.

In pursuing the subject with cases such as Abner's, whether at a first or subsequent visit, the counselor would do well to avoid a direct interrogation. For instance, on the subject of grievances against his father, I would ask, "How did you feel about your father?" or, "Was your father disappointed in you?" rather than "Are you disappointed in (or angry with) father?" Or I would ask, "Could your sister have had any reason to resent you?" instead of "What else might you have resented your sister for?" or "Who was the family favorite? or "Was *she* your mother's favorite?"

Since we already know that sister was father's favorite (two horses) and since older brothers are more likely to be mother's favorites, the indirect intimation is that Abner was not entirely left out of parental warmth. This leaves him in a less threatening position. It also gives him an opportunity to correct the therapist who should not pretend to know *all* the answers.

A follow-up question, especially after an expected denial, might be, "If there were any reason for disappointment on either side (you or your parents) what *might* it have been?"

At subsequent conferences, if he brings up the subject, his feelings about his wife and her redecorating can be discussed. Meanwhile we have displaced his attentions onto earlier conflicts and patterns that undoubtedly influence his current situational stress. The same result could be obtained by letting him release his resentments against his wife in the first place and then encouraging his associations with other persons and places, but, as a newlywed, he would be reluctant to complain about her so early in the psychotherapeutic relationship. His report of the nocturnal canter had definitely set the pattern for the inquiry.

A *Simple Error of Interpretation Provokes a Curbstone Consultation*

Another example of a reaction which resulted in the speedy establishment of rapport came as a result of misinterpretation.

Case of Antoinette

Earlier this year, Antoinette, one of my students at a weekend training workshop on clinical hypnosis in a distant city, joined me at breakfast in the hotel coffee shop. She spent several minutes telling me how much she and her sister had enjoyed the psychodramatic demonstrations at Las Vegas in October of 1966. She had been especially impressed by the group therapy sessions and hypnodrama with *Juan* and *Jezebel*.[4]

At an appropriate moment, and by way of reminding her that the patient deserves most of the credit for successful therapy, I remarked that it "takes two to tango," which certainly dated me but was relevant enough in view of what she had just said. Her immediate response was startling.

"Yes it does! And I've got just the muscles to do it." This was said as she proudly patted her somewhat muscular right arm.

"To Tango?" I asked in mild surprise.

"Oh! I thought you said 'tangle!'"

Antoinette blushed as she promptly began to analyze her own error. She volunteered the information that she had been told previously that she was not very lady-like and that this was in sharp contrast to her sister. She then proceeded to tell me several more important details of her personal life. As the hour for the first lecture was near at hand she asked whether she could come to Springfield for some private conferences; but inasmuch as she had already made long-range plans to work overseas beginning in the very near future, the time factor did not seem very propitious. Instead, I suggested that she write me a letter. It could be as long as she chose and as informal as she wished. She was not to censor or even reread it. However, after sealing it in an envelope, she could wait a few days and then decide whether to mail or destroy it. She delivered it to me the very next morning.

Inasmuch as Antoinette had not only analyzed most of her current and earlier conflicts but had also settled in her own mind the questions about her current decisions and plans, the letter had served its purpose admirably. She proved it by a change in attitude and uninhibited participation in subsequent teaching sessions whenever volunteers were called for. (*See* Case of Bundy, below.) Even if she never returns for private counseling, she has been set on a constructive path which will render present and future activities much more fruitful and productive. The autobiographic report will also serve as excellent foundation for further therapy with some other counselor, whenever she finds it desirable to continue her psychological reeducation.

REACTION

Additional Cases on Brief Psychotherapy in Counseling Situations

Insight Through Spontaneous Role Playing

Case of Bundy

On the very next day following the above impromptu breakfast conference, Antoinette participated in an unrehearsed marriage counseling psychodrama. As the substitute wife she greeted her returning husband with an obviously unexpected embrace and kiss on his cheek. "Hubby" was completely taken off guard. He had expected to find his wife "glued to the television." He was also prepared for the usual bored or noncommittal answer to his "Hello, dear. How's everything?" He promptly stepped out of character to explain to me, as director, and to the rest of the group of psychologists, physicians, psychiatrists, and students, *"You see my wife isn't really like that!"*

Bundy had already said this twice before and had to correct himself by adding, "*Well, I mean she used to be like that*; but, with the children and all that. . . ."

I promptly cut the scene with Antoinette as his "wife" and invited Bundy to select some members of the audience to play the roles of his children.

In less than two minutes it became obvious why his wife was no longer warm and demonstrative "like that." Bundy insisted on playing both himself and his youngest daughter. In the role of his three-year-old daughter, who was quite obviously his favorite, he rushed to the substitute "daddy," and in exuberant tones went through their favorite ritual of pretending to be like Popeye—eating some spinach, wrestling with "daddy" and overpowering him to the floor.

If Bundy got the message, there will be a follow-up note in my mail one of these days; but I shall not be surprised to learn that he needs more than one lesson on the dangers of playing favorites and making his wife play second fiddle to his enthusiastic and responsive daughter. He did announce to the group at the end of the session that he had a great deal to think about.

Directed Psychodrama for a Premarital Stalemate

Body language is old hat to most counselors, especially the contradictory head shaking, the restless feet or hands, and the blush, stammer, cough or sneeze when the question is on target. Psychodrama is another form of body language which also employs verbal communication. It is at its best when it is spontaneous and unrehearsed as with Bundy, above. Here is how it was used on Sam's first visit; although it was not the first visit of his fiancée.

Sam and Judy

The young couple had already set the wedding date; but as the time grew nearer Judy became increasingly panicky, agitated, irritable and weepy. Sam, unable to comprehend, kept insisting that she had been all right *until* she began to see me. To him this was proof that he was justified in forbidding her to return. Judy's efforts to remind him that she had come *because* she was already upset for a whole year left him adamant and apparently unconvinced. Sam made his position quite clear at the beginning of the conference.

"I'm here under protest; and I will say absolutely nothing."

Later, it developed that Judy had threatened to call off the wedding if he did not accompany her for her regular appointment. He himself had used a similar technique with her to get his own way whenever she did not agree with him; but apparently this was the first time she had developed the courage to return tit for tat. Three previous private conferences and four group conferences had fortified Judy to a degree that she was now able to convince him that she meant what she said.

Sam, who sat apparently unmoved by Judy's tearful pleadings, nibbled at a few of my casual inquiries regarding his past military career and waived my efforts by a reminder to her that he had read some newspaper article saying that psychiatry was not what it was cracked up to be and therefore not to be trusted. He did, however, accept my proffered handshake when he entered and left; and he did accept a cigarette.

Sam also agreed to let me invite one of my nurses (V.H.) to participate in some role playing in order to demonstrate what Judy had been trying to explain. This acceptance surprised me until I reflected that he had obviously been informed by Judy about her previous classes in group psychotherapy. "You mean psychodrama?" he asked. To which I replied, "Yes, if possible. Will it be all right with you?" He nodded, and I repeated the question to Judy, to which she likewise assented.

Details of the resultant dialogue, innuendos, and reactions would require many pages which are not absolutely essential for the reading counselor. In brief, V.H. was cast as Judy, while I was prepared to double for Sam. To my pleasant surprise, however, Sam himself responded almost immediately to the new Judy's soft voice, mature demeanor, and conciliatory attitude. He reiterated his opinion that she could come to *him* for advice if she needed it, and that, because he loved her, he was therefore the best person to help her. In any event he was positive that she certainly did not need any psychiatrist, nor even a marriage counselor from their own church.

V.H. (as Judy) patiently agreed that they both loved each other and that she had tried to discuss problems with him, but *she* had concluded that she needed a *specialist* in counseling, and even if Sam were a qualified specialist in surgery, she would not expect him to diagnose and treat her for an acute appendix; she was sorry he felt this way but she had made up her mind and the rest was up to him.

Sam was obliged to change the subject. At first he tried to trap her with "Do you think I need a psychiatrist?" but V.H. as "Judy" was an old hand. She parried with "I'm grateful that you came just to help *me*. I'm certainly in no position to tell you what *you* need." Sam promptly changed his tactics and reverted to a more direct form of attack.

He reminded his psychodramatic "Judy" that she had always insisted on having her own way, for instance about the purchase of furniture, disposition of their earnings, and vetoing a sailing boat that he had wanted to buy. At this point, I stepped in as his double and deliberately exaggerated his complaints as well as his hostility and resentment. Having already been acquainted with some of these conflicts by Judy, during private and group sessions where she had been unusually fair and candid, I was able to identify so well with Sam that he kept nodding his head. He even complimented me later, on "doing it just right."

V.H., as Judy, listened patiently, agreed that maybe she had been too possessive and controlling; felt that he should have his sailboat since it was his money; and promised to be more considerate in the future. She was not, however, going to discontinue her visits to the doctor.

At this point she was invited to withdraw. The real Judy was still unable to say anything; and Sam repeated his refusal to return, either with or without her. He also reiterated his fear that I would tell her to give him up and that she would do so. They did not return; married a month later; and, so far, seem to be making a satisfactory adjustment.

Psychoshock for Parents in a Rut

Role playing—role reversal, projecting future episodes in the lives of the participants, and reliving past events—is a powerful therapeutic procedure. It serves as a rapid introduction to insight therapy and promptly alerts the client to the recognition that he himself is not the only person involved in his difficulties. Here is another example where it was used to confront and shock parents into a realization that they were making the same mistakes with their seventeen-year-old daughter Juanita that had all but destroyed their unhappy son, Tony. This was their first joint conference.

The Parents of Juanita and Tony

Both parents insisted that they had given the boy everything he wanted. Consequently there could be no fault on their part for Tony's failure to keep a job, to avoid alcohol, drugs and undesirable company, or even to complete his tour of satisfactory military service.

Casually they mentioned that Tony did love his sister, Juanita, who worshipped him, and that they usually stuck up for each other. A few questions on my part also disclosed that Juanita would not be permitted to date until she was "at least twenty-one years old, and can prove that she can take care of herself." They did not understand why Juanita had no friends, why she avoided dances and social events, and kept to her room and studies. Nor did they admit to anything unusual in daughter's program.

Since this was father's first visit, and might also be his last, I quickly decided that the daughter's predicament was more urgent than Tony's for which mother had first consulted me. With no preliminary explanation, and without asking their permission, I summoned V.H., motioned her to a chair and announced to the astonished parents,

"This is your daughter, Juanita. She has something to tell you. It's bad news; in fact, the worst. I want you to listen to her as though she were your own daughter Juanita and then pretend that you are both at home talking to your own daughter. Will that be all right?"

They nodded, without fully comprehending; but V.H., as Juanita, needed no further coaching. She bowed her head, fidgeted with her hands and said in low tones.

"Mother, I've got something to tell you." She waited for an answer but got none; so she added more loudly. "I'm gonna have a baby." She had to meet the stunned silence by shrilly repeating her statement. "Didn't you hear me, Mother?" "I'm pregnant!"

Mother finally got the message, looked at me helplessly, and then fatuously demanded, "How did that happen?" V.H. as the psychodramatic "Juanita" answered, "Oh come off it mother. You know *how* it happened; but that's not the point. What am I gonna do about it?"

Mother tried to cover her mounting anxiety by explaining that such a thing could never happen to her daughter *because she doesn't even date*. "That's what you think," said "Juanita," whereupon mother began an interrogation. "You mean to say you've been going out behind our backs?"

"Oh come off it Mom. That's not the point any more. I'm pregnant, I'm gonna have a baby and I don't wanna have a baby. What do I do?"

Father's initial smiles of confident amusement had vanished, but he remained quiet. Mother began to enter more seriously into the structured scene. "Well, we won't make you marry him when you don't love him. . . ."

"Who said I don't love him? I *do* love him; but he won't marry me."

Mother sputtered over that one and then announced, "Well, we won't let you give up the baby. We'll take care of it."

"But I don't *want* the baby!"

"Well you can't give it up. *We'll* adopt it. . . ."

"What about Pa? What's he gonna say about that?" Mother reluctantly turned to the still silent father and said, "Well, we'll have to ask him." But she didn't. Instead, Juanita had to ask him, "What am I gonna do, Pa?" to which he could only reply, slowly and in obvious and honest perplexity, "I don't know."

V.H. was then excused, without further comment; and both parents adopted a more chastened and cooperative attitude. The warning had been received but rejected and mother promptly began asking what they had to do to help their son Tony. Obviously they felt quite safe as far as Juanita was concerned; or at least they hoped they were safe. When father heard the prescription for them both to come to school via group psychotherapy, he kept asking how this would help his son. He ignored both the prescription and explanations. He also took refuge in reciting his own history of combat fatigue as a soldier in World War II, but mother cut him short and said she would get him to come.

At their first group conference, the very next evening, I did not bring up either Tony's problem or the hypothetical pregnancy. Instead, at the first suitable opportunity I cast each parent into the role of parent of an unhappy teenster who was rebelling against restrictions that had been instituted for unsatisfactory schoolwork. From that they were led to an airing of their views on discipline, chores, privileges *and dating*. The discussions were lively and productive so they left their first group with subdued but enthusiastic reactions and a slight ray of hope for their black sheep son. They had also developed a little more respect for Tony because he had been the first one to urge them to let up on their restrictions of Juanita, several months earlier.

N.B. The real purpose of the office role playing was to bring home to them the myth which they had fostered for over two decades. This was something that could not (must not) happen to their Juanita. Parents cannot help being shocked at the announcement of a premarital pregnancy; but the shock is much greater when it hits home. *Tony's mother had once been obliged to make the same announcement to her own parents in the late 1940s.*

The parents have repeatedly insisted to Tony that they married for love; that his conception was planned in order to compel their parents to agree to the marriage; and that since Tony was a child of love, they could not possibly hold anything against the boy. However, from Tony's behavior and the reactions of the parents to the above brief sociodrama (psychodramatic portrayal of a hypothetical situation), you can draw your own conclusions as to how much to believe. Obviously they protested too much.

After that one joint conference and the one group session father never returned. Mother resumed private and group conferences, but only for a short period. She promptly shifted her attack to nagging Tony about his untrimmed hair and droopy moustache. After four group conferences during which she reluctantly admitted his improvement, she abruptly cancelled all future appointments when Tony quit his job and decided to free lance away from home.

Tony, himself attended a different group and appeared to enjoy his active participation. He also learned autohypnosis in private sessions for "turning on" a hallucinated "trip" claiming that he no longer requires drugs. His sister's status quo remained unchallenged, although Tony says his parents have been a little easier on her than formerly. His sudden departure without cancelling his appointments or informing the group, suggests another blow-up with mother. It also indicates rejection of father, boss and therapist at least for the present.

Counselors are not expected to succeed in every undertaking. However, considering the usual difficulties of getting anywhere at all with clients who have character disorders, the contacts in this case have not been a total failure.

The counselor takes a chance and gambles on the reactions of his clients or patients when he confronts them with probable fact. This is equally true whether the confrontation is direct as with Sam above or is made indirectly as with Tony's parents. Nevertheless, when the situation is urgent, the direct and frontal attack is often preferable to slower and more permissive techniques. This was accomplished with Tony on his third visit, although the ground work had already been laid at the time of our first encounter.

Hypnotic "Turning On" as Substitution for an LSD Trip

Tony

In the case of Tony, above, I had already had two sessions with the young man before I met his father. The first session had been a joint conference with Tony and his mother, who had brought him for being uncooperative and going with a bad crowd that used drugs. I had used that occasion to soothe his ruffled feelings and to convince mother that he could not have been all bad or he would not have consented to come at all.

The second session (without mother), found him less eager for hypnosis, for which the referring psychiatrist had sent him, and much more anxious to learn whether I was going to be another in his long list of authoritative "old school" father figures. Nevertheless when the costs of his periodic, although allegedly infrequent indulgences in narcotics came up, Tony admitted that he had read somewhere that hypnosis could produce a similar "turned on" state; so he agreed to try. He not only tried but he also succeeded, and apparently did not mind the constructive suggestions for more mature behavior which I subtly inserted into the verbalization.

This does not mean that he is cured of his dependency on drugs. It does mean that he has learned a little more about me as well as himself. It also means that as long as I do not pressure him, he will cooperate for a reasonable length of time. He showed this at his third visit, by shifting the conversation to better ways and means for helping his unhappy withdrawn sister Juanita. Further verification of the gradual alteration in his personality and attitude came from his parents; both of whom volunteered the information that he is easier to get along with. "He will now listen to us when we talk to him, without blowing up and leaving home."

Tony himself reported that after staying out all night and returning home at 7 AM his mother had done no more than ask him whether he had had a good time and did he want some breakfast. Under the circumstances of almost ten years of daily emotional explosions and frightening temper tantrums, this change represented a considerable step in a constructive direction.

He became much more careful with his diction and elocution. This resulted from prompt acceptance by me and the group of his ambition to become a disc jockey. This was in sharp contrast with the discouragement which he usually got from his parents whenever the subject of a career came up. Unfortunately as reported above, the honeymoon did not last. Father refused to return. Mother soon wearied of carrying the load without him, and Tony himself took off for the summer. He will probably return when he is ready for further help.

Further Examples of Free Association Elicited by Direct Inquiry

Repetition of the client's key words or statements often proves to be more productive of associated information than trying to phrase specific or new questions. When the counselor sets his mind on a seemingly productive field of inquiry he may tend to ride a hobby that the patient rejects because he is not yet ready for such discussion. It is much easier not to try to conduct an inquiry from a mentally prepared script. *Simply repeat the client's own words or expression with a question mark at the end and let him take it from there.* Here are some examples:

Case of Hetty's Headache

Hetty announced (in group), "I feel *rotten*." Ed responded to her appeal.

(Ed) Q. You feel *rotten?*

(Hetty) A. I feel *terribly ill.*

Q. *Terribly ill?*

A. Uhuh, terribly terribly ill. Go find *a new head* for me.

Q. A *new head?*

A. Uhuh—brand new—anything would be *an improvement* over the one I got.

Q. An improvement?

A. If it's not an improvement *I don't want it.*

Q. Don't want it?

A. Don't want it.

Q. What kind of a head would you like?

A. One that don't ache *all the time.*

Q. *All the time?*

A. All the time; almost steadily *for the last six weeks.*

Q. When was six weeks ago?

A. About a month or almost six weeks ago.

Q. What *date* would that be?

A. About the *beginning of March.*

Q. What was special about the beginning of March?

A. About the time *my blood pressure went up again.* [There was complete silence. Ed glanced at me for help and I took over. Hetty had become pensive. One hand was near her mouth, and one finger rested lightly across her lips, as though cautioning them to be silent.]

(Dr. S.) Q. *You remember?*

(Hetty) A. What? *What caused it to go up?*

Q. Yes.

A. Part of it was that *I got upset in the office*, that's all I can remember.

Q. Something happened in the *office?*

A. Yes. Work kept piling up *on account of* this one girl. Happens all the time. My boss kept telling me not to worry.

Q. This one girl?

A. Yes. If she did less talking and running around she would do more good. It piles up and then I get *swamped.*

Q. When else have you felt *swamped?*

A. I couldn't *remember* any other time, exactly, not right at the moment.

Q. How far back can you *remember?*

A. Way back *when I was a little girl.*

Q. About how old was the *little girl?*

A. 2½ or 3.

Q. What happened *then?*

A. Someone gave me *a new chair. A little chair of my very own.*

Q. Yes?

A. That's all. It was a plain little straight chair—but it was mine. [Silence for a long minute.]

Q. Why do you suppose that comes to your mind *right now?*

A. It's the earliest that I can *remember*—that and sticking my tongue out at a lady—funny old lady who lived down the street. She used to throw a pail of water at the kids and at me for sticking my tongue out. Mother just pulled me back home. My brother used to sing. Old Mrs. So and So—It wasn't very nice. Mother was very special. *She was always in the house when we wanted her.*

Q. *Always?*

A. Well, *almost always*—usually. To me she was what she should be.

Prior to her announcement about feeling rotten, there had been comments in the group regarding washing, meals, and children coming home to an empty house. Hetty finally reported, "My daughter is fifteen. She has to come home to an empty house during the week; but she doesn't complain about it. *She has supper ready when her father and I get home.*" About an hour later, Hetty announced that the girl in the office reminded her of herself as well as her teenage daughter. She finished with, "and my headache's gone."

Psychosomatic complaints are usually disguises for more personal problems. Most of the time their origin is obscure; but in many cases the camouflage is more obvious, as in the following case of Caroline.

When Presenting Complaint Is Smoke Screen Cover of Personal Anxieties

Case of Caroline's Complaints

Caroline, thirty-nine, poured out the following series of complaints about her husband. The group was attentive.

He has a chronic paraplegia and backache for the past twelve years. And before that he was bent over and couldn't straighten up. You can't take a Polock to a doctor without an ambulance. And five years ago he had a hernia; but he wouldn't let himself get operated—not until last October. One nerve specialist says he's got multiple sclerosis; but the doctor at the soldier's home say it's just a form of neuritis.

I interrupted her to ask what her husband was doing now; and learned that he was being driven to and from work, but he was busy and successful in a local rubber plant, making automobile tires.

"I just could never make him relax."

Since Caroline's rapid speech and restless body indicated her own inability to relax, I concentrated on some of her own anxieties. A few brief questions revealed the fact that her sisters were still blaming her for putting her mother in a chronic mental hospital.

They said you're gonna kill her; but I was the only one who'd follow the doctor's advice. They were all too chicken. They wouldn't take care of her; and I did the best I could. But she wasn't even able to remember my name, or whether she'd eaten. She messed all over; and she even ran out into the street in all that traffic. What else could I do? (tears)

Once the air was cleared on this score, relaxation exercises and supportive group therapy began to accomplish what she needed. Within two months following the above scene she scarcely mentioned her husband, except when someone in the group inquired about his well-being. He himself told her she showed vast improvement; but, naturally, he persistently declined to come for himself.

A month later, Caroline reported that her relationship with her husband Louis has improved "and that he looked better this week." I asked, "Did you tell him so?" and she said, "Yes"; but when invited to show us how, in psychodrama, her remarks did not sound at all complimentary. For example, "Oh, you're home early tonight *for a change.*" The group laughed, and I asked her if she knew why they were laughing. She grinned and said she guessed she did not know how to compliment people.

Later when we had her act out her last visit to her senile and mentally deteriorated, hospitalized mother, she wept copiously. Then we cast her in a scene with her substitute sisters; but this time she was able to tell them off in no uncertain terms. From then on Caroline's relations with her husband steadily improved.

Still later some evidence of change in her domestic situation is indicated by the following note which she sent me a few days after the above group session.

Tonight has turned out to be a very enjoyable evening. Although Louis lost his temper at S. (our daughter) just before supper he was very nice to me. We did a little shopping together at the supermarket, and I replaced a tiny screw in his glasses for him. He was very talkative about his job; and it was so good to have something to listen to instead of the usual awful quiet or faultfinding. He praised the supper, gave me a kiss and even an invitation to visit him in his bed!

When Much Is Expected from a Single Conference

"Girl Shy" Gary

Two hours were reserved for this first session because Gary lived in another state. He also wrote that the matter was urgent.

The first half hour was spent in securing relevant historical data: oldest of five, the youngest a sister; college graduate living with an old chum; parents disappointed in his failure to pursue father's professional career; several affairs with eligible girls, but inability to trust himself to any of them; no impotence; social drinking in moderation; more comfortable with men. Father was an only child; mother was the third girl, with a younger brother who was also the first grandson in both families.

The second half hour was spent in teaching Gary elementary relaxation and encouraging him to discuss his reactions to simple physiological phenomena of tension and unconscious resistance: the forearm maneuver, the imaginary pillow, the clenched fist induction, the stretched shoe illusion and respiratory relaxation.[1]

The second hour was used in exploring his early recollections via the clenched fist displacement technique.[2] In brief, he was invited to recall an important event in his life. If happy, he could close his right (dominant) fist, if unhappy, his left. The left hand closed; and he reported feeling lost and afraid in a big old house.

"We lived there when I was four. Father was away in the service. Mother was playing hide and seek. I was afraid; and I didn't enjoy it." After a few moments of silence he became apprehensive, as though leaning from a high chair. "I'm afraid I'm going to fall." He repeated this, but did not elaborate, even after my reassurance.

He ignored the next few suggestions for another recall. Instead he continued to associate: being the only little boy in his neighborhood with no one but girls to play with; "They didn't make me feel comfortable." His next memory happened a few years later, at nine or ten, being exposed to fights with several little bullies whom he whipped, and by whom was then whipped in turn, "after which we became friends."

Once Gary had gotten these recollections off his chest he was receptive to the suggestion for another recall but this time it was a happy one. "A few years ago . . . My former girlfriend, it was at a beach house, we were alone. She'd just stepped out of the shower. I was in my trunks, resting on a cot. She put on a tangerine bath robe and fastened the belt loosely. Then she came to me. We embraced and knelt together. I didn't violate her. Yet she said I made her feel like a woman. And I sure did feel like a man. . . ." His voice trailed off as his features reflected the wonderment of discovery of the age-old rejuvenating power of love.

He was invited to remember as much of these and other events in his life as he felt were necessary. I also suggested that he could begin to remember some of his other hobbies, dreams and ambitions, especially since he had rediscovered some identification with some of his father's compulsive mannerisms and conscientious character.

He could contemplate the possibility of his mother's chagrin at being supplanted by a brother (Gary's maternal uncle) and that boy's important role as the first grandson in both families. He had certainly heard of natural psychological displacement of a woman's resentments from her brothers to her sons. He could even agree that his father, never having had any siblings, could require some years to get used to his own brood, and could also have mixed feelings about them even though they were his own children.

Gary was then reminded that his first memory, here, had been an unhappy one with a woman—his mother. Then he had associated unhappy times with only girls as playmates. After that he had discovered self-confidence via physical combat with boys. Having gotten all these off his chest he was then able to remember that a young woman had made him feel like a man. This was a woman with whom he had obviously been in love and who quite obviously returned that love.

The second hour ended with his spontaneous arousal. He was animated, enthused, refreshed, and eager for his next appointment a fortnight hence.

Gary cancelled his second appointment and asked for a leave of absence, pleading pressure of work.

Most therapists would agree that this first session was too ambitious and threatening. Each counselor must decide for himself how much this client or patient can take, but failure to return does not necessarily imply failure of therapy. Some people learn a great deal in a short period of time. Others may wait for several years before resuming a therapeutic program.

Occasionally, a session may last for three or four hours, and be renewed the next day. In most cases counseling sessions can produce reasonably satisfactory results in fifty to sixty minutes. Quite often, however, only ten or fifteen minutes are available. When this is the case, the first interview may be more productive after several preliminary group conferences during which the client has an opportunity to familiarize himself with the counselor's personality as well as his techniques. The groups also serve to remind the client that he is not the only person with problems; and this usually makes him feel better from the start.

The cases of Sam and Judy, Bundy, Tony's parents and Hetty, Caroline and Antoinette (described above) all developed in a group setting. Here is one that took place in a familiar group of three.

Case of the Open Secret

Karen had been referred for a weird assortment of nervous complaints none of which made medical sense. *She also wanted her husband to be present.* I soon became satisfied that there was no organic basis for her problem of "nerves, insomnia, loss of weight, irritability and inability to concentrate." I then began to search for clues to explain not only the symptoms but also the failure of medication prescribed by previous specialists.

Two people in her working situation kept coming up for discussion. One of these was a woman with whom Karen was obviously identifying. The other was a slightly older boss for whom she had an amazing mixture of contradictory feelings. One moment she was criticizing him as though he had offended her personally. Then, in the next breath she defended him as though someone else had attacked her own father.

I suggested that she relax herself and then told her that the signs all pointed to her having another in her long series of crushes—this one with her boss.

At first she rejected the idea as being ridiculous; but when I reminded her of the normal symptoms of love she blushed, opened her eyes and then reproached me for saying all this in her husband's presence.

I told her that I was certain that he would be so relieved that her condition was not more serious, that she had no "terrible disease" and did not "need to be hospitalized" *or to have shock therapy,* that he would actually be delighted. And he was. He showed it by promptly and indulgently reminding her that she had had similar crushes before and had always survived them. They left smiling and obviously relieved.

A few minutes later, while waiting for the nurse to recheck her blood pressure to determine whether or not a change of medication was needed, Karen called me in to whisper, "You were right, you know!" I smiled back and reassured her that "growing pains" lasted longer in some people and that wives were not the only members of the marriage team that understood their partner's problems. Her blood pressure had returned to normal, and her bottles of medicine are still waiting for her to reclaim them.

Six weeks later, after attending five consecutive group sessions with her husband, she again brought up the subject.

> Since giving up my job I'm not scared or nervous any more. My husband's changed, too, especially since you got him to play some of those scenes with the other women. Oh, and by the way, that man we talked about? Well, I think I've still got a crush on him; but it doesn't bother me any more.

Her husband corroborated her statement.

Self-Help from Exposure to Psychodrama (A report from one of my students.)

> In my personal experience with psychodrama, I have found it effective in doing what it purports to do. Although I wasn't involved actively in the role-playing in the group psychotherapy session, the problem presented was almost uniquely mine. It had to do with a group member's feelings about his father which so closely resembled mine. After the termination of the role-playing, the patient could verbalize his feelings towards his father as he did with the substitute father with whom he had been playing the role, e.g., *Dad, you're a pretty swell guy.*
>
> Though I remained silent during the whole process, I went home, called my father, and found that I could express just how I really felt about him for the first time that *I can remember*. As a result of the psychodrama, I also gained insight into the cause of my ambivalence (R.M.R.)

Resolution of Conflict by Agreement

Full agreement with the client is often an effective way to dissolve resistance. Here are two examples:

> In a first joint conference with her husband Dan for a domestic problem, Maureen was insistent on leaving the town of X or else she was going to divorce her husband. Having moved to X from Y,

only a short time previously, Dan was not anxious to pull up stakes. Besides, X was closer to his place of business. Nevertheless, *I urged them both to move to Z as soon as possible and to start looking for a new home that very day.* At the next visit, the following week, Dan reported that his wife talked him out of house hunting after they left my office, that she has been making all sorts of excuses to avoid looking for a new house, and that she is even talking of making do with the one they now have in X.

At Maureen's second visit (her first private conference) several important facts emerged: her mother and sister had been no help in her emotional growing up. The only confidantes and girlfriend she could count on was a woman her own age in Y. Her resentment to X was transferred to her husband, and this naturally provoked the marital conflict for which they were consulting me. As soon as she found (in me) a temporary replacement for the confidante whom she had left in Y, her need to return to Y was sharply diminished. She even became less hostile to X where she admitted that she has been resisting the efforts of a "new" neighbor to be her friend. There were other personal and domestic conflicts, of course; but these are irrelevant for this discussion and are gradually responding to further therapy.

At this writing, only three weeks later, Dan is ready to agree with Maureen that he is not being paid as much as he deserved. He is now ready to consider either a return to his former job or a comparably more lucrative offer elsewhere. In either event it will be he who urges the change of residence.

Here is another example of agreement as a neutralizer.

Joe, a teen-ager, was insisting on marrying Heather, a girl of his own age but with a different religion. His orthodox parents were naturally greatly disturbed. I invited the young people in for a conference; and much to their amazement, I agreed with them that their own happiness should be given priority. They left with plans for an immediate elopement; but this fell through when his parents (at my suggestion) invited Heather to be their house guest for a few weeks. After only a few days at Joe's home, the girl's disenchantment crystallized and became effective in postponing her decision to elope. Within a few months, each of them was dating a more eligible partner.

REFERENCES AND READINGS

1. BUCKHEIMER, A., and BALOGH, S. C.: *The Counselling Relationship—A Case Book.* Chicago, Sci. Res. Assoc., 1961.
2. GARRETT, A.: *Interviewing, Its Principles and Methods.* New York, Fam. Welfare Assoc. of America, 1942.

3. STEIN, C.: *Practical Psychotherapeutic Techniques.* Springfield, Thomas, 1968.
4. STEIN, C.: *Practical Psychotherapy in Nonpsychiatric Specialties.* Springfield, Thomas, 1969.

Chapter 5

COMMON PROBLEMS OF CHILDREN

THE IMPRESSIONABLE YEARS

THE FIRST SIX YEARS of a child's life are probably the most impressionable and formative of his entire career. They are certainly the most responsive to intellectual learning, to training for self-control, character formation and socialization. They are also a continual challenge to everyone for they encompass the greatest liability to injury, accident, seizures, infections and disorders of personality. Even suicide and infanticide are by no means rare, although these misfortunes are usually interpreted as "accidental deaths."

Rates of growth and normal averages on the appearance of teeth, speech, locomotion, learning and control of bowel and bladder are available in any pediatric textbook as well as in popular family reference books.[2, 4, 8, 9, 12, 14, 17]

Problems of digestion, hearing and other common complaints are usually referred first to the family physician or pediatrician, but the family counselor often needs help on many common problems which are frequently seen at general child guidance clinics and do not interest the average physician.

A large variety of complaints may bring a child and his parents to the child and family counselor. Most of these are classifiable as behavior problems, emotional instability, immaturity, tantrums, delinquencies and school difficulties. In one study these totaled over 70 per cent of five hundred children.[19] Today's terminology and classifications may be different, according to individual schools of psychotherapy, but the chief problems of children have not changed appreciably. They inevitably involve emotionally insecure parents and sometimes even "problem teachers."

Additional findings that are not always complained of by

[64]

parents or teachers often include removable physical defects, intellectual retardation, speech disorders, bedwetting, "nervousness," recurrent disturbances of the digestive tract, some form of sex play, disorders of hearing, vision, reading and the like. Only a few of the more challenging problems will be discussed here.

Psychosomatic complaints are usually first referred to the family doctor; but, when he gives a clean bill of health, the problem may revert back to the counselor because families are shy about seeing psychiatrists. Children who have been pampered during a physical illness and ignored at other times are more likely to seek an outlet for their tension in the form of a "functional" complaint. Look for unconscious motivation and mimicry.

Children are avid mimics. They mimic speech and other defects as well as skills and peculiarities. Here is one that puzzled pediatrician and neurologist until mamma began to think back over the recent course of events.

Bobby's Lame Gait

Bobby, age two and one half years, suddenly developed a limping gait. He had not been ill, nor suffered an accident. The doctors and specialist could find nothing wrong with him and nothing to explain it. "We puzzled and worried over it for several weeks until I found the answer." Hannah talked it over with her husband Harry, who remembered that the boy had started walking at one year and was always very active. The limping began several weeks after they had moved to Toledo, on a business transfer.

"I remembered that I used to take Bobby for a walk every day. Our route took us by a large home for crippled children. I figured that Bobby thought that maybe limping was the proper way to walk."

"Harry suggested changing the route. I did so, and within a week or so Bobby had dropped the limp and was walking normally again."

When telling me about the incident, many years later, Hannah did not recall ever showing undue concern for the crippled children; but a child can sense his mother's feelings just by the change in tensions in her hand and voice, an alteration in their pace, her concerned expression and the evasive or incomplete answers she had given to his precocious questions.

The problem never recurred; but mother had not realized that small children can also be homesick, even at two and one half years. Bobby's limp had won him all the attention (secondary gains) he needed except another brother or sister. For these coveted playmates he had to wait until he grew up, married and fathered his own.

Do not minimize psychosomatic complaints. Accept them at face value; but look also for *secondary gains* as the child seeks to recapture privileges and attention. Then seek better methods for reestablishing his former prestige. A good beginning is to concentrate on what the child *can* do now, while cultivating his latest interests for motivating future behavior.

BED WETTING

Enuresis is usually a nocturnal problem. In the normal child, it is rarely accompanied by soiling. Competition from a newly arrived sibling or loss of a playmate is a common factor; but outright parental rejection was found in 115 of my five hundred cases (23%). Rejecting mothers outnumbered the rejecting fathers by three to one.

Some teachers also reject children and penalize their pupils for using toilets during classtime. In one such case the hapless child was required to write his name on the blackboard and take a detention for each "offense." This was stopped as a result of a visit by the psychiatric social worker to the school principal.

The normal child can develop bladder control on his own within two years; or he may not achieve it until he is nearly five years old. Once trained, however, he may be so fastidious that he will void only on the lap of someone he likes very much, or as retaliation against those who have offended him. Many a child who habitually wets his own bed at home will remain perfectly dry in the home of a relative or friend, or in a hospital; but he will promptly renew the habit as soon as he returns home.

Several adolescents complacently reported that their parents and older siblings had continued to wet the bed until they were married; and at least one wife reported that her husband never wet the bed when he slept away from home but usually did so whenever he slept with her. Erotic excitement is a common cause of enuresis, but many people respond to other unusual excitement with an urgency to urinate, for example, while dancing or on arriving home. If the stimulus is too strong or restraint proves inadequate, an "accident" may result. I have observed this same temporary incontinence from excitement in a young puppy. The animal was well treated, and had been housebroken for several months, yet she nearly always lost a few drops of urine whenever her young master returned home after an all day absence.

The treatment of enuresis calls for an alteration of attitudes, abolition of reproaches, pessimism, morning inspection or punishment, and replacement by accentuating positive attitudes and successes.

When causes are fairly well known and have been mitigated as much as possible, the child may be confronted with the responsibility of contributing his share to family tranquility. Pediatricians may advise restriction of fluids at night and perhaps a bedtime sedative. Psychologists often suggest reconditioning gimmicks such as hydroelectric alarms. Therapists who are familiar with the art of suggestion can use a variety of displacement and reconditioning techniques which include essentially the following procedures and objectives: [6, 22]

Make the child your ally through *positive transference* or identification with someone he likes. A calendar record of *D's* (for *dry* nights) will usually show that *not every night is wet.* How come? Persuade the child to *alter* his pattern. First suggest that he should not play favorites. Why not fill all the squares on the calendar with great big imaginary *W's*? Or how about half of them, or three fourths? or maybe two thirds? or at least one square every month!

By inference, his imagination projects a calendar page full of more *D's* than *W's*. Meanwhile you are throwing out alternative suggestions for *permission to wet as often* as he needs, in order to prove whatever he wants to prove: That he can surprise his mother as well as himself? That he can prove he is as big as Daddy or brother by wetting the *whole* bed, instead of just the middle, or even a few inches? He will need a ruler or yardstick for that; and of course he will want to record the *diameter* of each night's *work*, along with all those *D's*. You might wonder which will win the race, the numbers (of inches representing the size of the damp spot) or the great big beautiful *D's*. The *N's* and the *D's*, the numbers or the dry's. . . ?

N is associated with "NO," but it could also mean "nice." *D* often signifies "don't" to the average child, but it could also represent "DO" as well as "dandy" and "DRY," just as silver and gold stars are familiar symbols of degrees of success.

With suitable rewards for successes, *not bribes in advance,* the child will soon be wanting a full calendar of tokens which he can exchange for something that is more important to him than stirring up the household. This is the same reinforcement procedure that is used to train schizophrenic and retarded children as well as psychotic adults. From food and praise for their efforts they graduate to tokens which they can exchange for candy, toys and privileges.*

Erickson usually adds suggestions to turn the tables by hinting at the probable chagrin and consternation when mother or the hotel maid or grandma, whom he is visiting, fail to find the wet bed which they were expecting.[6] He also adds in confidential tones that this can be a *personal secret* between the child and therapist; *because we really do not know when you are going to show that you do not have to wet in order to prove that you can sleep soundly because you can sleep just as soundly without wetting at all.*

Or, to use my analogy, we really do not know just how soon that race between the *N's* and *D's* is going to be over, but there is no question of the *D's* winning, or of the rewards and satisfactions at the finish. Maybe it will be before Mother's Day, or even before your birthday, or possibly April Fool's Day. The conspiracy deepens as therapist and patient forge a bond of surprise for the folks.

Even without hypnosis the counselor can use *suggestions to alter the problem first* (producing a *larger* damp spot, or wetting *every* night instead of only two or three times a week). Once the patient has accepted the suggestion for *any* kind of change, he is open to suggestions for reductions as well as increases in his habits.

Another scheme, which can also be just as effective without hypnosis (provided that one has the child's concentrated attention) is to remark that while a large wet sheet is quite an accomplishment for anyone, there is always the wisdom of saving a

---

* "Reinforcement Therapy," 16 mm. sound, available by Smith Kline & French Laboratories, Philadelphia, Pennsylvania.

little urine for the next time. Some therapists urge the child to practice stopping his voiding just before completely emptying his bladder, so as to get used to leaving a little. This also exercises his constricting sphincter muscles. Urethra and anus both operate on the same circuit. The suggestion is offered via the soliloquy, as though the therapist were talking to himself instead of to the child.

> But what if there wasn't any more urine for the next time? Wouldn't be much fun! Have to go all day maybe, or at least half a day, or maybe most of the night, or even the whole night until the bladder gets full again, so he'll be able to do *a really good job*.
>
> And wouldn't it be a shame not to see that strong and powerful stream, and hear its force in the toilet, just like a real faucet or garden hose?

Jacobs hints at a special "signal" which the child can learn. This tells when the bladder is full. Meanwhile, under hypnosis, he reassures the child of his parents' love. He then urges the parents to accentuate their positive affection and eliminate negative criticism.[10]

The problem of enuresis is difficult chiefly because people make it so. The techniques that are used, like the verbalization, are less important than the attitudes.

A similar approach using the double-bind suggestion is commonly referred to as "negative psychology." It is also effective for other undesirable habits, especially when family attitudes remain unchanged. For instance, there is the problem of getting children to bed and other compulsive behavior.

OTHER COMPULSIONS

Thumbsucking, nailbiting, disturbances of speech, sleeping difficulties, temper tantrums, nervous tics, psychosomatic complaints, disciplinary problems and school difficulties may be expected from stressful situations. These are especially difficult to manage when the family, teachers and patients try to shift responsibility onto the guidance and counseling expert. The therapist should serve as pilot, and the burden of following his recommendations should be placed squarely on the skipper, executive officer and crew—father, mother and children.

Habit spasms, like thumbsucking, headbanging, blinking, nail-biting and so on tend to be most prominent during times of un-happiness, fear, overstimulation from quarrels, competition or too much television. Treatment for all of these consists of re-moving causes, reassurance and unconditioning by offering more satisfying replacements.

Thumbsucking has been noted in newborn infants, who can demonstrate prenatal practice by efficiently placing the thumb within the mouth without any floundering about for location. Its origin is to be found in the normal sucking reflex which is essen-tial for bringing food to the infant. When the babe is hungry or anxious it usually seeks its thumb or fingers or blanket edge or whatever is available. Time and practice do the rest. Attempts at conditioning by painting the thumb with bitter substance or using thumb guards as elbow cuffs are usually worthless, unless the thumb is promptly replaced by something constantly pleasant.

The thumbsucking child should be offered some attractive diversion as the hand is drawn gently but repeatedly from his mouth. When long-established habit is the problem, Erickson suggests (under varying depths of hypnotic relaxation) that the child ought to *play fair and suck all ten of his fingers an equal number of times; but only when someone is looking.*[6] Or perhaps just a kiss for each digit. Or maybe one little finger near his mouth real close would serve the purpose.

The headbanging child may be in serious trouble, and he re-quires neurological clearance before counseling. The simple man-agement of one such case by displacement and suggestions has been described elsewhere.[22] The little fellow's father sat with the child, rocked the boy's foot and leg in time with the head and uttered a soft "boom" every time the foot touched the bed. Within a few days the boy was rocking himself to sleep with his foot instead of his head. Other methods employing similar substitutes and displacements can be adapted to given situations; but pediatric neurological factors should be ruled out first. After that, persistence and consistency are the prime factors.

The nailbiter is likewise reminded that he should not show partiality. He has ten fingers and ten toes. He could rotate, one for every day. Or, since he has not been able to enjoy anything but skimpy nibbles for quite a long time, perhaps he would consider another suggestion. This is usually more effective with the patient, whether child or adult, in a light to medium hypnotic trance; but any confident counselor can make it effective as long as he has the patient's concentrated and undivided attention. (The following verbalization is a modification of Erickson's approach): [6]

> Wouldn't it be interesting if you could chew on only nine fingernails until one of them got big enough and beautiful enough for you to take a really big satisfying bite out of it?
>
> As a matter of fact (said with calm nonchalance) I've known some people to be quite satisfied with nibbling on only six or seven fingernails; or maybe four or five nails; or even two or three nails.
>
> But they could always count on one nail to chew on whenever they felt a need to be angry with someone, or perhaps even when they are angry with themselves.

The message seldom requires repetition. The patient may reject many of your other suggestions, but girls and women are especially amused and intrigued by the possibilities. They are also eager to please someone who apparently seems to care about them, especially when their major underlying problems cannot be readily changed to any appreciable degree.

The constipated child has usually become accustomed to a lot of parental emphasis on regularity. Dependency on cathartics and enemata is easily developed and is often used to divert attention from more embarrassing or uncomfortable situations. Pleasure from repeated uses of enemata can lead to homosexual and other anal practices, as well as to recurrent troubles with the lower bowel. When the physician gives a clean bill of health, try counseling the family, especially the mother.

However, remember that appendicitis, spasm, obstructions

and common infectious diseases, as well as various poisonings or anxiety from other sources, frequently start with a sudden change in bowel habits. Cathartics should not be used solely on advice of neighbor, druggist or grandma. When in doubt about this or any other emergency, take the child to the family doctor or to the nearest emergency hospital. If the situation is not acute, they will probably recommend an enema, but if it is a habitual state of affairs, one should remember that the anal passage can get used to vicarious erotic stimulation. It can also be irritated and traumatized. While waiting, get as much information from the child himself. He or his playmates may have been sexperimenting.

SPEECH DIFFICULTIES

The serious study of speech disorders (dysarthria) is a matter of comparatively recent date. Sometimes retarded speech is the first indication to the family that the child is the victim of a damaged brain or delayed intellectual development. Rarely it is the result of a tied tongue from too short a frenulum. The usual cause is faulty teaching, and neglect to spend enough time to coach the child whose earliest pronunciations are naturally imperfect.

Families tend to accept "cute" imitations or lisping attempts and letter substitution. These produce such neologisms (newly coined words) as "nanna" for grandma, "doddy" for doggy, "Loozybuth" for Elizabeth, "vaccination room" for recreation room and "maternity pin" for fraternity pin. By the time the child is past school age the habit becomes difficult to change. When a parent, a relative or a playmate also has a speech defect, the temptation to imitate is all but irresistible. Whatever the causes, they must be discovered and removed if possible.

Faulty speech is *largely a matter of habit*. It can be prevented by good training which is usually available at a first-class child guidance clinic and is also becoming a regular feature of many large school systems. Such common disturbances as lisping, stuttering, stammering and baby talk may be classified for convenience as *compulsion neuroses*.

The counselor is concerned with *motivation*. Many a child

prefers to point to the article he wants without uttering more than a gurgling sound, rather than expose himself to laughter and ridicule. Just as in teaching a child to walk, patience, repetition, and persistence are important watchwords in training children to talk properly. Here are a few basic principles:

Lisping is the result of improper placement of the tongue in making the "S" sound. When the tongue is allowed to get in between the teeth, however, the sound approaches a "Th" sound. This is known as a *"low S lisp."* When the tongue is held too far back, and an "sh" or "sch" sound comes out instead of a hissing "S," it is known as a *"lateral S lisp."* Personal coaching and practice is the correct answer to both problems. Audiovisual aids and simple rewards can speed the therapy.

Stuttering consists of a blocking of the initial consonants of a word ("s-s-s-tuttering"). Stage fright, a sudden confrontation, disappointment, scolding or embarrassment may trigger its onset.*

Stammering consists of similar blocking on *any* part of the word, usually not the first letter ("sta-a-am-mam-m-m-er-er--ering"). Fear of being unable to pronounce the word correctly usually causes a prolonged hesitation. This results in a compulsive repetition of the offending letter or syllable, or even of an entire word. The problem often begins after a separation or loss of an important friend or pet, or some other personal emotional trauma.

Rapidity of thoughts causes an accumulation of words that are all trying to get out of the speaker's mouth at the same time. New words may be coined by rapid thinkers; and some of our eminent statesmen and actors have been heard to say "particerly" or "particly" instead of *particularly*. They also frequently fail to complete a clause or sentence. Whenever a speaker is unable to speak as rapidly as he can think or is anxious about his subject, or when he is before a potentially critical audience and has an inadequate command of his subject, then stuttering or stammering may result.

The two terms are often used interchangeably. Many children who are high strung are liable to stammer a little during early childhood; but patient and sympathetic handling as with enuresis

---

* Brutten, E. J., and Shoemaker, D. J.: *The Modification of Stuttering.* Englewood Cliffs, Prentice-Hall, 1967.

or any other compulsion, will usually effect a cure without further complications.

Guides for speech correction are few and simple: if possible, the important persons in the patient's life must also learn to speak, slowly, carefully, and distinctly. Hypnotic relaxation in the patient usually speeds therapy. Reassurance and relaxation, without formal trance induction, may be all that is needed. Stammerers, for instance, have learned that there is less respiratory and vocal tension present after they exhale or whistle than when their lungs are full of air. Try it on yourself. Take a deep breath and try saying something like "abracadabra" or "pneumonia" or "memory" while holding back as much air in your lungs as possible. Note the tightness in your vocal cords. Then try the same word or words as you let your breath out. Note especially how easy it is to pronounce them *at the end of exhalation* when the respiratory system is more relaxed. We will return to this phenomenon presently.

Rounding of the lips into exaggerated pronunciations of the the letters, as though speaking through a megaphone, increases volume and projects the voice further. It also helps to overcome a very common source of dysarthria—namely the habit of using only the tongue and jaw when speaking, as do ventriloquists. Part of this is in imitation of elders and part of it is caused by fear, as with prisoners who seek to avoid detection or with students whispering an answer to a distressed classmate.

Speaking with minimal use of the lips or mandible produces a stilted and flat, fallible vocalization which inevitably invites trouble with such consonants as *B, F, M, P, Q, V, W,* and the letter *Y,* all of which require proper use of lips, teeth, tongue and jaw.

Consonant formation for stammerers comes more easily when the troublesome letter is not the first letter of the word. Thus *m* in "emotion" comes easier than *m* in "mother"; and *b* in "ambition" usually offers considerably less trouble than *b* in "bandit." Therefore, one way to uncondition the offending letter is to practice saying long lists of words containing the desired letter in the middle, or at the end; for example, "oboe," "abandon," "abbey" and "hubbub." Terminal consonants should be exaggerated so that there will be no confusion in speaker or audience.

Fear produces tension. There is more tension in the respiratory system at the end of inspiration than at the end of expiration. Consequently, stammerers are advised to exhale forcibly but inaudibly before and during speaking. This can be accomplished by placing an inaudible aspirant *h* before offending vowels and before such consonants as *f, l, m, n, r, s, w,* and *x*. Similarly, an inaudible "hoo" before *y* facilitates pronunciation without stammering, and serves to boost the stutterer's self-confidence. The following are valuable exercises:

> "*H*-after" (*hafter*), "*H*-empty" (*hempty*), and daily practicing the letters *L, M, N, R, S, X,* and *W,* with "*H*-el," "*H*-em," "*H*-en," "*H*-ar," "*H*-es," "*H*-ex," and "*H*-oo-w." The same procedure is effective with the vowels: "Hay, He, Hi, Ho and Hee-y-oo (hu)." Be sure the *H* and exhaling are silent and that there is exaggerated use of the lips, especially rounding for *O* and *U*.

In effect, a deep but silent sigh also produces a light first stage of auto-induced hypnotic relaxation; and this is why improvement is often noted during the lesson when a sympathetic and patient coach is present. The problem usually becomes worse when the unrelaxed youngster is faced with critical friends or family.

Practice lists of selected words are made up by omitting the offending initial letter until repetition and confidence permit its inclusion. For example, have your student say the following practice words: "-ord," "-omen," "-ife," and "-eight"; later adding the *w*, and preceding it by *an inaudible H*; thus, "*HOO*-w-ord," "*HOO*-w-oman," "*HOO*-w-ife." The "*HOO*-w" is practically inaudible. It is whispered and is formed largely by an expiration and a puckered rounding of the lips as in saying the word "who," softly blowing out the vowel.

Some analysis of speech disturbances is useful. In obstinate cases entire words, rather than mere letters on which the patient stammers, must be analyzed for pertinent associations before the difficulty can be overcome. The habit of forgetting names, dates or experiences which have impersonal, unimportant or unpleasant associations is a familiar and well-known psychological defense mechanism.[7] It is certainly no accident that most stammerers will flounder on mother, father, dad, brother, sister, teacher, and other pertinent names.

Letter substitution or baby-talk dysarthria ("I wuv oo witta wabbit"—I love you little rabbit) results from normal childhood difficulties with letter formation. Failure on the part of adults to discourage the baby talk inevitably leads to difficulty in breaking the habit and, consequent, self-consciousness. Adults who cling to baby talk usually have other personality handicaps in the nature of emotional immaturity and dependency.

Only a little practice with a few cases of defective speech is needed to give the interested counselor and educator a valuable tool with which to help these unfortunate people.

Group therapy, psychodrama, and concurrent occupational therapy are valuable adjuncts, along with collateral conferences with parents and family.

SLEEPING DIFFICULTIES

On Getting Children to Bed

Sleep is often equated with exile, isolation, punishment, separation from family fun and even death. It may also remind the child of previous illness, discomfort and frightening experiences with darkness. When the problem is the result of habitual parental procrastination, a direct confrontation is often useful.

Alternatives need not be threatening. When exciting or stimulating programs and activities have been replaced by tranquilizing music or story telling or jigsaw puzzles, one can alter previous dilatory habits by use of the double-bind: *Do you want to go to bed at ten minutes to eight or at eight o'clock?* Here's how it worked with seven-year-old Alfy.

Bedtime for Alfy

The child had been left by friends of the family with my wife and me for a weekend at our summer camp in the Berkshires. We had been warned that there might be trouble getting her to go to sleep and that *her usual hour was seven.* When evening came, after dining and bathing, it was storytime but first we asked her how late *she* wanted to stay up before the cozy log fire.

"Seven-thirty?" she asked, hesitantly. We nodded assent; whereupon she hastened to add, "How about eight?" To this, we also agreed. Emboldened, she then said, "Can I stay up 'till *nine* o'clock?" We exchanged glances and again assented. Next Alfy went up to ten, then eleven, and finally to TWELVE O'CLOCK! ! After grave consideration we even agreed to letting her stay up 'till the magic witching hour of midnight. However we added one restriction.

"Okay. You can stay up until twelve o'clock. But, don't you dare go to sleep before twelve o'clock."

At seven, she was sound asleep on the hardwood floor; and she hardly stirred when we carried her to her bunk. For the balance of her stay with us, the subject of bedtime never came up again. Whenever she felt drowsy, she just went off to bed by herself.

Nightmares

People spend a great deal of time in sleep during their first and last years of life; and normally, only events of the greatest importance are permitted to disturb the natural appetite for sleep. Consequently the first things to be remembered in cases of infantile insomnia are hunger, cold, or pain. As the child learns more about people and begins to experience disappointments or to suffer from early illnesses, the recollections of some of these threats to his security continue to pass through his brain, especially during sleep. These constitute normal dream material or semi-waking fantasies.

Nightmares are more vivid recollections of some major emotional catastrophe that has threatened the sleeper during previous waking hours. During sleep, the factual data of the dream is liable to become distorted. Judgment and capacity for reassurance may be so dormant that the dream experience seems to be very real to the sleeper. Consequently he awakens in terror.

The cause of the nightmare may be a frightful ghost story, a telecast of violence at bedtime, or the loss of some valued property or privilege. Sometimes the nightmare may be an unconscious misinterpretation of shadows or of creaking sounds by a brain which is already exhausted by fatigue; or it may be caused by some prank (boogyman) that an older and foolish companion has played on him. When such stimulation catches the child off guard, for instance when he is preoccupied or only half awake, his misinterpretation of the stimulus is liable to be so extreme as to cause considerable emotional shock or even a seizure. The handling of such cases requires a great deal of patient and kindly reassurance.

Treatment

The treatment of sleeping disturbances requires ascertainment and removal of causes whenever possible. Boisterous and exciting evening programs should be avoided. A small night light in the bedroom for a few weeks or months is helpful. The light can gradually be diminished in intensity so that semidarkness or relatively total darkness (except for halls, stairs, and bathrooms) is an accepted fact. Lighting should also be arranged so that a dim illumination may be obtained whenever it becomes necessary to enter the sleeper's room.

Respect for sleepers by toning down radios or TV's and removing other disturbing noises, needs to be emphasized. Strong odors and unnecessary vibrations should also be minimized. The use of drapes, rugs, and other insulating material to absorb sounds usually proves helpful; but when funds are limited, clean burlap bags may be utilized effectively.

If the child is old enough, a brisk walk after supper and before bedtime is often valuable. A warm relaxing bath for twenty minutes prior to the bedtime story is also helpful. The use of sedative medicines should be left to the discretion of the physician. Acting out the dream as a charade, drawing or modelling the characters and other types of action therapy, including games and dancing, are all useful techniques to speed recovery.

THE CONVALESCENT CHILD

Sometimes when a serious illness in a child has caused long anxious hours and many weary nights for the parents, a new dependency arises. The parents have assumed once more the role of nurse and comforter, recalling to the sick child his earliest years of infantile omnipotence. Such children rapidly become used to being waited upon. They are inclined to exploit the situation for secondary gains which also play an important role in the production and chronicity of psychosomatic disorders, as in the case of Bobby's limping gait.

The remedy for this situation is to uncondition the child by gradually increasing his responsibilities and shortening the periods of attendance, thereby making his sickness and convalescence less profitable to him. When the doctor approves, a mild sedative for the first few nights is usually beneficial.

Constancy in the methods used to secure the proper rest is essential. As already mentioned, children fuss over going to sleep not only because they resent exile from family fun but chiefly because they have been encouraged to do so by irresolute and nagging parents. Convalescence is also more difficult when doctors and hospitals have been used as boogymen to coerce the child into cooperation. It cannot be emphasized too strongly that "problem children," whether in the matter of bedtime, mealtime, or the habit of hypochondriacal attitudes toward sickness, are usually the inevitable result of *problem parents.* Nowhere is this more glaringly apparent than in the parents who scream and yell and match the child's own procrastinations by mild threats or promises which they have little intention of keeping.

In dealing with temper tantrums, parents must realize that some degree of distemper is normal, because no normal person enjoys being denied the things that he wants. When the denial is done tactlessly, or frequently, or harshly, a sensitive child soon finds himself greatly disturbed over apparent injustices. He is usually too young to understand the reasoning, if any, behind the denial. All he knows is that his security has been threatened, his omnipotence is waning rapidly, and an increasing number of refusals and other restrictions are beclouding his previously happy horizon. Most of the treatment consists of strengthening the family ties, enhancing parental confidence, and gradually reconditioning the child to less autonomy and more cooperation and self-control. Consistency, firmness and finesse are the guiding procedures. Furthermore, most tantrums terminate spontaneously when there is no audience.

When there are important affairs to attend to, the parent does not have time to put up with a fussy child. The trick is to hold onto your own patience and give the child a chance to simmer down. Occasionally, the situation calls for a firm warning such as "That's enough!" But no grudge should be held for long, and diversionary tactics are always in order especially in the form of games and toys.

SCHOOL PROBLEMS

Intelligence

Intelligence is the ability to learn, to remember, to think, and to profit from experience. Those are the functions of the thinking cells in the gray matter of the child's brain. Like a radio set that depends in large part on the number and quality of vacuum tubes, condensers and other electronic gear for its efficiency, your child's brain power also depends upon the number and quality of his thinking cells and their nerve connections. These are estimated at thirteen billion, over four times the population of the world. They are fixed at birth, and they determine the child's mental capacity. Illness and injury may damage and reduce their number as well as their efficiency. Diet, drugs and special training can speed learning, but thus far no method has been found to increase their number. Eighty per cent of brain growth is believed to take place by the end of the third year of life.

The mental capacity or thinking ability is measured in terms of an "IQ" which means intelligence quotient. The child normally keeps the IQ with which he is born, although IQs may fluctuate as much as 10 or 15 per cent in either direction. Except for a few tests which are strong on vocabulary, the standard tests of mental measurement would reveal similar IQs for the uneducated child and for the educated one. However, education can increase the child's ability to acquire special skills and interests and motivate him to make speedy associations. These result in shortcuts and quicker thinking. Consequently when a time limit is set for answers in the intelligence tests, this training will give an advantage to the educated child and to the child with broader cultural stimulation.

Now let us consider the five-year-old with a normal mental age of five years. His IQ is 100 per cent. Many school systems are discovering that three-year-old children have phenomenal learning capacity, especially for languages which they love to mimic. Nevertheless most school systems still prefer the conservative program of starting with first grade at five and a half or six years. At six years, his IQ will still be 100 per cent, but his mental age will have kept pace with his chronological age and will also have increased to six years. If the child has been kept active and happy learning new facts and acquiring new experiences, for instance in the nursery and kindergarten classes, he will be better prepared for first grade no matter how many months he may be behind the others. Parents should therefore avoid making him feel that he is not being treated fairly.

This emotional complex which many parents have about grade and age levels affects children all through their school years. It may make them overwork in the hope of obtaining a double promotion just to please their parents. In the long run, a double promotion seldom pleases the child who must leave his friends and classmates behind. He invariably steps into an inferior position as a freak prodigy in a class of older and sometimes resentful schoolmates. He will have trouble enough with all the other social and emotional adjustments that have to be made when he leaves home for school, without this additional handicap.

Here's How the IQ Actually Works

At 100 per cent, the mental age or intellectual capacity keeps pace with the physical age (chronological age) in years and months. A ten-year-old with an IQ of 100 will therefore have a *mental age* of ten years. If one figures *six* as the average for beginning first grade then the ten-year-old (with normal 100% IQ) should be capable of doing fourth grade work, and the twelve-year-old should be doing satisfactory sixth grade work. This goes on until about fifteen or sixteen years of age when the average child reaches his full level of mental development. The intellectual capacity of the superior child however continues to develop until about eighteen years; but the average mental age in the adult population is only about fifteen or possibly sixteen years.

One should always keep in mind that IQs are not any more accurate than the average home scale. A child's real IQ may be at least 10 per cent higher (or lower) than the figure that is reported. Furthermore, if he rates an average or higher than average IQ when he is small, he is liable to test even higher as he grows older, although he usually retains his original rating. On the other hand if his IQ is below average during early childhood, it may drop a little as he grows into the teens.

Psychometry means mental measurement or the determination of one's capacity to use his brain. Clinicians and counselors are less concerned with a child's IQ if he is making normal progress, but if he is slow or if he is overbright, intelligence testing is usually helpful.

For instance, if a client's IQ is 80, then his mental age is only 80 per cent of his actual or chronological age (measured in total number of months). This means that a six-year-old with an IQ of 80 has the mental aspects of a child of about four and a half years. He will not be able to do satisfactory first grade work until he is seven or eight years old.

On the other hand, if his IQ is 110 or better he will be ahead of the others. This may please the parent but it could cause the child a lot of grief. He could get through his work too quickly and might soon become bored unless his teachers can keep him happily occupied with more challenging work.

The child's early patterns of behavior and his most pressing anxieties connected with school do not depend half as much on his IQ as on the family's attitudes. This is shown in the following case:

Case of Ronny

Ronny, age five, was failing first grade while his older brother and older sisters were all getting good marks. Ronny's mother had been an honor pupil, but his father never finished high school. Ronny's older brother is his mother's favorite. At first Ronny was his father's favorite, but now father is always bragging about the success of his two daughters. The arrival of mother's bachelor sister for Easter vacation increased the tensions in the home, because Ronny's aunt was a school teacher. When psychometry showed that Ronny was mentally a whole year behind, as a result of a neglected injury, the family stopped shaming him and began a special program of training at kindergarden level.

The majority of school failures do not occur because of retarded intelligence. Rather they are the result of failure to recognize other needs in the child such as his emotional security, physical ability to compete with his playmates, and unfinished business with parents and siblings. These are old scores which the child often does not recognize but which he *transfers* automatically onto the teachers and playmates whom he unconsciously identifies with the first important people in his life.

Left-Handedness

Anxieties over left-handedness become accentuated when starting school. They are the result of a lot of misunderstanding plus good intentions that are often misdirected.

Control of the left hand is centered in the right side of the brain, but there is no evidence to prove that one side of the brain is actually superior to the other or that "lefty's" are smarter or duller than others.

The average normal baby shows a preference for using one hand (and foot) or the other between his sixth and twelfth month of life. During the first five years of life, children tend to develop more accuracy and poise when they cultivate the use of one hand for such activities as self-feeding, building with blocks, throwing a ball and drawing than when they are allowed to use either or both hands (ambidexterity) indiscriminately.

Gesell has produced some evidence to show that those children who develop right-handed preference during the preschool age generally develop greater skill, strength and poise than those who favor the left hand.[8] Whether this might be attributed to physical or social adjustment is a moot question. Even if this observation should be true, the child may become more maladjusted *if he is a lefty who has been forced to become right-handed.*

In the older child there is no important disadvantage in left-handedness as far as intelligence, skill and strength are concerned, but there are some definite social handicaps which usually cause embarrassment. Chief of these handicaps are the use of the left hand in writing and in feeding. In games and sports the child can always compensate for being different by developing special skills such as becoming a baseball southpaw pitcher. This can make him highly desirable to his playmates. However, refined table manners will not protect him from embarrassment and discomfort when he picks up a fork at a crowded banquet table.

It was with these thoughts in mind that Marianne's parents adopted the following procedure on one of their children during her second year of life.

The Training of Marianne

Each time the girl reached for a spoon or a pencil with her left hand the article was gently shifted to her right hand. The pleasant smile and the patient words "This way, dear" accentuated the positive attitude. Since no restrictions were placed on the use of her left hand for any other activity, she soon learned that this was the preferred way to play the game.

At meals, everyone else used the right hand. At nursery and kindergarten school Marianne was again with the majority. At play, she used both hands; but gradually, as she grew older, she began to favor the right hand for group activities, while retaining her left hand for special personal pursuits like sewing, knitting and tennis. Recently, when Marianne faced her first class in practice teaching, none of her fifth grade pupils would believe that she had ever been left-handed. "But you don't even stutter!" one of them insisted.

Stuttering or any other serious emotional disturbance can be prevented in a left-handed child when there is no undue pressure for change and no haste or deep anxiety in the parents. The use of the right hand for eating and writing can be cultivated with the same patience and care with which the child is taught to attend to his personal toilet.

Left-handedness may be one of the ways a child chooses to be different or rebellious. There is no danger in retraining an older child if he wants to change, provided that the change is made gradually and with patience.*

Bullying

Recently I was held up in traffic a few blocks from a school-

---

* *Eye dominance* usually parallels hand dominance. When in doubt ask the child to focus both eyes on the tip of an outstretched finger. As he slowly bends his elbow and brings the finger closer to his nose, the dominant eye will tend to toe in ahead of the other.

house. As it was long past school hours, I was at a loss to account for the delay, but as my car edged slowly along, the explanation soon became clear. A small boy of about ten years preferred to take his chances on autos stopping for him rather than to budge from his position of relative safety—in the middle of the road! On the sidewalk a small gang of boys about the same age, feeling strong in numbers, taunted him for being a crybaby and dared him to come back to the sidewalk where they were obviously prepared to tear him to pieces. He was rescued by a passing adult.

You have seen cats at bay against a similar group of barking dogs. It is not generally known that when the danger is great enough, a child, adult, or animal can be immobilized by fear and literally eaten alive. Children may tell the most absurd lies and fantastic excuses rather than risk closer contact with "barking" parents or unknown punishment from strict teachers. Here is a case in point.

Al

Nine-year-old Al (Algernon) was desperately in need of approval from his gang. He played truant and took money from his mother's pocketbook. He used the money to buy candy and baloons for his friends, obviously as bribes so that they would not molest him. "When my mother discovered the loss of her five-dollar bill, she hit the ceiling, so I ran away."

Hours later the boy was discovered crouching behind a high iron railing that protected the town's bank. A crowd had gathered, and although it was getting dark, Al refused to crawl back under the rail. Faced with so much public humiliation and the alternative of calling the police or the bank president to come and unlock the gate, Al's father offered the boy an ice cream soda and total immunity, if he would come out by himself.

When telling me about this incident, a few years later, Al was not the least bit concerned with his own moral involvement—"I was afraid he'd call the cops. That's why I came out; but you know, Doc, I still *can't get over it, my old man actually kept his word*! *He* bought me the ice cream and he didn't beat me!"

The foundation of character for any child begins in the home, with the honor and integrity of its leaders. Practically all of his social experiences are of secondary importance; yet much of the blame is often placed on the schools.

Physical Defects

Defects may also be at the root of such school problems as low marks, tardiness and truancies, or a growing number of detentions and other penalties. Delayed descent of testicles, various types of malnutrition or conspicuous defects of teeth, nose, eyes, ears and skin may prevent a child from giving his best performance at home as well as at school.

Fortunately, many of these defects are correctable but even with available clinics and various insurance coverages, costs are still a big factor. However, competent social agencies can usually help the counselor and family find a way to meet them.

Fears

Other anxieties include fears of dark, thunder, lightning, heights, noise, dogs and other animals, and competition with other children. Frightened attitudes are often learned from adults and other children. Self-confidence, like socialization, has to be acquired gradually, the earlier the better. Isolation, as with an only child, and failure to teach useful habits of cooperation and resourcefulness are often the cause of many of his difficulties.

Parents who themselves were poor mixers are inclined to slough off their responsibility or to encourage the child to read or to watch television. They also provoke friction and tensions by breaking into the child's privacy and playtime with unreasonable requests and reminders or with questions that could easily wait for more suitable occasions.

Parents may unwittingly encourage excessive competition between brothers and sisters by playing favorites and by other forms of rejection. Parents are like older siblings and spouses; they are especially inclined to act up and be bossy when other people are around, particularly important visitors. They then become embarrassed and angry over the child's disobedience— unable to comprehend that they themselves had provoked it.

Disobedience

Disobedience usually results from unreasonble requests, or failure to be firm and consistent with discipline. Disobedience may also result from misunderstandings. As a result of hasty reading or careless speech, messages may become distorted, especially when carried through a third party. Most people can recall such common errors as the following:

> Some years ago while reading a newspaper article, I read, "The Clown Prince was reviewing the troops," instead of the "The Crown Prince was reviewing the troops"; and, on a college bulletin, "The first lecture will be on the interpretation of Dreams" instead of "Drama." Also, I read "Four tenths of one of the groups were detached" instead of "Fourteen of one of the groups were detached."
>
> "Soap" may be mistaken for "soup," "candles" for "cans," and "pears" for "tears" or "hairs."

Many adults refuse to accept the blame for such common errors; yet even a single unjust accusation may be enough to produce a rebellious and uncooperative child or an inappropriate response. The point is illustrated by the following anecdote:

> A small boy placidly continued eating his supper while his mother repeatedly tried to tell him that his beloved pet dog *"Danny"* had just died. Thinking there was something wrong with the boy she shook him violently. "Don't you understand? I said your dog Danny has just been run over by a truck. He's been killed!"
>
> The boy suddenly stopped eating; and his eyes filled with tears. Between sobs he wailed aloud, "I thought you said *Daddy.*"

The proper way to overcome the problem of disobedience is to remove the major causes, if possible. Other ways must be found for making the child feel important, than by being the center of unfavorable attention. Johnny may be backward as well as a troublemaker; but if Johnny is promoted to chief monitor and is *permitted* (not required) to attend to the blackboards each day, his attitude is liable to change for the better. At last he becomes recognized as somebody of importance. If his name is up on the board, not for disturbing the peace but for efficiency as chief messenger, with a star for each week of successful service, he can obtain almost as much satisfaction as if the stars were for perfect spelling.

Whenever an older group plans a project such as a play, where it is usually impossible to cast the entire membership, many positions are created for all to share—stage manager, scenery, costumes, ushers, tickets, advertising and the like. Each member of the group should be made to feel that he belongs and has an important contribution to make.

I am indebted to Miss L. P. Hayes, formerly Psychiatric Social Worker at the Monson State Hospital for the following apt illustration:

> In a special class which I once visited, the teacher was blessed with a most unpromising collection of retarded children of all sizes and ages. When I asked her how she managed to keep them all looking so contented and busy, she confided that she made it a point to see that there was some one thing in which each student could excel. Thus, one was a best speller, another could do the best painting, and a third might do best at woodwork, or knitting. Having just examined one particularly dull and discouraging fellow, I asked with a mischievous twinkle in my eye, "and what, pray, can Johnny do better than all the rest?"
>
> "Oh," she replied enthusiastically, and in loud tones, "*Johnny's the only one in the class who* can open the window from the top!" and Johnny, whose head and shoulders towered above all the rest, sat and beamed in supreme happiness.

Delinquency

Prevention of delinquency is largely a matter of common sense.

> Mrs. W. was disturbed by boys running into her orchard. They picked unripe fruits, trampled her flowers and destroyed property. No amount of scolding, threats, or complaints to police and parents seemed to have any good effect. She finally solved the problem by summoning the two oldest and biggest boys. She offered them the job of policing the orchard during the summer with the promise of *all the fruit they could eat on the premises,* when the fruit ripened. They accepted, and she had no further difficulties.

During the early 1930s, I spent some time with August Volmer who was then Chief of Police in Berkeley, California. He later became Professor of Criminology at the universities of California and Chicago. He solved common delinquency problems in a similar manner.

The boys of the slum neighborhoods in Berkeley were organized into junior policemen. Each one had his day on duty. Promotions came to those who made the best record in preventing or reporting damage to property and other violations. The young-sters wore badges, were given certificates, and met once a week right in the chief's own office. At that time Berkeley was known as a city which was singularly free from crime; and in those years Volmer's "College Cops" had long been the first choice as a source of police chiefs for other cities all over the country.

A comparable solution is underway in Hartford, Connecticut and elsewhere. "Teen-agers on patrol" are paid a small salary to aid police in dealing with the rising tide of delinquency and crime. They are not expected to be informers, but they do wear uniforms and badges. Results so far have been encouraging.

Any competent teacher can handle problems of discipline in her classroom or school yard. Self-confidence, patience, tact and freedom from personal bias are the chief essentials. It is im-portant however that such problems be dealt with early and promptly in order to prevent the development of more serious delinquency in later life.

The Retarded Child

The retarded child offers one of the biggest heartaches not only to his parents and teachers but also to himself. If there is one universal criticism to be offered against the usual method of handling such a case, it is that parents try to conceal the problem by denying its existence. Teachers also are often too slow in recognizing the special needs of the retarded child. Even with factual data from psychological and psychiatric examina-tions before them, I have known teachers to spend hours after school trying to reteach a subnormal child some work that was several grades too far advanced for him. "He knows it after I'm through with him," she wails, "but next morning he's forgotten it all." It is almost impossible to impress upon such a misguided teacher that she is subjectively involved (crush in reverse, or positive countertransference) and that she has, therefore, over-estimated the child's capacity for retention.

I have known nurses to become similarly involved with a handicapped patient, especially when it is someone else's re-tarded or defective baby. Adolescent trainees and even medical students and internes are constantly exposed to this hazard long after their professional courses are completed. They show their involvement by extraordinary services and heroic devotion to duty.

Yet if it is hard on a conscientious teacher, it is even harder on the child himself. He is subjected to accumulating pressures from anxious teachers and ambitious parents as well as competitive classmates. It is necessary therefore to discover these retarded children as early as possible in order to permit them to learn according to their capacity. They should be placed in special classes or in regular classes with special programs. Failure to do this may result in delinquency, sickness and sometimes suicide. The natural fondness of a child for what he thought would be new playmates and better opportunities in school soon changes to disillusioned resentment for the teacher—a *task-mistress* who cannot or will not understand his needs. He naturally turns to those who accept him, even though they also exploit him for their own benefit.

Many school systems are handicapped by the lack of adequate physical facilities, classrooms and specially trained teachers. Most parents strenuously resist having their darlings labeled as "dummy" or "dumb" members of "opportunity" or "auxilliary" classes. In some cases the child may remain with his regular classmates, as in the rural one room schoolhouse, for eight separate grades. He can work on special individual assignments, yet still be able to participate in such communal activities as simple games, sports, music, entertainment and assembly.

The child can be given a report card that reads, for example, "Special Fourth Grade." He can also be promoted each June so that both he and his parents can feel that he is making some kind of progress, if only on paper. Even a special certificate at graduation is not too much to ask as a reward for one who has worked as hard as he can. He, with less intellectual equipment than those who have been more generously endowed by nature, certainly deserves more praise for any accomplishment that he makes.

N.B. The greater the intellectual retardation, the more protection that is needed from sadistic or unscrupulous people. Boys as well as girls can be abused; but it is not only strangers who take unfair advantage. Families, neighbors, employers and even teachers and doctors are often impatient, because they usually expect too much.

As a rule, the retarded child does well enough when kept in his own home, unless competition and rejection by normal siblings and family make his life miserable. In such cases, institutional training for a few years may be for his best interests. This is especially true during the years of sexual maturity.

Truancy

Truancy is a response to an inner force or urge to move on. In the young child there is a natural spirit of wanderlust to investigate that which may lie beyond forbidden limits; and this spirit is liable to overcome his normal desire for security. Such curiosity is not uncommon in adults, but their "running away" is more frequently confined to daydreaming or fantasying, movies, golf, bowling, bridge or weekend trips. Truancy is more common when the pressure of unhappy situations at home, school, or work become too great for comfort.

Unless the child's timidity is too great, the tempting lure of new places, green fields, rivers and lakes, or the bustle of a big city can offer powerful competition for his dark or crowded home with its inadequate playground. However, escape from poverty, sickness, or family unhappiness are not the only causes. Even the program of the wealthy family must be made interesting in order to keep the active child at home. Time and distance may mean very little to the young wanderer. If he also possesses a pleasing appearance and makes friends easily, he will be well cared for by policemen and others whom he meets. Such a successful trip is liable to be repeated several times, so that the habit is easily formed.

The truant is not *necessarily bad.* He may be a good boy or girl who is running away from a bad situation at home, or among his friends. "They'll miss me when I'm gone" is a thought that compensates for guilt when truancy is used as a weapon of retaliation or revenge. However, truancy is not free from dangers, such as kidnapping, accidents resulting from carelessness, the formation of undesirable friendships or associations, and the use of the child for improper purposes by bribes with money, food or toys and even drugs.

Treatment of truancy quite naturally consists of making the home and school more attractive, improving inadequate recreational facilities, and removing other specific causes if they can be found. Taking the small child on personally conducted tours of the city, parks, zoos, museums and factories may be one way to curb wanderlust. Reading adventure stories and tales of travel may prove satisfactory for some children; while games of make-believe and exploring may serve equally well for others.

Sometimes a conference with the schoolteacher is all that is necessary to reestablish an understanding with the child. Sometimes a new leaf must be turned, and a change of school or classroom is indicated.

Some type of token punishment is usually indicated; and physical chastisement, if necessary, should be promptly administered when circumstances warrant.

When we remember that the ten-year-old children in school today are going to supply the largest number of adult criminals in the community only ten years hence, we must reflect more soberly upon our responsibility in the guidance of children. Overprotection and too much leniency has become a universal habit, extending all the way up to the highest court in the land. The future conduct of the truant or other delinquent child depends upon whether or not his first offences are handled properly.

Destructiveness

Destructiveness is not always what it appears to be. In the first place most children are naturally somewhat careless (meaning untrained) in handling delicate or fragile articles. Children also have not developed a mature sense of values. The pernicious habit of giving too many toys should be discouraged for it tends to prevent the development of an appreciation of property values as well as privileges and character. Children, like most adults, are also less careful with objects which they value little, particularly with things which belong to others whom they dislike. Adults, too, usually take better care of their own property, unless experience has taught them that they must make good any damage done to the property of their neighbors. (Sign in gift shop: "If you break it, you've bought it.")

Children are also normally curious to discover how things are made. They want to handle them and take them apart. Many adults also like to "inspect" clocks and machines, especially those that belong to someone else. Like children, they often try to put things together again with as few parts left over as possible. Many good intentions are misinterpreted as misdemeanors or even as wanton destructiveness. This is especially so when parents are unwilling to take the time to learn that the child was only trying to help.

It should be unnecessary to remind parents that touching and handling objects represent the childs' natural mode of learning their size, shape, and consistency; that fragile or valuable articles should be kept safely out of reach; and that the toys that they give to their children should be few, simple and durable.

The treatment of destructiveness requires analysis of the contributing causes. Was the delinquency intentional, habitual, or accidental? Was it a means to an end (revenge? spite?) or the article itself which was offensive to the child? Has he a grudge against teacher? Sometimes it is the person who gave it that was disliked as in Eugene O'Neil's "Strange Interlude."

> Young Gordon, son of Nina, received for his birthday a beautiful model of a ship which he had long coveted. However, after admiring it for a few minutes, he dashed the ship ruthlessly to the ground destroying it completely. The donor of the gift happened to be Nina's lover whose rivalry had aroused Gordon's jealousy . . . loss of the ship should be punishment enough.

Adults, too, frequently break or lose unwanted gifts; and children's misconduct is usually quite transparent to observers. Here's one I recorded some years ago.

> "Put your shoes on and hurry up about it," commanded an impatient mother to her rebellious daughter who had been brought to my Child Guidance Clinic unwillingly. The child promptly sat down, and in a few moments had one shoelace broken and the other in a knotted snarl. It was as though she had said, "I was in no hurry to come here so why should I be in a hurry to go home? And, anyway, I can't go home until you fix these shoelaces."
>
> Mother had neglected to inform the child of the reason for

bringing her to the clinic. Her disregard for the child's previous commitment with playmates had resulted in retaliation to thwart mother's desire to get home on time. The shoelace incident appeared to be accidental; but the deliberate carelessness in tying her shoelaces, something she had been doing successfully for years, was obvious as well as eloquent. This mother, fortunately, did not fly into a rage. Instead, and much to the child's surprise, she made the child walk home with her shoes untied.

PROBLEMS OF TEACHERS

The Harassed Teacher

It is unfortunate that the responsibilities of the average school day are so great as to exhaust many a teacher. In consequence of these and other pressures, she herself is frequently lacking in common courtesies to her pupils. Even when teacher insists upon children using good manners to each other, she has to buck families. For instance when such a youngster carries back his newly acquired courtesies into his home he is liable to receive considerable ridicule and continued abruptness from his less considerate family. Playlets, stories and special programs for parent-teacher groups may help to put over the idea that common courtesies are the foundations of socialization. In the same way that programs on good health can prevent sickness and accidents, practicing the Golden Rule can prevent delinquency.

Problem teachers, like problem parents, are usually overworked and underpaid. They have to undergo rigid preparation and examinations for their work. They are usually obliged to continue their studies and to participate in a considerable range of extracurricular activities. Only a few decades ago they were expected to live wholesome and "normal" lives upon penalty of losing their jobs if they should marry. In some school systems they are still receiving less pay than janitors and garbage collectors. Moonlighting jobs to help raise a family leave little time for self-improvement, although many conscientious teachers have pursued courses on guidance, mental hygiene, and allied subjects.

Unfortunately too many teacher's colleges do not yet stress educational psychology, sociology or guidance. Consequently, in many school systems the well-trained teachers, though still in the minority, are often far ahead of their superintendents and school committees; however, those teachers are liable to be so preoccupied with budgets and political complications that their concern for pedagogy is relegated to second place.

Obviously the solution to many problems of the classroom depends to a large extent upon the abilities of the teacher in the following areas: avoiding fatigue, varying her programs, giving individual assistance when needed (preferably after school hours or during study periods in order not to bore the others), softening her voice, avoiding sarcasm and impatience, discouraging unfairness, correcting poor legibility by using finger tracing, drawing or other projection techniques, encouraging remedial reading, elocution, original projects, organization and planning committees of the pupils themselves, and introducing visual, electronic and other aids to better teaching.

Adequate attention to proper ventilation, lighting, coloring, plants or flowers, grouping of playmates, and the general tempo of the program will go a long way towards preventing many problems of the classroom. This in turn will lessen fatigue and enhance efficiency.

Effects of Unstable Teachers

A teacher who is not emotionally or personally secure is not likely to exert a very stabilizing influence upon her pupils. The following incidents were personally witnessed during my seven years of service as visiting school psychiatrist to surrounding communities in western Massachusetts under the supervision of the Massachusetts Department of Mental Health. Such incidents are more common than most people realize. They occurred when I was a schoolboy, half a century ago and they still occur in contemporary school systems including colleges as well as in private homes. The remarks and events herein quoted were overheard unintentionally or seen quite accidentally by the writer while pursuing routine examinations in adjoining rooms. In many cases the teacher was quite aware of my presence, although she may not have been cognizant of the efficacy of the acoustics. On the other hand, like her pupils, she too might have been acting up for my benefit, using me as a substitute principal or parent and daring me to do something about all the impositions which had to be put up with.

Bursting into my examining room without knocking was a very frequent practice by principals as well as by teachers, much less so by pupils themselves.

Openly discussing, in front of a wretched child, the sordid facts of his home life, much of it confidential to say the very least, was a favorite pastime of several principals, usually the older spinster ladies.

Delaying me at the close of school for "curbstone" consultations to discuss their personal problems was a complimentary yet disconcerting practice of many teachers. The fact that even a visiting school psychiatrist might have other commitments, and a schedule to keep, did not seem to concern them.

It was also common practice for teachers and principals to show their own resistance to our mental health evaluation program by ill-concealed annoyance at the intrusion of the team (social worker, psychologist and psychiatrist) that had come to help them. Some of these would direct me to a very dirty assembly hall that was usually drafty and quite cold or to an already crowded teacher's room that was frequently cluttered with rubbers, clothes and lunch bags. What the poor teachers thought of losing their scant privacy for several hours of a school session is best left to the imagination. In many instances, and despite previous notification of the visit, nearly twenty minutes of valuable time would be required just to secure a table and chairs in order to begin the routine of examining several dozen "problem children."

In one school, as I passed by the glassed door of a classroom, I saw the teacher determinedly, if undignifiedly, chasing a small boy up and down between the rows of desks while the entire class was in an uproar. "And that goes for you, too!" said she vindictively as she heartily slapped another small boy in the far corner of the room. Fortunately she had not seen me, but I did not wait to see the rest of her battle for control.

Another teacher was no improvement: "Put that down," she shouted in tones that would have terrified the hardiest child. "Will you sit down or do I have to push you down? Put your hand down. You're not going anywhere. You've got to stay here 'till quarter of twelve!" (What price good toilet habits in a six-year-old?)

In another urban school, the following monologue was taken down verbatim during an interlude while I waited for a pupil. The teacher was an attractive but embittered bachelor girl of about thirty-seven years.

"I *knew* I'd catch you (triumphantly). You don't pay *any* attention! Oh, this is *disgusting*—Why don't you *look at your work?*— What business is it of *yours* what *she's* doing? (Tones of contempt). You *know* you've got to find a common denominator for fractions. —I'm going to punish you if you don't do your work—You've *got* to be punished. You've got to be *punished!* If you don't do your work that's disobeying, and for disobeying you've got to be *punished,* You've got to be strapped."

There was a pause followed by general laughter at apparent mistakes of the child. This was joined in by the teacher herself. Her tones changed with different children—soft and gentle with some, harsh and contemptuous with others. She continued, a little later: "You make me sick and tired.—What did we just say we should do in problems like this?—Where were *you?* Where *were* you? I just *told* you what to do! !—We're still on fifth grade work. There's no reason for not being able to do it." (Obviously there were plenty of reasons, and teacher may well have been most of them).

Vocabulary and diction in teachers is important. The following letter, sent to a distressed mother by a teacher, is self-explanatory:

"Dear Mrs. L. I am sorry to have to tell you that we cannot keep Adeline in school.

She is a dear little girl but she does not settle down and her constant running around is very annoying to the other children.

You must know, I am sure, what a difficult task it is for a first grade teacher to train a whole class of children in school habits." [Teacher pleads for sympathy from Mrs. L. Up to this point the letter is not objectionable.]

"*Personally* I do not think Adeline is ready for special class. [Insertion of "personally" indicates further subjective involvement and suggests a conflict with teacher's own professional judgment.] She probably would gain the most help through attending a psychopathic clinic. I think there is one at Springfield Hospital. Yours truly."

This teacher may have meant well enough; but the mere mention of a "psychopathic" clinic rather than "child guidance clinic" was enough to terrify the mother. Mother did come to my clinic and was relieved to learn that Adeline was a normal child who had done nothing worse than to start school a whole year too soon.

The effects of unstable teachers can be illustrated by scores of incidents reported to me personally by their unhappy pupils:

> A high school teacher conducted recitations by a stopwatch. She demanded prompt replies to all questions *within three seconds*, on penalty of receiving zero for the recitation. Her otherwise brilliant pupil, a sixteen-year-old stammerer, was prepared to leave school rather than face the daily ordeal. We changed the pupil to another class.
>
> Another conscientious girl vowed she would never again write a thesis. On the morning when she finally brought in her manuscript, after working on it nearly all night, her teacher in a fit of ill temper had torn up the pages without even reading the report. The girl had not known that during her absence, because of unavoidable sickness, the *due date of the assignment* had been advanced, and that her paper was consequently one day late.
>
> Another teacher boasted that he never gave an "A" because no one was perfect. Still others respond to various forms of seduction, favoring certain boys or girls, wasting time with clowning instead of teaching or discussing irrelevant and controversial topics.

These and many more examples make up an imposing list of indictments to which every reader can doubtless add comparable experiences from his own personal knowledge.

Fortunately, these tragedies are overwhelmingly counterbalanced by the long honor rolls of wonderful teachers who have made ever increasing sacrifices for their pupils and whose kindness and encouragement have made their classrooms a haven for countless thousands of children who knew no other love or solace.

GUIDES FOR THE SOCIALIZATION OF CHILDREN

Ancient Egyptian customs under the pharaohs called for schooling at age three or four. They believed in the following aphorisms which leave no doubt as to their meanings: "Oh scribe, be not idle, or thou wilt be chastised!" and "The way to the brain of a boy is through the seat of his pants." *

The ancient Hebrews also cautioned, "Train up a child in the way he should go, and even when he is old he will not depart from it." (Prov. 22:6)

---

* Reported in the *Literary Digest*, April 27, 1935, pg. 19.

The Aztecs of Mexico taught these four cardinal principles for the raising of their young: (1) the avoidance of gormandizing and the careful regulation of food; (2) the avoidance of idleness; (3) strict punishment; and (4) vocational training.*

Do not lie to a child. This does not seem important until we reflect that a child needs accurate information which he can use over and over to guide, protect and save him from ridicule, embarrassment and danger. Deception is not only dangerous, it is also undignified since children are liable to be more astute than most people realize. Deception also sets a bad example. If a child does not trust you to keep your promise not to punish him when he tells the truth, he will lie in order to get you off his back.

Do not withhold your body but do not be too free with it either. A baby may not receive breast milk, but he still needs to be held close. An older child also needs embracing. Undemonstrative parents usually pass on to their children the kind of rejection which they themselves received. Children are often eager for affection. Counselors can show warmth and acceptance by their smile, voice, handshake and body posture, but adults should remember that seduction works both ways.

Children of all ages will often take advantage of familiarity, and they have also been known to solicit seduction. Young girls have accused an innocent teacher simply because he did not respond; or to get even because she did not earn a better mark; or just to prove to her classmates that she was desirable.

Boys as well as girls frequently steal from teachers and parents whose affection they particularly desire, especially when they feel let down.

Even when there has been no physical touching, children can be so enthralled that they may quote their counselor as though he were the last word on everything. This does not enhance his populartiy with the family whose cooperation he needs.

The whole truth? One may not feel capable of telling the whole truth about some matters, for instance about sexual intercourse. One may also be uninformed about the latest discoveries

* Ruhrah, J.: Aztec methods in child training. *Bull John Hopkins Hosp,* 42:5, 1933.

in electronics or the mechanics of outer space. As for the perennial riddles—Who made God, why does He permit so much sin
and suffering, and how do you know I will be an angel when
I die—each is on his own.

When faced with questions to which you do not know the
answers it is sensible to tell the truth. For instance,

> "I don't feel qualified to answer that one; so
> let's look it up" or "Let's ask our doctor or pastor."

By the time you have done your research and presented the
child with diagrams of the reproductive or solar systems, he may
be willing to change the subject. The main point is that you
have not evaded him; and, of course, you yourself would really
like to learn the answers for the next time.

**Accentuate value, rather than costs and do not coax, bribe,
nag or cheat.** These are immature procedures. They are also self-
defeating because they distort values. Either give the child an
allowance which he needs or make him earn it; but pay your
child what he is worth or what you owe him. Do not let others
impose on him either, and be sure to encourage thrift and planning by matching his savings with comparable deposits.

Even a rat can be taught the difference between a nickel and
a quarter by the amount of cheese he can get for his efforts. He
pulls a chain with his mouth. This spills a can of coins. The rat
picks up a coin and runs over to a saucer, where he exchanges
the coin for a reward of cheese. The bigger coin buys a larger
piece.

A child has a right to some fantasies, but his values should
be consistent with the realities of the life for which you are preparing him.

Firmness with finesse are simple and positive principles which
require constant practice in order to become effective. Too many
parents are afraid to risk their children's displeasure. "He won't
love me if I don't let him have his way." They ignore the biblical
injunction to discipline and chastise those whom they love. The
favorite refrain of the indulgent parent is "But I *do* love him.
Look at all I've done for him." This usually masks the underlying wish "I will do almost anything for him in order to make

him love *me*, as I tried to do with my parents, and failed" or "As they should have done for me, and didn't."

Indulgent parents also reject the obvious pre-freudian conclusion, "He who spareth the rod [of correction] *hateth his* son; but he that loveth him chasteneth him betimes." (Prov. 13:24) They consider it as just another one of Ben Franklin's sayings, about indulgence spoiling the child. In effect they are thinking, *"I could have used some spoiling myself. But my child's not going to scrimp* and *save and go without things the way I did."* Try reversing roles with your children. Ask *them* what they think, and listen to what they say and do.

Constancy is a virtue, especially in parents and counselors. Keep your promises. Be polite even when company is not present. Respect a child's privacy. Be generous with praise and encouragement and sparing with criticism and scoldings. Children will usually punish themselves, if allowed to do so.

The time is shorter than you think. Parents need reminding that practically all of the above problems and conflicts should be ironed out during infancy and childhood. When puberty comes, many new challenges are added, but they become complicated by unresolved problems of the past. One of these unresolved problems is the perennial challenge of education on sex—a simple three-letter word that can be so beautiful, yet continues to cause so much trouble.

REFERENCES AND READINGS

1. APTEKAR, H. H.: *The Dynamics of Casework and Counselling.* Cambridge, Riverside, 1955.
2. BAUMEISTER, ALFRED A.: *Mental Retardation.* Chicago, Aldine, 1967.
3. BAYER, L. M., and SNYDER, M. M.: Illness experience of a group of normal children. *Child Develop,* 21:93, 1950.
4. BLANTON, S., and BLANTON, M. G.: *Child Guidance.* New York, Century House, 1927.
5. CARMICHAEL, L. (Ed.): *Manual of Child Psychology.* New York, Wiley, 1954.
6. ERICKSON, M. H.: *Advanced Techniques of Hypnosis and Therapy.* Haley, Jay (Ed.), New York and London, Grune, 1967.
7. FREUD, S.: *Psychopathology of Everyday Life, Basic Writings.* New York, Modern Lib., 1938, pp. 35-178.

8. GESELL, A., *et al.*: *The First Five Years of Life*. New York, Harper, 1940.

9. GILBERT, M. S.: *Biography of the Unborn*. Baltimore, Williams & Wilkins, 1938.

10. JACOBS, L.: Emotional and behavior problems in clinical pediatrics—treatment with hypnosis. *J Amer Soc Psychosom Dent Med, XI*:40-55, 1964.

11. JACOBS, L.: Sleep problems of children—treatment by hypnosis. *New York J Med, 64*:630-634, 1964.

12. KANNER, LEO: *Child Psychiatry*. 3rd ed., Springfield, Thomas, 1962.

13. KANNER, L.: *In Defense of Mothers*. Springfield, Thomas, 1954.

14. NELSON, W. E.: *Textbook of Pediatrics*. Philadelphia, Saunders, 1964.

15. ORTON, S. T.: *Reading, Writing and Speech Problems in Children*. New York, Norton, 1961.

16. Psychiatric disorders in students. *Parke, Davis, Therapeutic Notes, 74*: 142, 1967.

17. SPOCK, B.: *Baby and Child Care*. New York, Pocket Bks., 1950.

18. STEVENSON, G. S.: *Child Guidance Clinics*. New York, Commonwealth Fund, 1934.

19. STEIN, C.: Practical aspects of child guidance—a critical analysis of 500 cases. *New Eng J Med, 219*:844, 1938.

20. STEIN, C.: The role of mental hygiene in general practice. *New Eng J Med, 214*:665, 1936.

21. STEIN, C.: *Practical Psychotherapeutic Techniques*, Springfield, Thomas, 1968.

22. STEIN, C.: *Practical Psychotherapy: In Non-Psychiatric Specialties*. Springfield, Thomas, 1968.

23. WICKES, F. G.: *The Inner World of Childhood*. New York, Appleton, 1929.

24. WOLFF, E., and BAYER, L. M.: Psychosomatic disorders of childhood and adolescence. *Amer J Orthopsychiat, 22*:510, July, 1952.

Chapter 6

SEX ANXIETIES OF CHILDHOOD

Dᴜʀɪɴɢ ᴛʜᴇ ᴄʜɪʟᴅ's ᴇᴀʀʟɪᴇsᴛ ʏᴇᴀʀs his most effective counselors are his parents. These chapters are, therefore, directed to them as though the professional counselors were standing by to furnish further enlightenment when needed.

THE DIFFERENT MEANINGS OF SEX

Sex is only a three-letter word, yet it has a variety of meanings. To the biologist, sex is how life begins microscopically. To the breeder and farmer, sex as "stud" or "service" is a legitimate livelihood in the business of feeding the world. Sex is also a food, drug, commodity or symbol used to attract and control others. Ships and colleges as houses away from home are referred to as "she." Plumbers and machinists designate certain fittings as male or female, according to the purpose which they serve. Even the florist makes his living by cultivating and selling the sex organs of plants.

To most people, sex is still a collection of dirty words and jokes, a source of embarrassment, or a rallying focus for revolt. For modern youth, sex is both a self-serving reward and a defiant challenge to authority, an uplifting combination of many wonderful emotions, dreams, and adventures.

Sex is the spark plug that activates social relations. It adds zest to our lives and life to the world in which we live.

Sex is also a badge of identity of which a child should be as proud of as he is of his name, race, and religion. Yet the sex of many a youngster is a bitter disappointment not only to the family but also to the child himself. Parental preferences for boys (or girls) may be traced through several generations. Such prejudices are the result of successful brainwashing in self-rejection which compensates for previous parental and family rejection. The task of pleasing grandma or grandpa often takes precedence over pleasing one's own spouse or in-laws; but the real sufferer from sex rejection is the child who, in poetic justice, eventually returns the compliment. His emotional volcanoes eventually erupt. He gets even by means of sickness, sexual aggression or deviation, alcoholism, drugs or some other form of maladjustment and rebellion.[3, 4, 6, 9]

GREAT DISCOVERIES IN THE SEX LIFE OF THE NORMAL CHILD

Natural discoveries of normal children are almost always great events because they are important stepping stones to knowledge and wisdom. Here are a few which are sometimes overlooked or minimized.

Sex means trouble whether it is spelled with three or four letters. Sex is supposed to be a secret, or dirty, or something awful; but you are not supposed to ask.

> Girls really are different, so something must have happened to them. Something bad might happen to me too—like losing my peanut. But, so far, it's still here. So, parents can be wrong!
>
> They tell other fibs too, Like where babies come from. But sexploration is exciting, and it gets a rise out of folks.
>
> Other kids are doing it; but you can't always tell by their eyes.
>
> Storks don't bring babies; and they certainly do make mistakes. Maybe other babies are made that way, but *my parents wouldn't!*

The Conspiracy of Silence

Despite the conspiracy of silence among parents and educators, including doctors and their medical school faculties, the overprotective secrecy is a "bamboo curtain" which does not deceive the child for very long. From time to time, great pictorial magazines like "Life" and "Look" publish intimate reports on human reproduction with illustrations that offer sensible approaches to sex education.

Pictorial encyclopedias and special books are available in libraries and bookstores to remedy the fables of yesteryear; but unfortunately, too many adults still reject these visual aids.* Consequently, their own past mistakes and prejudices keep returning to plague them and to interfere with the wholesome guidance of their children.

Children are *naturally inquisitive and curious* about everything that they can see, hear, smell, or touch, and that includes the bodies of parents and playmates as well as their own. A child will accept restrictions if they are offered with firmness and finesse, but his vocabulary is dominated by endless "why's" and "why not's" and "I wants." There are also too many "no's" and "don'ts"; but, after all, a child has to know.

You Have to Know

You have to know whether you're a boy or a girl. You may not know your last name or where you live, but you have to know your own sex. You must be able to tell the difference between male and female or people will think you are "dumb" or "stupid." You might make embarrassing mistakes—like going into the wrong room, or wearing the wrong clothes, and then you will be laughed at, unless maybe if you are a hippy or a yippy or sumpin. Sex means that you are different; and you have to learn to tell the difference by the hair (if you can), and the clothes, or maybe by the toys and games that other children are playing, or by their names.

And here is another wrinkle: Some grownups like you better if you are a girl. And some children will only let you play with them if they think you are a boy; or if you act like one.

With sex, as with other matters in everyday life, a child has to be as well informed as his peers. He will make up stories rather than admit to ignorance, but he will eventually replace fiction with facts. The incorrigible psychopathic liar never outgrows this need to appear well informed and be ingratiating to others when it suits his needs, regardless of the consequences.

The normal child takes his cue from the people who surround him. He soon learns that being a sissy invites rejection and his sister discovers that a tomboy often has more fun than nice, good little girls.

---

* See also "Human Reproduction" (16 mm sound). Association Films, Inc., 35 West 45th St., New York 19, N.Y.

Other Reasons Why Sex Is Important to the Normal Child

An adult's first question, Is it a boy or a girl?, is a common indication of the prejudices of parents and grandparents. Children are like house pets. They, too, know when they are not wanted. They recognize the nonverbal signs of rejection when they have been labeled "second class" or "grade B." This knowledge usually produces lifelong emotional scars. Rejection usually impairs self-confidence, but it can also serve as motivation for compensatory achievements.

> Some day I'll show them. I'll become the best athlete, or performer, or specialist in the whole wide world. You'll see. . . .

An implied second question is also loaded with anxiety, is it a *normal* boy or girl? Your child may not know why this is important, and at first he does not even care. Nevertheless, a pattern of apprehension develops over the constant pressure to meet accepted standards. Children as well as parents compare size and weight gains, but they may be anxious for other reasons. This anxiety is especially prevalent since the outbreak of phocomelia (flipper limb) deformities following such drugs as Thalidomide.

More commonly, the enlarged and cyanosed genitals of the newborn boy, while normal, are not at all reassuring to the average lay parent. The same is true of the misshapen head of a first baby, whether girl or boy. Even the normal umbilical area of the newborn baby can be an upsetting sight to a growing child.

Such sights are valuable learning experiences for medical students and nurses, but they may shock the layman and they are common causes of anxiety. Repeated exposure to such sights over the years permits the professional worker to accept unusual or distressing experiences, but the lay parent often goes to opposite extremes of secrecy in an attempt to overprotect the rest of the family.

These and other aspects of baby care, such as breast feeding, bathing and diapering, enhance not only the child's curiosity but also his apprehensiveness concerning babies and sex—theirs as well as his own.

The first visit to a maternity hospital has profound effects on fathers and other relatives as well as on the expectant mother. Waiting is, in itself, provocative of anxiety. The sight of blood stains plus strange or alarming sounds and smells give rise to additional apprehension for the mother's welfare. Consequently, these, too, may become linked unconsciously with the sex of the newborn babe. Some hospitals and obstetricians are especially negligent in such matters. Their failure to protect patients and visitors often recalls one's previous childhood hospital experiences or accidents or illnesses at home which may have been none too pleasant.

Most people usually have valid reasons for fearing sickness, hospitals, and doctors. Their fears may not be directly related to sex as such, but most deliveries, tonsillectomies and the repair of injuries are now made in hospitals. Consequently there is a natural association of sickness with separation, with problems of excretion, with invasion of bedroom privacy, and frequent exposure of the genitalia. These are common experiences in the life of nearly every child. It is, therefore, impossible to rule out some aspects of childbirth and the reproductive organs in the origins of a great many common anxieties.

Among these anxieties are the fear of being pushed and falling which normally accompanies the baby's expulsion from the uterus; the loud noises which are in sharp contrast to the muffled sounds that reached the baby during prenatal life; the fear of strange odors, sounds, lights, instruments, appliances, pressure, cold, hunger, separation from family and isolation.* Additional anxieties, relating to the earliest weeks of life, can result from prematurity, illness and surgery, including cutting the umbilical cord and circumcision.

Sex Is No Secret

Sex is seldom the secret which parents try to make it. For one thing, sex curiosity is heightened by restrictions, especially

---

* There is an average drop of 20 to 30 degrees from uterus to delivery room—quite enough to make anyone who is naked gasp and cry out.

those involving looking and touching. When parents encourage the baby to investigate and play with every part of his body except one, he does not have to be hit on the head to recognize the situation. A "no touch" quarantine does not have to be printed in large letters on his diapers. The average child soon knows exactly how his parents feel about most matters without even looking at their faces. He can tell when he is in trouble just from the tone of voice and the sudden change in the way he is handled. In the mind of most children the attitudes of their parents toward sex is the worst kept secret in the world. Even a liberal or "modern" mother usually feels that she has to say or do something in order to avoid giving the impression that she approves of sexploration or sex curiosity, or even natural penile erections.

Sex Is Equated With "Bad"

The normal child has sensitive feelings in the rest of his body as well as in his genitals. In training the child there are many interests which he must learn to restrain. He must be taught that certain foods are harmful, certain bright objects are hot or sharp, certain parts of people's anatomy are personal and certain parts of his own body are also taboo, "private," "special" or "reserved," rather than *forbidden*. In the child's mind the severity of parental disapproval may not be as great for one trespass as for another; but he soon learns that the forbidden activities are all classed together as signs of "bad" behavior.

Indulging in forbidden activities means danger of some restrictions or punishment. The greatest of these is some form of rejection which, in the beginning, means fewer privileges. Later, when he is older, these restrictions will be reenforced by threats, hints of punishment and warnings of divine disapproval.

Right now, however, when the child's little hand reaches out for a fragile glass ornament, for example, and the ornament is grabbed quickly away from him or his hand is suddenly seized, it does not take long for him to grasp the idea that violence will be used if necessary to keep him and his hands away from other forbidden objects, including his genitals. Sometimes the restraint comes a second too late; the article drops or is broken and the effects are catastrophic.

The more violent the restraint or scolding that accompanies the "accident" the more importance the child will attach to the article or activity that has been restricted.

A child will often cry even when no damage has been done except to his feelings. Nevertheless, much of the sexual anxiety of later life still reflects this earliest conditioning over inconsequential matters.

Sex Becomes a Dirty Word

It also causes the child to lie, and make him feel wicked. Children may never outgrow the emotional effects of these very painful discoveries. They may be quite willing to put the words and the subject out of their conscious minds until some later date; but they will not stay out of dreams. Here is another wrinkle. The loss of confidence in parents causes a drop in prestige and a weakening of their guiding influence which often carries over into adult life. The child is convinced that this is one thing that his parents do not understand. They do not know what he is thinking or how he feels.

You Are Not Supposed to Ask About That Either

You have to find out some other way. You can ask about almost anything else, like Santa Claus and the angels and even who made God, and maybe they will say they do not know. But you will be safer if you have an accident in your pants or go to the bathroom on the kitchen floor, than to ask where babies come from, and how they get born and why is a girl different.

> Now if I were to grow up to be a nurse, or a doctor . . . Anyway, nobody seems to care about what little boys can do except little girls, and maybe some grownups who won't admit it. And yet it isn't fair for little girls to have to go all the way back to the house when little boys are allowed to go to the bathroom almost any place. But I can show them. I can prove I'm just as good as a boy. Huh! I can already run faster and climb higher. . . .
>
> But when parents don't seem to care, or when

they're afraid—well, that's the part that really hurts. They're even afraid to put it in the dictionary. They've put "ain't" in the dictionary and "rape" and "piss" and even "shit," but nobody's willing to admit there's even such a word as —— you know what.

Direct Communication

Most of the disturbances of communication between people of any age can be traced to early patterns of emotional conflict other than sexual, but the chief source of tension between parents and children is often the result of a child's inability to talk things out. This is the result of the parent's equal ineptness at hearing him through without interruption and without undue censorship. Dirty words can be left unspoken but they can be written and repeated to oneself. They still spell defiance against restriction, and they still denote rebellion against what the child considers as inexcusable injustice.

Familiar examples of this kind of "bad" and "dirty" *oral aggression* include the "Bronx cheer," yelling, spitting, ostentatious burping, and the bold use of four-letter words. Other profane outlets for inadequately repressed emotions, at almost any age in life, include "bad" and "dirty" *anal aggression*. Anal aggression includes acts of excretion, words or gestures that invite attention to one's rear end, acts of desecration, vandalism and so on.

PARENTAL MANAGEMENT OF EARLY SEX PROBLEMS

Bladder, bowels and sex are as intimately connected as food, mouth and stomach. If the daily newspaper is admitted to your home, you must learn an acceptable vocabulary with which to discuss "rape," "ravish," "sex fiend," "pervert," "fornication," "adultery," "lewd and lascivious," "unnatural acts" and the ever-fascinating interest in surgery and hormones for changing one's sex from male to female and vice versa.

The sex fears and anxieties of childhood are a challenge to sensible management, especially since they are also a normal part of the child's daily life. For instance, here is a very common occurrence.

> *Judy,* a ten-year-old, came home from school with a question, "Mommy, Ronny said the word for making babies is 'tuck' or 'puk' or something like that. Is it?" Mother, a schoolteacher, did not faint. She said, "Yes, Judy it is. Only the first letter of the word is 'f.' "
>
> She then explained that the word was so used in slang but that it was an impolite term and usage was not acceptable in social conversation. She added, almost as an afterthought, "We use other words, like mating or sexual relations, or copulating."
>
> Judy listened attentively, and seemed quite satisfied. The child then asked if she should report this information back to her classmate, Ronny, but the mother advised her to drop the matter, telling her that Ronny's mother probably would correct him when she heard him using the word.

Judy's mother was on good terms with her daughter, but Judy's mother was not born that way. She had to learn from her own past errors. Many parents have had a similar experience. Here's how Judy's mother remembers hers.

> It wasn't quite as easy as it sounds from the way I tell it; but I had such a hard time, when I was a girl, I made up my mind that my Judy wasn't going to go through the same thing. When I was ten I ran all the way home and fell and hurt my knee; but I didn't dare tell my mother that I was running away from a little boy who had tried to kiss me. And at eleven, I was standing in the subway when a man came up to me and I suddenly saw that he was exposed. I ran up to the "El" (elevated electric train) and was late for school. I got detention, got scolded by teacher, and then I got a licking when I got home, *but I couldn't tell anyone why I'd been late.*

N.B. Home and love are the most important four-letter words. Against them, competing gutter language and vulgarisms have little chance to flourish.

When sex is thrown at you, as a counselor, therapist or parent, in the form of a startling frank question from a precocious youngster, do not pretend to be shocked by his use of the four-letter words. You have heard them before. However you do not have to admit them to full membership in your own daily vocabulary, although I have heard some psychologists do so from the lecture platform and in so-called progressive groups.

Junior may be testing you to see whether you will tell him the truth. He may also be trying to embarrass you in order to get even with you for avoidance and for some of the fairy tales you have been throwing his way.

Treat the situation the way you handled other words in his vocabulary. For instance, you can say, "Some words are better than others. You would cause quite a commotion in class if you told your teacher that your hand was raised because you wanted to make 'manure' in the toilet, wouldn't you?"

If you can smile at this vulgar expression, you can imagine how Junior will giggle when he hears it. Yet this is precisely the point you are trying to make to him: namely, that some expressions are not suitable for everyday use, even though they may be technically or colloquially correct. By doing this you avoid hypocrisy and you also avoid emphasizing the "bad" or "naughty" features of the situation.

"B.M." for bowel movement or "duty" or "numbers" are generally accepted terms for the feces (rhymes with species). Nurses and doctors usually refer to it as "stool"; just as "specimen'" is their term for a sample of urine, and "void" or "micturate" is the act of emptying the bladder.

For better or worse most children learn from others, including their parents, that "shit," "crap" and "piss" are often more explosive and effective expressions than "hell" or "goddammit." Some of these terms have been appearing in our theatres and cinemas for decades and others will doubtless follow.

Like "bandit," "rascal" and "stinker," they are also undergoing changes in their meanings, as well as in popular acceptance. For instance, "You're full of bull" has become accepted as a proper designation for the obstreperous and rebellious dispenser of bovine manure and "hot air" exaggerations.

Nowadays a new shortcut has been introduced. Some entertainers on television refer without embarrassment to "The Pill." By stating whether or not they are on the pill, they automatically sidestep the question of intercourse and replace it with "are you being careful," or are you "planning to have a baby?"

Once the choice of words is straightened out, the rest is simple. If you do not feel capable of answering a child's question without wisecracking, stammering, blushing, hesitancy and evasion, tell him that you will think it over or that you will find out and let him know, or you do not feel capable of doing justice to his question, not having been asked so directly before, because when you were his age young people just did not talk about those things and would he mind if we all take it up with daddy a little later on in the day.

If daddy is also not quite up to it, then find a counselor or someone else who is capable until you yourself feel able to handle the subject with finesse. Here are some simple situations:

> Six-year-old Eva said to her mother, "Say, Mom, was you ever frigged?" Mother almost swallowed her gum and was unable to say a word. The child instantly sensed her mother's embarrassment but passed it off like a veteran. "I dunno what it means, but Joan told me to ask you." Then she ran outdoors. Her mother reported sadly, "This incident happened ten years ago and to this day Eva has never mentioned a single word about sex. Whenever I've tried to tell her things she should know, she just says, 'Yeh, Mom, I know' and quickly changes the subject."

> Five-year-old Charley was less tactful as he demanded to know the meaning of "f-k." His mother coughed a few times but managed to convey some sort of explanation at which the boy burst out contemptuously, "Is that all! Well, why does everybody make such a big fuss about it?" Mother merely shrugged her shoulders, preferring not to trust herself to say anything more, and Charley promptly changed the subject by asking for some cookies.

Meanwhile, it may help you to know that the popular vulgarism for sexual intercourse comes from the Latin word "facere" which means "to make." You may want to adopt the word "coitus" (ko-ee-tuss) which means "coming together" or "cohabitate" because the more popular term "sexual intercourse" risks embarrassment to others. The word "mating" is often rejected because it is so frequently identified with animals in heat. Many people prefer the terms "loving" or "making love," but you can see how easy it would be to confuse the young child when you want to use the word "love" in its less intimate and nongenital sense.

Similarly, you may prefer the word "vulva" which is the term for all the external female genitals. *Cunnes* is the Latin name for the same "private parts" and explains another colloquial term for the female genitalia. Popular lay terms may strain the imagination, but some of your clients will have limited vocabularies, and your child's first sex words may not come from dictionaries.

Penis (peé-niss) and phallus (faý-luss) mean the same thing.* Shakespeare refers to a "bull's pizzle"; but in medical books, a sore on a boy's sex organ is referred to as a "penile" (rhymes with *senile*) lesion. Scrotum refers to the bag or sac containing the testes.

Womb is still a good biblical term for our very first home, but uterus (yoó-ter-us) is the correct anatomical term. Vagína (rhymes with Jamima) is the tubular passage or canal which leads from the entrance (introitus) between the lips (labia) to the womb (uterus), (commonly called *snatch, muff, box, pussy, crack* or *hole.*)

"Making out" has replaced many of the former vulgar terms for intercourse. Girls usually call it "making love" or "going all the way," but they are no strangers to gutter language. The frequent use of anatomical diagrams and pictures can simplify the task of setting the youngster straight. Most therapists and counselors already have them in their possession; and they also appear in medical dictionaries, encyclopedias and books on sex education.

Remember that to some children, the mere thought of coitus is wholly unacceptable if not actually disgusting. The normal child who is raised by parents with conventional standards has become fairly well convinced by one means or another that the sex organs are for urination and should not be handled for anything else or by anyone else. The idea that sperms and ova (seeds and eggs), which are the sources of life, and babies, which are the products of love, must also come through these same passages may be rejected for a long time.

Even when the child is forced to conclude that other parents may make their babies in this manner, he will often cling to the conviction that *his* parents are different and that they, of all people, would never stoop to anything so vulgar. Even if he has to accept the equally threatening idea that he may be an adopted

---

* Your young client may know it as *cock, prick, peter, pecker, dingus, privates* or *thing.* "Secrets" is a biblical term for the genitalia.

child in order to protect this ideal, he will try to keep his parents on the pedestal occupied only by the holy, the untouched and the untouchable.

Parents should remember, however, that there is nothing *necessarily* shocking in the organs and function of coitus. The shock to the child comes in having learned something else and then finding out that he was deceived or that the reason why his parents failed to guide him along the path of truth was because they themselves were ashamed of the subject.

Except as a matter of convenience, the sexual differences are important to the child only because other people make them so. Being a girl or a boy is important chiefly because one of them feels more accepted than the other; more wanted by his family and by his playmates.

The *intake history* should include a few casual questions on how the father's and mother's families felt about girls versus boys and which ones were generally considered to be the family favorites. The more the patient attempts to change the subject, or to deny any possible connection between sex or favoritism and his complaints, the more suspicious one should be of potential unfinished business in this line.

Multiple Values of Sex

To the small child the genital differences between boys and girls are almost exclusively related to urination. Some time later, when mother ceases to be a special personal possession and the chief source of food, from which he has been eventually deprived, the child thinks of sex in terms of her most prominent symbol, the bosom. He then focuses his conscious interest and attention above, as well as below, the waistline as most adults of both sexes still do.

On a broader level, genital differences also represent an indication of value. Sex now stands for a badge of superiority or inferiority depending upon which group the child has learned to value and which one he wants to belong to and is accepted by. If a girl feels at a disadvantage for other reasons, then she might covet being a boy solely as a means of gaining acceptance or prestige. Boys often wish they were girls for similar reasons: and the hippy hairdo has profound personal values.

During toilet training, little boys and girls often want to imitate an older brother or father's method of voiding. This is their means of identifying with him; just as they do by wanting to wear his shoes or hat, or pretending to smoke his pipe or cigar. Some parents make too big an issue of this. They cause embarrassment by scornful restrictions or disparaging remarks. Wiser parents make a game of it and let the little girl "make believe" until she is ready to make her own adjustment and to accept her limitations as well as her advantages.

Prevention of Voyeurism

As shoppers well know, the urge to look is a natural compensation for restrictions on touching or possessing. A large percentage of sex anxieties of older children are the result of parents' failure to recognize the urge to look as normal compensation for not being permitted to touch. The case of Sara shows how needless restrictions on this score were avoided during her infancy. Sara's mother, a nurse, tells the story.

Baby Sara is our first daughter. At eight weeks she was completely fascinated by a red silk handkerchief at which she would gaze long and earnestly. At ten weeks, Sara discovered her own hands and spent hours admiring them. Later she showed a similar absorption in other parts of her body. She gradually learned to recognize voices and familiar sounds, and to associate them with feeding, elimination, diapering, bathing, being picked up and so forth.

Sara was young enough not to mind the natural curiosity of her two older brothers at bath time; but at eighteen months she suddenly discovered her father's genitals while he was bathing. We tried to pay no more attention to her than when she began to creep into closets, or discovered a new toy, or the cat's tail. Of course, she had to learn the "no touch" taboo just like the others before her. But we found that we, or rather I, couldn't be quite as calm and pleasant when she wanted to touch her father's genitals as we had been about teaching her to investigate her own toes, or to imitate us, for instance, in saying "bye-bye." For some reason it was much more difficult than it had been with the boys.

In matters of important discipline we expect her to detect some anxiety or annoyance in our voices, for instance, when it came to keeping her out of trouble, like when she wanted to feel the candle flame. But we didn't want her to sense that we might be upset when it came to denying her the right to satisfy her curiosity about father's sex organs. I was actually more embarrassed than I'd even been with the boys.

Well, we used "no" as little as possible and said it with as much smiling patience as we could muster. In a pinch, we just changed the subject and found something else for her to do. It wasn't easy, but little by little we're catching on, and so is Sara. [Many parents "muddle through" in similar fashion.]

When the desire to look is suppressed too early in life, or too severely, and when other sources of approval are inadequate, a child may express himself in a different way. The forbidden interest in others often becomes centered on his own body, and he may seek approval or attention by showing off. He may develop a passion for nudity, discover the mirror, call attention to his clothing and toys and resort to whatever language or mischief he can think of in his attempt to recapture the center of the stage and prolong attention. Such acting up is especially common when visitors are present.

The best method to offset these attitudes is to give approval for acceptable behavior, dress and language. This emphasis on the positive is an indirect devaluation of the negative or undesirable behavior. It encourages the child to discard his desire to shock you in favor of behavior that brings out your praise. Thus by restraining your own natural concern for this type of exhibitionism you automatically alter the child's attitude.

In the case of a child whose age and size keep him at a constant disadvantage when it comes to dealing with people who are older and bigger than himself, the need for reassurance and a friendly voice and gesture is always present. Small children feel left out when company takes over. They interrupt frequently and are often completely ignored, or repressed, by equally rude elders who are trying to concentrate on what is being said at the other end of the table or across the room.

Look for unintended suppressions or omissions on this score whenever you are faced with a behavior problem in the home. If you cannot find it, try asking. If you ask the child what is wrong he might be willing to tell you. *But be sure you pay attention and listen to what is being said.* Then even when you cannot believe him you can at least say that you are sorry for losing your temper and start all over again.

Attempts At Secrecy May Backfire

It has long been thought that there is less juvenile delinquency and fewer sex offenses among rural children than among those who are raised in cities. Part of this may be the result of a more leisurely pace of living; but it also suggests the value of exposing children to natural animal functions of suckling, excretion, mating, birth, sickness, and death.

On the other hand, it must not be supposed that everyone who lives on a farm is free of complexes. Many adults not only miss the boat themselves but also cause difficulty for others.

Recollection of Della

Della, a young woman still in her teens, was having early marital troubles. Although she had been married for nearly a year, she was still unable to permit coital entrance. Here is her statement.

I was raised with my cousins on a farm. We had free run of the place except at stud time. Whenever a cow was to be serviced, we were locked up in the barn by my uncle. He would never let us watch a calf being dropped either. I can't seem to remember about the other animals.

Obviously Della's uncle could not possibly hide every sexual activity from the children. All he had succeeded in doing was to accentuate the mystery and arouse greater curiosity. What Della had managed to do was to suppress all of her forbidden knowledge into "forgotten" experience. To her, intercourse was mating. It still meant disobeying her uncle, and any attempts to fulfill her natural function and desires were met with painful muscle spasms. The management of this physical expression of anxiety required nearly a year of treatment by conventional non-hypnotic, analytically oriented techniques; but the problem was successfully resolved and Della is now a happy and healthy mother.

Unfortunately, Della herself did not profit by her experience. She still undresses in the dark and she permits no nudity in her home. She even excludes her husband from watching their baby daughter's bath. Just knowing what ought to be done is not enough. The courage to put knowledge into practice is also required.

Misinformation Is Easier to Acquire Than to Correct

Seeing is believing, but illusions are especially convincing to children.

Recollections of Anita

Anita had once seen a cow giving birth to a calf. From where she stood, the hind legs of the cow appeared like the forelegs because the cow's head was turned around toward its tail. Anita was convinced that the calf was born from an opening between the shoulders and believed the same to be true of humans. She rejected the suspected truth and used denial as a defense against her fear of genital mutilation. Her refusal to accept any of the stories told by the girls in junior high school about babies "coming out of their mother's bellies" did not help her popularity. Even when she was given an opportunity to visit a farm, Anita carefully avoided the barn and cow pastures, until one day her anxiety about her own neck and shoulders caused her so much distress that she sought professional help.

Her neurosis yielded to a program of reeducation and reconditioning similar to the one for Della, above.

Here's one that was more stormy and lasted longer.

Recollection of Cheryl

I had a new lunch date. He's married, another rigid male in my life. [She relaxed spontaneously as soon as she sat in her accustomed chair in my office. I didn't even have to cue her with the signal "Relax."] Now we're back in the mud again. I put mud on a boy's penis. I had a girlfriend. She was Polish . . . not very feminine . . . she wore a boyish bob . . . we used to have a lot of sex play. Her brother had intercourse with her and then with me. Mother caught us . . . I wish she were dead . . . I still go for the men . . . must be to prove I can *get* them . . . but I can't *hold* them . . . yard full of mud . . . dirty mud on the side of the barn and my clothes and face and legs . . . my older sister saying "Shame on you . . . dirty muddy water again . . . I had a dream. There was a yard full of mud . . . not feminine. I remember father urinating in the field . . . that made mud and the horses urinating in the field . . . and once I urinated in a barrel and I remember the boys calling out "Cheryl, Cheryl, pee in the berrel" (bursting into tears). I was a dirty little girl . . . [Spontaneous arousal with considerable relief of tension from her abreaction.]

On the way out she told my receptionist, "I'm not coming back because Dr. S. always makes me cry." But she was back the following week—more relaxed and much less compulsive regarding her dates.

Improved Communication Minimizes Anxiety

During childhood a common anxiety over injury or loss of the genitals is also shown in the frequency with which overheard medical information is liable to misunderstanding, as in the following case.

Tommy and His Grandfather's Tinkler

Ten-year-old Tommy insisted on going to the hospital to visit his grandfather who had just had an operation. According to hospital custom, Tommy was refused admittance and had to wait outside in the car, wondering whether he would ever see his beloved grandfather again. On the way home Tommy's worried mother did her best to explain the operation (removal of the prostate) and the reason for a temporary drainage tube "sticking out of" her father's abdomen, when suddenly the boy burst into tears. He turned for comfort to his silent father and wailed in dismay, "Oh, Daddy, Grandpa's had his tinkler cut off."

When young people identify sex play with mating and the responsibilities of parenthood, they are likely to develop a more wholesome respect for sex than if the emphasis is chiefly upon sex play as a naughty or forbidden pastime. In this way conscious desires for sexual intercourse are less likely to arise until the later stages of courtship when they can be dealt with more intelligently and where an earlier marriage might prove desirable.

So much anxiety and resentment is aroused by unnecessary secrecy about the most elementary facts of biology that it is small wonder that few parents are able to discuss the facts of life with their growing children even when the danger season of puberty actually arrives. The simplest procedure is to teach the young child that some matters are confidential. The child should be expected to respect private business just as his parents are obligated to respect his secrets.

The normal child already knows that her playmates have different standards as to mixed bathing and semi-nudism in the home. She does not expect that they will serve the same menus or buy the same furniture or decorate in the same way. She usually has already compared her own parents with those of her friends and found the latter wanting. In other words, the normal child is already prejudiced in her parents' favor and is usually ready to accept their ideas and even their restrictions long before her parents voice them. ("I know just what you're gonna say. . . .")

Parents must be careful lest they destroy this enthusiasm or impair the child's natural loyalty by making foolish and superfluous restrictions. When parents build an emotional foundation of confidence quite early in the child's life, the child will come to them of his own accord whenever he needs help or is in doubt. Most of the time he will reach the right conclusion, independently, just from having lived with his parents and from hearing their comments and reactions to other situations such as profanity, exhibitionism, and smutty or sensational stories.

When a child can come to his parents with a report such as the following, they need have no fear about their success in communication.

Miriam's Confession

Six-year-old Miriam reported confidentially to her mother, "You know something, Mommy? Jimmy is a dirty pig!" Mother waited but gave her full attention. "He wanted me to pick up my dress and let him zamin (examine) me!"

"Really? And what did you say to that?"

"Told him no and now he's mad at me and I'm mad at him so I'm not talking to him."

After a brief pause, mother asked, "You think he's really a bad little boy?"

"Well, isn't he?"

"Oh, I don't know, honey. Lots of little boys are curious about little girls, and I suppose it's natural for little girls to be curious about little boys, too. Remember how you felt about your baby brother?"

"But that's different, Mommy. Jimmy's not my brother!"

"You're quite right, Miriam, and I'm not saying you didn't do right—you did and I'm proud of you. I wouldn't want any dirty little hands playing around my body, either."

"Then you're not sticking up for him?"

"Oh no! I just said it didn't mean he was a bad boy for being curious. But I agree with you that he was out of line in trying to get you to agree with him after you told him you thought it wasn't the right thing to do."

Miriam seemed satisfied for a short while, but obviously she had something else on her mind. Presently, she hung her head and in a low voice said, "Mommy, I've got something to 'fess to you."

Mother kept on with her knitting and again waited patiently.

"Member when Cousin Cora was here? Well, back of the garage we . . . I mean she . . . lifted her dress and . . . and peed . . . I mean yurnated (urinated) like a boy."

"So?" asked mother casually.

"I didn't tell you coz I didn't want to tattletale."

"You did quite right, dear, but why do you tell me now?"

Long pause. "Well . . . a while back . . . I did it too."

Mother smiled.

"But it was right in front of Jimmy's father!"

Mother stopped smiling and asked, "You wanted to impress him?"

"I don't know . . . I suppose I should of told you about that?"

"Only if you wanted to, dear, but did you try to figure out why you did it?"

"Well, baby brother does it that way and Jimmy did too, once . . . and, Cora said boys was better'n girls and she was gonna be a boy when she grows up."

Miriam's tears overflowed as mother suddenly began to recognize that Cora's mother's fuss over Miriam's new baby brother had upset the two little girls far more than anyone had realized. She reached out her arms and gently hugged the unhappy little girl, meanwhile trying to figure out what to say. "You think Jimmy's father told on you?"

"He must have," the child wailed, "and now they'll all think I'm a bad girl, and I'm not, truly, I'm not."

"I'm sure you're not, sweetheart. But tell me, what did Jimmy's father do?"

"Nothing. He just kept on walking like he didn't see me."

"Well, then, he probably didn't see you. He must have had something else on his mind. Otherwise he'd have mentioned it to your father or to me."

The child's eyes widened in wonder. "You mean he didn't *tell* you? You didn't *know* about it?"

"Cross my heart."

"And you're not mad at me?"

Mother's smile said no, but her words were, "Well, it was a

foolish thing to do. [Just the right amount of censure.] But any little girl can make a mistake." [Poor alibi but still a way out.]

"Gee, Mommy, I was so afraid . . ."

"And that's why you called Jimmy a bad boy?"

"Guess so, Mommy, but isn't he if he does that?" [Miriam still attempts to excuse herself by dwelling on Jimmy's misbehavior.]

"It's not considered good taste, if that's what you mean."

Another pause. "Are you going to tell Daddy?"

"I hadn't planned to, dear. Let's just keep this as woman's talk, shall we?" A relieved Miriam threw her small arms about her equally relieved mother and the incident was closed.

In telling me about this incident many years later, Miriam's mother reported the following:

> From that time on I've never had cause for worry. Miriam has sometimes kept me waiting for a few days when she's been angry with me about something, but the restraint I exercised then—and it was a big strain on me, I can assure you—has paid off in big dividends. She tells me just about everything and usually takes my advice, even when I don't give her any, and just let her figure things out for herself. What wouldn't I have given for liberal parents when I was a little girl!

Miriam grew up to be a wholesome and popular girl who did not have to buy favors with privileges, became a gracious hostess like her mother, and a happy wife and mother of four normal children.

Fathers can also be tactful, as shown in the following story about six-year-old Hazel.

> "Daddy, I don't feel so good." "What's the matter, dear?" "I don't know, but I got cramps. Mommy says this cold has gone to my stomach, but I think I'm going to have a baby or sumpin."
>
> Father promptly brought her one of her dolls and gravely remarked, "Well, well, a seven-pound boy! Just what we need. Now how about feeding him some ice cream?" Hazel responded with delight and recovered immediately.

Nudism As Prevention Is Not Always Foolproof

Color and religion are not the only barriers to acceptance of the child by his playmates. In most homes to a large extent one has to conform not only to what the grandparents thought about alcohol, sex, food, or drugs, but also to what the majority of the neighbors may think and are doing—if we expect to avoid criticism, resentment, and ostracism.

For example, some parents have liberal ideas about nudity in the home, but if theirs is the only house in the block where the children are no longer curious about each other's genitals or the human body, they may soon find themselves less popular with the neighbors, and their child may be singled out for unwelcome attention.

Aunt Maggie Disapproves

Betty, aged six, and Benny, aged eight, had been accustomed to nude bathing together from infancy, until recently when their visiting Aunt Maggie bathed them. Like Adam and Eve in the Garden of Eden, the children suddenly became very self-conscious in her presence and hastily grabbed towels to cover themselves.

Little Betty and Benny already knew how their grandparents felt about mixed bathing, but they had not yet learned how Aunt Maggie might feel. As a matter of fact, Maggie did not even say a word. She did not have to. There is a universal sign language for disapproval as well as for love and acceptance. Needless to say, Aunt Maggie never became their confidante on personal problems. On the contrary, a wordless mimicry of her disapproval in a charade was usually good for a laugh at a party. Maggie was not actually a prude; but anxiety is contagious, and her anxiety over an unfamiliar experience communicated itself to the children.

Sex Play

People of almost any age can exploit sex as a means of consolation and a source of prestige and power. But most parents are still uncomfortable when confronted with sex play in their children. They resist the fact that sex has been promoted to the ranks of respectability, where it rightfully belongs; and they ignore the psychological and practical significance of increasing publicity on the worldwide population explosion and belated attempts at large-scale birth control.

Religious influences are still trying to retain some respect for traditional morality and conservative behavior. Yet seductive nudes in color can be seen on newsstands, theatre lobbies, "art" displays, and in barber-shop magazines. Frank portrayals of erotic behavior with cinema nudity is common in many theatres which do not exclude teensters. Many adults are not yet able to deal reservedly with the full impact of unabashed erotic stimulants.

Sex play, indulgence and pornography are not new. They have become a thriving and lucrative business. Concurrently, the social revolution of teen-agers has released sex from its former underground secrecy to involve the junior high schools as well as higher levels. Many adults have not yet accepted the fact that college dormitories and campuses have been sexually unsegregated for several decades. They are still shocked to learn of recent statistics on the rise of venereal disease and unmarried mothers. They missed the first boat too when their own children were young.

A common outlet for both sublimated and direct genital tension is the practice of sex games, even though "playing doctor" or "nurse" in young children may have very little sexual stimulation as we adults recognize it. While the playing does provide an opportunity for forbidden exploration (looking, exhibiting and touching), the activity may also be an innocent imitation of a previous experience with sickness. Playing doctor is also a natural identification with the recurrent rash of popular television shows about doctors, hospitals, and nurses. But here, too, supervision and enlightenment are indicated to prevent injury, as in the following case of Dina.

Dina Plays Hospital

Dina's mother returned from an errand one day to find her three-year-old child screaming. The two little girls, Dina and Marie, had been "playing hospital" and mother was horrified to discover that Marie had been trying to take the child's temperature. Marie had been accustomed to having her own rectal temperature taken many times. But, unlike the real nurse, she had neglected to lubricate the thermometer. Also, her knowledge of anatomy was incomplete. Moreover, Marie was using an old-style oral thermometer, and the danger of breakage had not yet been impressed upon her five-year-old mind.

There is no adequate substitute for superivision of children at play—whether at sex or any other games. As a rule larger groups under trained leadership afford greater protection for the child. Furthermore, group play usually offers many more opportunities for the child to achieve prestige with the crowd from more wholesome sources. The "play" is usually an imitation of things seen or heard. The closed doors, secrecy, removal of clothing and handling of the body are incidental and are liable to be over-stressed. The main objective is to gain attention and acceptance by playmates and to pretend being grown-up.

Parents can substitute lessons in first aid and how to use the telephone for emergency calls. They can also encourage the use of children's doctor and nursing kits to build up the child's interest and to divert attention from the more intimate features of sickness. In other words, one should encourage those activities that will *not* evoke secrecy and criticism but *will* arouse wholesome interests in health, recreation, exercise, education and fun.

Group Sex Play

From the age of three years to the midteens, group sex play is more common than many people realize. One or two "fast" leaders often attract many unhappy followers who may be more afraid to be left out or to break away than they are shamed to remain with the gang. More often some bolder acquaintance brags to the child or teases him, or an older cousin or other member of the family may have been indiscreet and aroused his curiosity. Whatever the situation may be, parents should be well informed about their child's playmates and be prepared to furnish replacements for undesirable behavior in the form of wholesome group activities.

If you want to help some child whom you suspect of being involved in such an entanglement, your best procedure is to win him away from his crowd by offering something that is much more attractive and satisfying. Devices for building up a child's ego and helping him to gain prestige with other children of his own age level usually prove to be far more effective than threats or punishments, provided you work at it. Bad habits are not easily changed. They should be replaced with good ones, but the positive training must be started early.

Keep the emphasis on the *desirable* activities that other children are doing if you want to weaken your child's argument that all the other kids are doing it. Try also to play up the desirable things that your own child can do and is doing. Cultivate his interests in hobbies, special skills and normal recreation. If you keep building up his prestige in his own family, he will not need to resort to undesirable outsiders or to anxiety-provoking activities. He will be too busy with his acceptable projects and too anxious to keep your good opinion to fall an easy prey to unwholesome seduction. This is also your best device for protecting your child against the threatened anxiety from dirty words, obscene pictures and the temptations of bolder playmates.

Genital Tension

Genital tension can be embarrassing, but it is also pleasurable. It may be localized and natural, as from a full bladder or rectum, a soiled diaper, or stimulation from clothing or from cleansing during bathing; or the tension may be generalized, for instance, when the child has been punished by exile to his room, or left alone too long, or has been listening intently behind closed doors, or is being kept off-limits. The child also may have seen or heard something unexpectedly without comprehending its full meaning, such as mating animals or boudoir activities in the home. As in other habits, like thumbsucking, the consequent tension may be displaced to the genitals, where imagination can easily take over.

Similar anxiety or excitement, with accompanying genital tension, can occur during preparation for a date or party, or upon receipt of a new gift or some wonderful news.

Genital tension and excitement can result from tight clothing, from squatting positions, and from straddling an object or someone's knee. Unthinking caresses from adults, such as repeated and excessive kissing of the neck or patting the buttocks, can be stimulating to a child, like stroking the head and back of the family cat. We sometimes forget that this is a procedure which pleases both the child, or animal, and the one who pets him.

Other common causes of genital tension are delayed diapering, holding back a call to nature (bladder or bowels) in an older child who is trying to win approval, and excessive fondling at any age especially during bathing. These causes suggest their own remedy.

Sometimes a child's normal activities and play are too stimulating or the praise is too lavish and seductive, in which case the aroused feelings and excitement may become permanently associated with some particular function. For instance, if a baby has too much fun in the tub or on the pot, he naturally wants to prolong the relationship as much as possible. He often does the same thing at feeding time, if only to avoid the boredom of being left alone too long in between nursings.

As the child grows older, he becomes increasingly reluctant to accept inevitable time limitations and restrictions on these pleasant relationships. When he is considered to be too old for babyhood he will often resort to fun by tossing food, splashing water all over the bathroom floor, or scampering about the house without his clothing, even though he knows that he may be scolded and punished for it.

In later years such pastimes as reading in the bathroom, sliding down a stair rail, or dallying at meals, and compulsive bathing or swimming may be explained as emotional hangovers from early pleasurable associations of childhood.

While none of these activities are necessarily sexual in themselves as far as genital excitement or stimulation are concerned, they often are colored and influenced by the general sensual excitement of physical caressing of early childhood. Caressing means acceptance. Acceptance means love. Love means warmth and comfort and well-being. All together they spell emotional security for the child.

Genital Manipulation in Children

It may surprise many people to learn that genital manipulation is as common among girls as it is among boys and for identical reason. Here is how the tension problem was handled in the case of Jerry.

Jerry's Ding-Ding

The five-year-old boy's mother thought that she had solved the problem a few years earlier. The boy had excitedly announced, "Mommy! There's something the matter with my ding-ding." She had told him to "forget about it, leave it alone and it will be all right." Later her husband had reassured her that she had done the right thing and she was amazed when she read in a book that spontaneous erections of the penis may begin in earliest infancy. When Jerry first became excited about his penis, she had simply told him not to be upset, that it was natural, and to just leave it alone and it would take care of itself. This worked very well at first. But soon afterward the boy learned that his pajamas had something to do with the erection and that when he rose from squatting before the television set, the erection disappeared by itself. "When I stand up, it goes down." He was very pleased with himself over this discovery.

The following case was more complicated, as related by his mother.

Eating Replaces Sex Play

Recently Junior has been masturbating openly in front of his two sisters. Emma's only eight years old but it drives her frantic. Junior's six-year-old sister had remarked, "You got troubles, Junior?" but paid no further attention to him as she concentrated on the telecast. Emma, his older sister, also pretended not to notice and she, too, seemed to be absorbed in watching television. But the three-year-old sister was observed to edge closer for a better view of Junior's performance.

Junior's mother said that she had read about sex play and knew that she ought not to worry. But she could not help being anxious because of her daughters. Since this was not her first visit she demanded a quick remedy and wanted me to justify her position that Junior was a very bad boy.

Junior's mother was in no mood to discuss sibling rivalries or little girls' insecurities and normal curiosity, so I asked her what she would do if it were her daughter who was masturbating in front of the others.

Mother: Why, stop it, of course!

    Dr.: Immediately?

Mother: Certainly.

    Dr.: How?

Mother: Why, take her hand away, I suppose.

    Dr.: And would you slap it, if necessary? [slapping was her usual method of rebuke.]

Mother: Well, my father always punished me by slapping our hands. I found it very humiliating, but I suppose I would slap her hand, but not too hard.

    Dr.: Now tell me, why is the problem any more difficult with the boy?

Mother: I don't know.

Dr.: You've never really attempted to stop him?

Mother: Well, I've talked to him about it.

Dr.: How about using the same method that you would have used on your daughter?

Mother: Do you really think it would be all right?

Dr.: Do I really think WHAT would be all right?

Mother: Slapping him.

Dr.: Why not?

Mother: But on his penis!

She looked doubtful as I wondered what a boy would think of a mother who would slap his penis, but I did not voice my thoughts. Instead, I asked, "Would you slap your little girl on her genitals?"

Mother: "Why, NO!"

She was actually horrified at the question, but truth soon began to dawn on her and she had the grace to blush. "So that's what you've been driving at all this time. You think I'm still jealous of my younger brother and would like to take out my hostility on my own son?"

All her life she had been thinking of sex as something that was bad, but the question required no answer. Tears began gathering in her eyes and as they overflowed, she turned away and started to leave the room. I heard her whisper, "God, forgive me."

The next time I saw Junior's mother, two weeks later, she was beaming as she made this report.

> I followed your advice and began treating him like an equal. He now comes to breakfast without being called, picks up his own clothes, dresses himself, and even ties his own shoes. But he still masturbates when watching television, only not so much as before, and I want to know why you think I rejected him. . . .

This time she was smiling and ready for help. A few weeks later she reported, "You know, Doctor, giving him popcorn to munch while he watches television works wonders. He hasn't exposed himself once in ten days."

After some discussion during subsequent conferences it was discovered that the practice had started right after Emma, the older sister, had been given a junior bicycle by a doting uncle. Junior was seeking physical solace by asserting his "manhood" and showing open resentment against his sister.

It was also learned that the practice was indulged in chiefly when some exciting story was being shown on television. So the experience of movie houses in setting up refreshment stands in the theatre lobbies was drawn on and used to divert interest and relieve the tension. Chewing gum and popcorn became part of the regular television program at home, and the procedure worked very well for all concerned, including mother. Junior found more satisfaction from eating and promptly reduced the habit of playing with his genitals. His sisters were also intrigued by the new refreshments and paid less attention to him.

Meanwhile, his mother was encouraged to reexamine her own mixed feelings about the boy who strongly resembled his father who had deserted them all only a year earlier. She secured a scooter-type bicycle, close to the ground, for Junior and a tricycle for the younger sister who had already begun to imitate her brother by genital manipulation. Within a few weeks more important interests had claimed the children's attention.

In the case of a small child or baby who keeps handling his, or her, genitals, one should avoid any show of alarm or excitement. Simply divert attention as unobtrusively as possible by offering an attractive toy, game or a pet to care for, and keep the child busy with other sources of interest and satisfaction. In the case of an older child, try to find out what is disturbing him and why he needs to keep loving himself. It could be from a rejecting playmate so that he may have good reasons to keep playing with his genitals. Avoid letting him play alone, and try to get him to tell you his troubles. You may be able to prevent a great deal of unnecessary worry. In any event, it is believed by the majority of experts that moderation in the practice of masturbation, in itself, is not harmful. Guilty feelings and shame, however, are another matter, for they are liable to persist indefinitely.

SEX EDUCATION FOR CHILDREN

Parents can show the average child some pictures of the sex organs in a library book on human embryology. During most of the first three months after conception, the external genitals of girls are actually identical in appearances with those of boys! [10] This usually comes as a surprise to many grown-ups who have to keep in mind the fact that the child tends to reach conclusions on the strength of what he already knows and that if he is familiar with only one set of genitals (his own) he naturally concludes that all others ought to be the same. Anything that conflicts with these notions he tries to explain by making up all kinds of stories, just as he often makes believe and fabricates tales about almost everything else. This is why fairy tales, Superman, and Batman, etc., are so popular.

On the other hand, the boy's testes are sensitive to the slightest injury and yet are vulnerably exposed during certain play activities involving the groin. Despite this, some children will romp and wrestle with abandon, while others do not dare to indulge or play follow-the-leader lest they get hurt. Some parents conclude that the boy who holds back from rough-and-tumble games is a sissy and hopelessly neurotic while others will try to find causes and show the child how to protect himself. Usually he needs the protection—especially from older brothers or cousins—for small children are not born with an understanding of the Golden Rule.

There is yet another reason for this lingering anxiety over genital injury; namely, the fact that in many boys the testes remain in the abdomen and do not descend into the scrotum until middle or late childhood. Normally the testes descend in the seventh month after conception, but quite often the testes do not descend completely. They may remain partly suspended in the inguinal canal where they have no room to grow but where they will also be out of harm's way. Such a boy can straddle fences without genital injury or discomfort. His scrotum is very small, and except for the convenience of a small penile appendage, the length of his haircut, or the style of his clothing, he does indeed resemble a little girl. The family doctor can give reassurance on the normalcy of a child's genitals and can also advise whether the boy needs hormones or surgery for their proper development.[5]

Psychotherapists should remember that too many people do not receive adequate medical attention, nor periodic physical examinations.

Prudery, resistance, misinterpretation and haste are some of the reasons why many physicians will refuse to explain sex or any other medical problem to the patients and families. The inability of the average patient to grasp some medical facts because of personal subjective involvement may cause him to reject even simple terminology. This is also one of the obstacles to good sex education, and it points up the need to reread troublesome or disturbing passages several times—especially when the reader disagrees with some of the ideas that are expressed in the text.

There are some wonderful teaching films which can be rented and studied in discussion groups; but none of them can produce a change overnight. Parents and other therapists may need time to digest the available material and to practice overcoming some of their own earlier inhibitions and embarrassments on the subject of sex.[1, 2, 7, 8, 11, 12]

Meanwhile, there is always the problem of hands and cleanliness which can be more troublesome for little girls because of genital secretions and odors.

> Hands are a problem, too. Hands are wonderful, but they are often in trouble. You are supposed to use them to learn to make things, to eat and dress, to pat and to love and to touch, but not every place. And you have to keep them clean as well as busy, and lots of times that is just about impossible. And why don't little boys have to wear gloves, too? Mommy says it's because of glands and moisture and the way she's made, and things like that. But if she can't wash every time she's touched the forbidden area, someone might get suspicious.
>
> *Is it true what they say about changing sex?* Can a boy become a girl if it's cut off—like in circumcision, maybe? And can I really grow a penis if I pull on my wee-wee long enough? And will I really get a baby if a boy kisses me on the mouth like they do in the movies?
>
> And there's lots more to worry about than getting a licking.
>
> What about when she grows up? Will she really develop hair and a bosom like the older girls? And what will Daddy or the boyfriends think about her using a bra then? But Daddy's known me all my life. It'll still be safer to marry Daddy—and have no babies, of course—or else not to marry at all! Women are supposed to get sick and have awful pains like Sis, and maybe bleed to death. And some-

times they die when they have babies. Well, didn't
Dotty's mother go away to the hospital—and something terrible must have happened to her because
she never came back. I remember the crowd, and
the flowers, and the long shiny casket. . . .

During the so-called latency period, before puberty, the child
learns to try to outlaw sex as his parents have tried to do before
him. He may not show any interest in sex, but he remembers.
He wants to trust his parents, but he remembers all too many
occasions when they were absolutely wrong about other matters,
when they did not tell the truth or at least not the whole truth,
when they were inconsistent, unfair, immature and sometimes
even disgusting. But how can a child tell that to a parent? No,
he is much safer to avoid sex if he wants to stay in their good
graces and if he wants to be accepted by his playmates and their
families. Sex may be all right (exciting and stimulating and acceptable) for the newspapers, magazines, movies, television, and
even a lecture at the P.T.A., but it usually spells trouble for the
child.

Parental Responsibilities

Fortunately most grown-ups respond remarkably well to the
responsibilities of parenthood, considering all other claims that
are made upon them by modern living. Yet parents do have to
remember that their own attitudes on sex are important to their
children.

If these experiences have been minor and uneventful, then
the parents will not be greatly impressed with the necessity for
anticipating trouble in the lives of their children, but if some
mishap befalls a young baby-sitter in the neighborhood, many
parents will suddenly begin to attend to locked doors and drawn
shades and may impose an unusually early curfew for their children.

This is what happened when a group of parents were discussing a recent incident that befell two of their little girls.

The children were riding home on their bicycles from a school
playground when they were stopped by a handsome young man in

a flashy new car. The man asked directions to a certain street in the neighborhood, but when they started telling him the directions he did not seem to comprehend and kept asking them to repeat. The girls could not understand why he seemed so flustered until one of them happened to look into the car and saw that he was manipulating his genitals. They immediately rushed home and told their parents, who reported the incident to the police. The parents all agreed that some restraint and more instruction on avoiding strangers was indicated, but not all of the parents were able to give a satisfactory explanation to their children as to the reasons for their admonitions.

Some parents even lose their tempers and resent having their motives challenged. The parents may be fully justified in their fears, but the child who (usually) already suspects what is back of it all may conclude that they just do not trust him. As a result, he often stops trying to please them and quite often will not even confide in them any more.

Inability to give a reasonable explanation to the child for new restrictions on activities and hours or playmates can weaken a parent's prestige and value in the home and may deprive a child of the confidence and guidance which he so urgently needs.

Every so often, one of these sexual assaults takes a more disastrous turn and a child is permanently mutilated or even killed. All parents have the duty to protect their child against such dangers. Words alone are not enough. Here are some steps you can take to prevent such catastrophies.

Prevention of Sex Problems in Small Children

1. Know your baby-sitter well and check on him or her from time to time.
2. Teach your three-year-old his own name and address and how to use a telephone. Show him how to call for help. Practice and frequent drills are needed.
3. Encourage your children to report all assaults, bribes, or offers from strangers.
4. Teach them to reject candy, gifts, and rides from people whom you do not know well. Caution them against loitering anywhere, especially in public lavatories or near railroad stations and alleys.

5. Encourage the "buddy" system that is used by swimming instructors at progressive children's camps. Do not permit your child to become a lone wolf or encourage him to play alone. Get him out of the isolation of his room. Teach him wholesome and socially acceptable activities. Make time for daily practice and offer constant encouragement. Home time is street-light time and no later.

6. Do not conceal or minimize the dangers. Your child is entitled to know what he is up against. Here, truly, is a case where one picture may be worth thousands of words. They may not be pretty, but they do appear in our magazines and newspapers constantly.

7. Do not monkey with your baby's sex. Psychologically, if not morally, there are few greater hurts to a child than to reject the sex with which he is born. The rejected child usually operates on the theory that any love is better than no love since he concludes that nobody cares for him, anyway. He will be less liable to care who sees him masturbate, for instance, and if the rejection is extreme he may not care what happens to him or to anyone else. *N.B.* If it is extremely important to know the prenatal sex of your child, see your doctor about special tests on the amniotic fluid during early pregnancy. Some risk may be involved, but recent researches are producing highly accurate predictions in this area.

8. If your local P.T.A. is inactive, join up with other parents for renting suitable teaching films and securing experienced speakers for discussions on the subject of sex education. Ask your doctor to write to the American Medical Association for suitable pamphlets, and start collecting your own reference library from your local bookstore; but preview the films and pamphlets for yourself, before handing them on to others.

REFERENCES AND READINGS

1. BIBBY, C.: *How Life Is Handed On.* New York, Emerson, 1947.
2. DE SCHWEINITZ, CARL: *Growing Up.* New York, Macmillan, 1939.
3. ERICKSON, E. H.: *Childhood and Society.* New York, Norton, 1950.

4. GESELL, A., *et al.*: *The First Five Years of Life*. New York, Harper, 1940.

5. GRUMBACK, M. M.: Chemistry and physiology of the testicular hormones. In *Cecil Loeb Textbook of Medicine*, 11th ed., Philadelphia, Saunders, 1963, pp. 1408-1421.

6. KANNER, L.: *Child Psychiatry*, 3rd ed. Springfield, Thomas, 1962.

7. LEVINE, M. I., and SELIGMANN, J. H.: *A Baby Is Born*. New York, S. and S., 1949.

8. LEVY, D. M.: *Maternal Overprotection*. New York, Columbia, 1943.

9. NOYES, A. P., and KOLB, L. C.: *Modern Clinical Psychiatry*, 6th ed., Philadelphia and London, Saunders, 1963.

10. Paterson, A. M.: *Manual of Embryology*. London, Oxford U.P., 1915.

11. SPOCK, B.: *The Pocket Book of Baby and Child Care*, New York, Pocket Bks., 1946, p. 270.

12. STRAIN, F. B.: *Being Born*. New York, Appleton, 1936.

Chapter 7

PUBERTY IS NATURE'S GRADUATION

GROWING PAINS OF PUBERTY

CHILDHOOD MEMORIES ARE OFTEN SUBMERGED, but emotional conflicts are accentuated by the physical changes of puberty. This is nature's announcement of reproductive maturity and biological graduation. Parental rejection of their children's coming of age is reflected in poignant anxieties, physiological dysfunction, and a widening of the gulf of family unity. Family rejection of the child as a person, regardless of sex, is often responsible for mental breakdown and suicide. The tensions of puberty also give rise to an increase of skin disorders, seizures, and serious conflicts with social mores as well as with parental and other authorities. It is a time for truancy and school dropouts; for trying out tobacco, alcohol and drugs; and for a variety of misconduct of which sexual "making out" may be only the first step.

Ambivalence and Seduction

There is an impressive list of theories and terms which are so inherently associated with psychoanalytic literature that nonpsychiatric specialists and counselors often become confused and resistant to further clarification. For instance, much is made of oral, pre-genital, genital, phallic and anal stages of erotic development. These are naturally associated with weaning and toilet training.

There is also an alleged "latency" period during which some of the child's erotic and emotional development is supposed to remain on a fairly level and unconscious plateau. Classifications of this type are as useful to the counselor and other nonpsychiatric specialist as the anatomical ridges and smaller promontories of osteology and embryology are to the general practitioner. The emotions of the young schoolchild may indeed give a placid outward appearance, but, in practice, one usually sees a restless merging of erotic and other personal and moral conflicts which surge and retreat like huge tidal waves in a maelstrom of emotional eruptions.

Emotional volcanoes **have** sometimes been referred to as the underworld of our moral training. They may erupt at almost any age, depending upon stressful or provocative circumstances. They may be disguised by a large variety of mental, emotional and physical, psychosomatic complaints.

Compensatory erotic activities may also be reactivated by situational stresses such as punishment, rejection or separation. As a rule, in such cases much more than sex is involved, although some form of seduction is the presenting complaint.

In most seductive relationships between children and adults, both parties are not only expressing tensions and reactions but they are also seeking acceptance and approval. The aggressor seeks to fill a need for dependency on someone who will accept him and who will not reject him (he hopes). He feels safer with a weaker, smaller and younger adversary whom he can usually intimidate. Yet children themselves are often the aggressors. They frequently initiate the seduction "for kicks," or because something is missing in their lives. Recent studies indicate that nearly a fourth of assaults with rape are victim-induced, and a similar percentage of homicides are actually provoked by the victim.

As a rule, we are unaware of our ambivalences. We tend to suppress or repress unpleasant memories and do not consciously recall much of our preteen years. Teensters and adults who claim to have absolutely no knowledge of ordinary sexual facts of life usually have had one or more unhappy sexperiments that produced conflicting desires. Unfortunately they tend to keep their secret to themselves and must deny it if it is disclosed prematurely.

On the other hand, children who have been seduced show surprisingly little guilt and anxiety and do not mind discovery. Most of them are themselves seductive and have actually initiated the intimacy. They are also inclined to exploit the relationship. They will seek an adult partner on the street and even brag about it.[1]

Nevertheless it is at puberty, the ages between twelve and fifteen years, that most of us observe major changes in our size, shape, appearance, and personality. It is also at puberty that some form of separation anxiety often becomes pronounced.

Separation Anxieties Accentuated at Puberty

Camp, boarding school and other separations speak for themselves; but there is another kind of separation that is often overlooked. For obvious reasons, physiological and anatomical differences can no longer be ignored. When boy and girl playmates are separated in games and for bathing, then the real emotional and social significance of their physical differences begins to dawn on them. Sex and puberty now mean loss of childhood associates and playmates, and this is often accentuated by a change of school from grammar to a junior high school; or to an all girl or all boy prep school.

Girls discover that they are denied the privilege of playing equally with boys *because they are different*. They may cling to, or cultivate, compensatory tomboy activities for a long while in order to defer the inevitable separation. Perhaps this is one of the reasons why "puppy love" comes so soon during and after puberty, as young lovers seek to recapture their earlier comradeship. I suspect that the popularity of live-ins and love-ins during adolescence is another defense against this same separation anxiety; and perhaps some of the appeals of togetherness and nude physical contact that is inherent in Esalen's group therapy is designed to serve a similar objective.*

Living together without benefit of clergy, both on and off college campus, is not new in human society. It is a reminder that separation from family is usually a painful experience and that people of all ages, whether students, patients, juvenile delinquents or workers in an Israeli kibbutz do better when living in groups than when they are isolated or separated according to their sex.

At puberty, nature and society demand that we suppress our earlier patterns of behavior and adopt more useful inhibitions

---

* Howard, J.: Inhibitions thrown to the gentle winds. *Life Magazine,* July 12, 1968, pp. 48-65.

and grown-up restraints, but some memories will not stay repressed, as explained by Adrian, a housewife.

> We'd play doctors and nurses up in the hayloft. We'd make-believe cutting each other's tummies and take out doll babies coz that's how we thought they came out.
> We'd even tickle cats and dogs to get them sexually excited. We used to rub each other's backs and stomachs and put each other to sleep that way. To this day I enjoy it.

Personality Changes

Personality changes become increasingly conspicuous at puberty, along with broadened social interests, idealistic projects and increasing emotional tensions. These tensions are often accompanied by shyness, secretiveness, changing alliances of friendships, quarrels with families and best friends, and rebellion in school and on jobs. Extra anxiety and stresses may produce insomnia, nightmares, various types of illness, and sometimes even convulsive seizures. The result is an enhanced need for tobacco, alcohol, drugs and cliques of bolder peers who are frankly out for kicks and excitement.

At puberty, our young folks need facts rather than fantasy in order to guide their conduct. Here are a few facts to keep in mind.

Facts Worth Knowing

By puberty, one should know and remember that privileges are an invitation to intercourse; that intercourse can lead to pregnancy even when it occurs several days before or after the so-called safe period; that contraceptives including "the pill" are not foolproof; that abortions are expensive (up to several thousand dollars) and are not as easy to get as most young folks think; that even a legal abortion can be costly as well as physically dangerous; that girls who have abortions sometimes commit suicide anyway; that boys who are asked for financial assistance usually prove they are not men by reneging, refusing to marry, and running away; and that no one goes through sickness, venereal disease, pregnancy abortion, or just the anguish of waiting for the next menstrual period without paying a price in terms of dignity, self-respect, and a change in personal or family loyalties.

N.B. It is commonly feared that knowledge of birth control will encourage promiscuous premarital intercourse. It probably does; and extramarital sex is likewise less inhibited. More indulgence in sex is reported to counselors than formerly; and more participants are enjoying their sex than formerly, but the same liability exists with all types of learning. For instance, knowledge of the dangers of speeding and drinking while driving is usually sufficient deterrent to most people; but there is always a certain percentage who ignore safety rules.

Driver education and adequate law enforcement cannot be applied as easily to sex education, but a good start has already been made during the last few decades. However, education in schools and homes is a continuing process. Some teachers and parents are more successful and persuasive. Some girls and boys still prefer safety even if it means less popularity. Others, especially girls, do not separate sex from love. They need protection against themselves because too many boys do not share their idealism.

Puberty is the time for enhanced self-awareness, for closeness to God and love, for great idealism and altruism, for poetry and visions and for planning careers, but it is also a time for misinformation, a hunger for knowledge as well as experience and acceptance, for false starts, self-reproach, fears of irreparable damage and overwhelming guilt.

Puberty affords one of our best opportunities to help individuals and families, but even then, it may be too late. This is because puberty is also the occasion for declarations of independence and overpowering desires to escape and run away—from home, church and school. It is a time when some unhappy youths may entertain thoughts of suicide rather than face the loss of a close friend, or the threat of failure, or the danger of disapproval, and even the necessity for competition with one's own loved ones.[14]

Questions That Need Answering

Here are some typical questions—a sampling from groups of boys and girls to whom I have lectured during the past forty years. They are not any different from one generation to the next.

> What is syphilis? Explain what a test-tube baby is. Can you have a child before having a menstrual period? What is the normal age to begin a menstruation period? How do labor pains feel? Do they hurt? Why does a pregnant lady usually feel nauseated during her first three months of pregnancy? Does the first intercourse hurt the female participant? Is it painful when intercourse is taking place? What age should a girl be permitted to be sexual with boys? Can you have a baby any time and does it have to be a certain time after your period? What is the definition of a lesbian and a fairy? Is it safe to take birth control pills, or will they cause a deformed baby?

No two counselors would have the same answers, and some answers require a lot of discussion. (Menstruation and other genital fluids are covered further on in this chapter. Questions on venereal diseases are answered in Chapter 10. Intercourse is discussed in Chapter 16.)

Birth control pills are a problem for the family doctor, the clergyman, the parents, and the youngsters themselves. Even today the questions that are submitted, *in writing,* do not include masturbation; although the subject does crop up more frequently during private conferences.

Not all questions, however, are directly related to the genital aspects of sex. This is because sex has broader aspects and is also a continuing education.

> Is it wrong to kiss a boy on your first date? How would you handle a boy that you liked very much but had a very bad habit of staring into your eyes as if he wanted to kiss you? How can you overcome shyness with a boy? How can you show a boy that you like him without appearing cheap? How do you get a shy boy to get around to kissing you? Is it right to like a boy a great deal and not to show or tell it? If you are skating with a boy and you hit his foot, should you say excuse me or should the boy say it? How can you get a boyfriend and keep him?

Duval's *Facts of Life and Love for Teen-agers* is an excellent guide for answers to these and similar problems of socialization which are intimately related to sex.[5]

Teensters Are Realists As Well As Idealists

Here are some answers to my question, What do you consider to be the greatest thing in the world?

From girls—a happy home . . . to be able to live together in peace and harmony . . . love . . . motherhood . . . God; and from the boys—a career . . . a good job . . . money . . . self-respect . . . a good name.

Individual Differences

The growing pains of puberty are physical as well as emotional. The physical changes represent a natural process in which glands mature, bones grow longer and muscles stronger, hair appears on face, armpits and pubic area above and about the genitals, girls' breasts grow larger and boys' voices become lower in pitch. Puberty is the time when menstruation begins in the girl and seminal emissions in the boy.

Several years may be required for the completion of these changes which usually occur between the ages of twelve and fourteen, but the changes may start at nine in some girls and not until sixteen or seventeen in others.

This wide range of individual differences that is possible in the same group of thirteen-year-old girls, for example, makes it difficult for counselors, parents and teachers to plan a program of activities that will prove to be generally satisfying.

For instance, consider a girl of thirteen who has a well-developed body, has been menstruating for several years, and has attracted some attention from older boys. Now compare her with a girl of sixteen who has just begun having her menstrual periods but who does not have as well-developed a bustline. Clearly these two girls are going to think and feel differently about themselves as well as about dates, even though one is three years older.

Privileges that are accorded to sixteen-year-olds are generally denied to thirteen-year-olds; but late hours, dancing, parties and solo dating could be an embarrassing ordeal for the older, yet inexperienced and physically retarded girl. The usual differences in school seniority will not compensate the older girl for her self-consciousness. On the other hand, while the younger girl is usually restricted, she may be tempted to do things secretly if she cannot date openly.

Boys are also concerned with the size and shape of various parts of their bodies. Tall boys can be just as self-conscious as tall girls. Like the flat-chested girl, the tall boy may not stand up too well in the gymnasium locker room. He may even be afraid to compete with his own father for family approval. He may be physically ideal for basketball or pole vaulting; but without motivation, mere size will not help.

Short youngsters are frequently exposed to teasing and rejection. Consequently, many of them become bookworms. Some may plunge into heterosexual or homosexual activities as compensation. Others concentrate on television or records. They may also resort to delinquency, alcohol, drugs, off-beat groups and even suicide.

PREVENTION OF MALADJUSTMENT AT PUBERTY

Too many parents do not know enough about their children and have not prepared for these heartache years. Yet there is a simple preventive remedy. Parents should encourage an active program in practical values. These include health, cleanliness, time, money, responsibilities at home and on jobs. They should also include a personal and continual interest and participation in music, dramatics, sports, recreation, hobbies, and especially in social dancing. Dancing is a universal language for self-expression and communication which makes it much easier to tide the young folks over this awkward period in their lives. Dancing also develops self-confidence and self-control.

The same preventive measures are also equally beneficial to boys, even though acceptance, approval and recognition can often be obtained by a job, money, or athletic success and without most of the social graces.

The popular "life of the party" is not necessarily the one who flaunts wild behavior, sex, drinks and drugs, but rather the substantial, dependable, good sport who can organize games for legitimate fun, has some talent for entertainment, knows the rules, observes most of them, and acts with reasonable restraint and dignity.

Family Conflicts

There are other important reasons for emotional growing pains of puberty. Chief of these are the usual conflicts with one's own family. They are the same types of conflicts that occur during childhood, but now they become intensified by a mixture of ambivalent feelings on both sides. The child, at puberty, is ready to receive nature's diploma, but the average parent is not ready to grant it, and usually with good reason.

For one thing, few children at puberty are ready to accept the responsibilities of marriage and parenthood. So if parents are expected to take care of unscheduled babies they are surely entitled to some say in regulating their production. This is their chief argument against premarital sexual relations, because there is no 100 per cent safe contraceptive technique except abstinence. Ninety per cent safe is definitely not safe enough.

Another reason for parental resistance to graduating their children at puberty is that few girls, and fewer boys, in their early teens have acquired sufficient poise and good judgment to take care of themselves, let alone assuming the responsibilities of having a partner for life.

Parents can be jealous too. A third reason is less flattering. Yet it is unfortunately true that too many parents are liable to be much more resentful and jealous of their own children than most people realize. They envy the youth's opportunities in life and they show this rivalry unmistakably by acting up, becoming bossy or critical, and making unnecessary restrictions. This is especially common whenever company or a third party is present. Demanding such obedience lifts up their own ego as it deflates the youngster's. Unfortunately, at such times justice and reason are often cast aside, while rationalized conceit and vanity take over.

Teachers, coaches and employers are liable to act the same way. Occasionally their behavior masks an unconscious homosexual or other seductive wish; but sheer possessiveness and control often compensates for personal insecurity from earlier unresolved conflicts in their lives.

While this is a startling enough statement for most parents

to hear, it is practically incredible to children. They recognize parental rejection easily enough, but they usually misinterpret the reasons for the resentment. They are unable to comprehend, or even to contemplate, that their parents could possibly find anything worthy of coveting in "poor little me." The fact that children often displace their own parents in the hearts of grandparents or favorite uncles or doting aunts is not very popular. Even when such displacement is suspected or actually pointed out, the average normal parent would have to deny it. He usually scoffs at the suggestion and rejects the whole idea as utterly fantastic.

Then, in order to prove that it is not so, the parent often goes to opposite extremes. He becomes too kind and indulgent in some matters, yet overly strict and severe in others. For example, he will lavish expensive gifts that have not been earned or are not needed. He will then rationalize his desires for scholarship, or athletic prestige, or for thriftiness, and lucrative part-time jobs or his restrictions on hours, behavior and sex by insisting that his constant criticism is for the child's own good. Usually he does not even dream that any of these extremes are dead giveaways of his own insecurity; yet such an attitude may alienate his child just as effectively as direct rejection. My young friend Jimi has labeled the situation, "parental hangups."

Parental Hangups and Time for Living

Here are some abstracts from a letter written to me by a mature, attractive and intelligent teen-ager. They represent notes on her reflections, jotted down on a program during graduation rehearsal at an Ivy League girl's prep school. All names are fictitious, including her own pen name of Jimi when she signed permission to publish.

Dear Dr. S.

I have witnessed a variety of emotions which are atypical for the usual excitement preceding graduation . . . While I am planning a fun summer, many of my friends are obsessed with trouble which in my lingo are regarded as "Parent hangups." These are not a new thing; they've probably been around since Adam and Eve; but they seem to me magnified as a result of today's social attitudes.

So many of my friends feel they can escape home troubles by taking the magic action—running away. Once away they try to convince themselves they're free and happy. But the majority of those I've talked to would like to live at home.

The "lost ones" sit at my lunch table. Sometimes they seem to resent me or anyone else who knows where she's going. More often they have no one to talk to so their situations become "bottled up." They know they're "hung up" but can't face the underlying reasons. But many of them "let loose" because they trust me; Reney, in particular.

Reney has money, and social prestige. Her father is a small town professional man. Her mother hates to cook, and almost never does. She's too busy with golf and social activities. Reney is a commuter, not a boarding student; but she isn't planning to return home. She's going to run away, live in the Village (Manhattan's Greenwich) and do everything she feels like doing (including sex, alcohol and drugs).

Recently Reney came home after an exhausting day of exams. Mother didn't even say "Hello." The minute she entered the door mother hopped on her for not making her bed! Reney said nothing, but on passing through the kitchen she noticed that mother had actually prepared a meal—a very rare occasion in this household. Reney, however, had no appetite for food. She asked mother if it would be all right for her to lie down for awhile; but it was apparently the wrong thing to say.

Her mother broke into a total rage, destroyed all of Reney's records, posters and anything symbolic of youth. Reney says she's definitely not going back to that house as long as she lives. Of course she's afraid they'll send the police after her, and she doesn't want to hurt her father who is not really in the picture—and this is a big part of the problem.

I tried to dissuade her; but she is convinced that her mother doesn't care. "Why doesn't she ever cook? . . . Why didn't she care how I looked Saturday night for the prom? She never would have seen me if I didn't walk through the living room. Maybe, if she'd start preparing meals, and demonstrating more love . . . there'll be a transition. Maybe I'll stick around, for a little while. But believe me it will take a long time to gain a mutual reflexive [*reciprocal respect and reflection?*] relationship. . . ."

["Jimi" filled a dozen pages with more of the same and concluded with the following statement.]

We wish adults would take some of their precious time for living, and listening; give us an opportunity to contribute, and try to combine some of the phases of our life with theirs. So now, "excuse me while I kiss the sky."

                                                                Jimi Hendrix

"Jimi" demonstrates the fact that she practices what she preaches. Having a sympathetic audience, her friend Reney talks herself out of her plans for an immediate runaway. When Reney herself learns to offer a comparatively sympathetic ear to mother, whose rejection of cooking and preference for golf represents her own compensation for hubby's professional preoccupation, their "reflexive" relationship will stand a better chance of realization.

The best remedy is for the parent to talk the matter over freely and frequently with the youngster himself, until both become better acquainted with each other. This may take a little time, several years perhaps, but the rewards are great. One may not be the happiest of parents now, but there is still time to become the most wonderful grandparents in the whole wide world.

Happier grandchildren can make lives better for their own parents. Reformed grandparents can also find new areas of comfort and mutual respect with their own children, as they too learn from experience.

Emotional Leftovers Cause Disturbed Communication

The emotional growing pains of the girl and boy at puberty are based on unresolved leftovers from childhood as well as current physical changes and personal conflicts; but none are so great as those which come from the inability of budding youth to talk to the people whom they love the most. When these avenues are closed our young hopefuls are liable to indulge in excesses—of eating, sex, overwork, or of indolence and misconduct. Reney's talking with mother has not even begun, but even after it starts, there is no guarantee that it will be very productive.

Here is a familiar example of a "talk" that also comes under the heading of "too little and too late."

Polly Attempts Sex Education For Her Boys

I had heard numerous times in our group therapy class the importance of frank sex discussion with your children. Having made a few quiet successes and many loud blunders, I felt this was one area I wouldn't goof on. I had already had a short talk with my sons when they were ten and eleven about the birds and bees. This went pretty good, but now I was a wreck—my seventeen-year-old son was leaving home for the first time to live in San Francisco. I felt

I should have a more involved discussion before he went out in the world. I kept putting it off and time was running short, so being the conscientious mother I am, I drew in a deep breath and took the plunge.

I foxily chose a time when Randy, seventeen, and my fifteen-year-old Peter were in a reasonably good mood. This came one morning when the three of us were lingering over breakfast coffee, chattering about Randy's forthcoming adventure.

Polly, I said to myself, this is it. You're going to be casual and confident. So—as I casually struck a cigarette and tried to smoke a match, I said, "Boys, if you have another minute I'd like to talk about sex."

Randy said, "Oh, no, here we go again."

I said brightly, "You can hear this too."

Randy groaned, "Do I have to?"

"Of course, you do. There might be some things you might not know.

Randy laughed out loud, "Boy, Mom, are you square. Pete knows as much as I do."

Pete grinned sheepishly, "I'm not a little kid, you know."

"Well, then," I bravely continued, "that makes it a lot easier. Are there any questions you want me to answer?"

I was fully prepared to answer anything. "I have no questions," Peter said, "so are we finished?"

"Now just a second. We haven't talked about girls and things."

"Yea, let's talk about girls," Randy growled. "They're all nuts—that takes care of that."

"Leave her alone," Pete told his brother. "She means well."

"O.K. Mom," he answered, "I'll listen, but I have to meet Joe soon."

"Boys, you'll be taking more interest in girls soon. Do you know what contraceptives are and why they are used?"

"Oh God, Mom, do we have to talk about this? We know all about those things."

"Well, look what happened to your cousin, having to get married so young—this is important."

"Nothing happened to him that he didn't want to," Randy said. "Besides, they'll make out o.k."

"Randy, also while I think of it, you'll probably come across homosexuals out there."

"Don't forget bisexuals," Pete added laughing.

"Mom," Randy groaned, "we know quite a few already. Did you know they can't help themselves—it's kind of a sickness."

"Well, boys, that covers it, I guess. Isn't it nice we can talk frankly like this?"

Peter said, "Yea, it's swell. Are we finished?"

Randy said, "Mom, you shouldn't worry about such things, but it was nice talking."

Later, I thought my sons handled me very well—so wise, kind and gentle. Thought you'd like to know (P.H.)

When Parents Play Favorites

Some specialists in child psychology are convinced that little girls resent being different and feel that they have been cheated; they are therefore hostile to boys; try to compete in boys' games; yet want to be accepted as one of them.

Other specialists feel that this genital difference is a minor matter compared with how well the child is accepted as a welcome person in her own home. In other words, if she is made to feel that she is loved and wanted because she is herself and that girls are just as important to her parents as boys are, then the differences in her body do not assume major proportions in her life.

A girl who feels wanted in her own home as a cherished member of the family is free to develop more useful patterns in the cultivation of her personality. Some imitation, resentment and competition with boys is normal, but a girl who is emotionally secure at home would not be proud of being a tomboy for the simple reason that she has no *need* to be a tomboy, nor would she have need to become sexually promiscuous in order to be important to someone or to express her rebellion.

On the other hand, if a boy is raised in a family where girls are favored, then he may grow up with the feeling that possession of a penis and testes is actually a handicap. As a result he may try to suppress his masculine strivings and often longs to be a girl. Such yearnings are easy to understand in families where mothers and the girls take on most of the responsibility for management of the home and family fortunes. Unsubtle parental rejections are not lost on the children. Fathers who urge too much responsibility on their wives, for instance, by turning over pay envelopes and by referring their children to "mother" for all important decisions as well as for discipline are helping to belittle the importance of maleness. Instead of setting an example as a strong father figure, they enhance the premium on being a female. Such a pattern of family management may encourage the boy to want to be more and more like his mother who seems to be the real boss of the house.

Some years ago a friend of mine reported the following incident just after reading about a soldier who was "de-sexed," or altered, by surgery (complete castration) and by insertion of an artificial vagina, plus female hormone injections for mammary development.

The following case shows that parental rejection can eventually provoke a suicide.

Case of Charles

I was visiting some old friends the other day. Later in the evening their only son Charles, aged fourteen, came in and paid his respects in his usual friendly manner. His father amiably called out, "Hello, Charlotte, how are you this fine evening?" My heart skipped a beat as I turned to take another look at the boy. In the eighteen months since I had last seen him, he had grown much taller. He was handsome, slender, and very friendly, but the only masculine feature that I could detect was his alto voice. I was startled by his formal politeness and the almost complacent pride with which he took his father's rejection.

Later, at the table, a friendly banter took place between them and I began to think that I had made a mistake when suddenly his father again addressed him. "Charlotte, will you please pass me the sugar?" The boy complied without protest, but this time I could keep quiet no longer. "Why do you call him Charlotte?" I asked as calmly as I could. The boy merely smiled as his father appeared a trifle taken aback by the question.

After an awkward pause Charles told me confidentially across the table and in tones loud enough for all to hear, "He thinks he's kidding us all, but he really wishes I had been a girl." The boy's mother protested loudly at this, "No, he doesn't! Don't you believe it! He's just fooling!" But the father continued eating in silence; and I made no further reference to the incident.

Children have long memories for this unsubtle type of rejection. Six years later, the boy suddenly disappeared from college. After a long search he was found dressed in his mother's clothing, his lifeless body hanging from a tree.

Such cases are not rare; but here is a more common form of parental rejection.

Case of Cherubic "Roberta"

Bobby, after reading about an English doctor who had changed sex, recalled that as a "small boy my mother's women friends would come to visit us and would remark on my soft voice and fine delicate features. 'Such a cherub-like creature,' they would say, 'positively angelic. What a pity. He should have been a girl.' And Mother, confound her, she didn't disagree. I've always felt she'd have loved me more if I'd been a girl. Sometimes they'd tease me by calling me Roberta, instead of Robert."

When the opposite is true and father runs the family in dictator style, or with too little regard for mother's emotional needs, then it is often the little girl who may reject her feminine role and may want to be like father whom she considers to be strong and important. Mothers, in such cases, often compete with fathers by keeping their sons overdependent, for instance, by taking sides with them in family arguments or by making excuses and doing too much for them. This unfair attitude causes the girl to feel resentful over the fact that it is the boy who is the reigning favorite with mother. She resents everyone except father, who often treats her the way mother is treating her brother; and she also resents herself for feeling hateful toward the mother and brother, both of whom she also wants to love.

The little girl may not understand the emotional reasons which are involved in these powerful alliances at home so she often singles out the difference in genitals as the object of her resentment and disdain. This resentment she frequently represses, however, so that she may not recognize any jealousy of her brother. Instead she decides that males may be superior because they are bigger, or older, or can get away with more privileges at home or with teacher; but she can also resent males because they are too aggressive or uncouth and because their bodies are unattractive and their sex organs are positively disgusting. To such girls the mere thought of genital contact with a male at any age may remain a revolting idea for a long time. All of which points up once more the great danger of playing favorites in any home—no matter what the sex of the children may be.

THE IMPORTANCE OF "MAKING OUT"

"Making out" becames important for both boys and girls. They need to be "in the know." They feel the urge for sexperimentation, and they also need to feel desired, whatever the price or consequences.

"Making out" has wide interpretation from necking and other intimate contacts to "going all the way." It compensates for multiple anxieties, even though it also gives rise to more worries than it relieves. For instance, it can reassure the young girl that she is wanted and that she is important to somebody. Consequently, she often considers "going steady" and granting privileges as a small price to pay for insurance against boredom and neglect.

"Making out" assures the boy that he is deserving of a girl's acceptance and also that he is virile. It compensates for lingering anxieties over possible self-injury from previous practices of self-love.

"Making out," in both sexes, is also an area of competition—with peers as well as with adults. It is a means for defying parents and an opportunity to control members of the opposite sex—former rivals from childhood days. It is a laboratory course in sexperimentation. Like playing with fire, it both courts and defies responsibility at the same time. Besides, it is more easily attainable than owning a car and more fun than earning a living.

When the first physical contacts of puberty confirm previous visual imagery from pictures or stolen peeping, there is often an accentuated return of memories of infantile and childhood contacts with mother's (and father's) body. This occurs in girls as well as boys, but it also arouses guilt and desire in both of them.

Efforts to suppress the desire often lose out to the insistent urge to possess or control the body and sexual symbols of both parent figures. As if this were not disturbing enough, most youngsters at this age already know the dangers of pregnancy. Nevertheless, when sexperimentation has been allowed to progress beyond the point of no return, the desire becomes stronger than the restraint. Judgment takes a back seat to lust, and hunger requires completion of the closest physical relationship that is possible.

This is how nature designed sex; and this is how she intended it to operate. Some societies recognize both the need and the dangers. They encourage mixed youth outings and premarital intercourse. They also accept unmarried pregnant girls, and they take the "illegitimate" babies into the tribal family.

The best that our American culture can do for young people is to strengthen the home ties, to reduce the opportunities for such premature sexperimentation, and to concentrate on adequate sex education along with well-known conservative substitute activities and other wholesome relationships between the sexes. At the same time, we must accentuate the moral, legal and financial responsibilities which inevitably accompany all such privileges and pleasures and take steps to strengthen the youth's self-respect, confidence, and abilities along other productive lines.

Such responsibility must start at the top, however, and the paradox of greatness, wealth, power and mounting public indebtedness along with growing industrial and racial unrest is far from reassuring.

CHANGE OF SEX

Some questions sound easy but are harder to answer. For instance, "Can I change my sex?" Every so often a rash of publicity on this subject breaks out and gets people upset. Our children are no exception to this popular interest in the subject. But the mere fact that a child is interested does not prove that he is anxious about it.

On the other hand, the failure to show concern over the size, shape or classification of his sex organs may mask a repressed curiosity, especially if he has been called a "sissy." When a boy's parents or grandparents keep wishing that he had been a girl (or the reverse) he is liable to be alarmed at news reports of cases of misdiagnosed sex. He also ponders the possibility of a change-over.

Transvestites are people who derive sexual pleasure from wearing clothing of the opposite sex. Children often do it for fun. Parents often encourage it for real.

Psychotherapy for compulsive transvestites and those who seek surgical alterations for change of sex is definitely not recommended for the unaided nonpsychiatric specialist. However, some counselors may manage where psychiatrists have failed. In general, transvestites are seriously disturbed people with whom even psychiatrists are liable to have no success. Nevertheless, they usually show their first indications of the complex during early childhood; and it becomes especially conspicuous during puberty. Consequently the counselor should be on guard. Not all of the loose attitude towards long hair, beads, smocks, colors and frills are just an acknowledgement of a changing trend in styles. Some of our most famous stylists are known homosexuals. Their creations should cause no surprise; but the fact that there are enough purchasers to wear them should be food for thought.

One would need a lot of instruction on anatomy as well as surgery and endocrinology in order to understand what really happens in these "men" who live as women and vice versa, but here are a few important things that parents will want to know.

Pseudohermaphrodism

The sex organs at birth may not be completely formed. They may look like one sex and yet be partly made up of the organs of both sexes. A glance at an illustrated book on embryology will show that in girls, before birth, there is a well-formed counterpart or equivalent of the penis which at times looks more masculine than feminine, until it shrinks and becomes a clitoris. Before the end of the third prenatal month, the boy's genitals are also incomplete. They, too, at times strikingly resemble those of the female.

Changes are normally completed, and sex differentiation is possible, by the end of the thirteenth week; but, if the change is incomplete, then the imperfect genitalia may resemble those of the opposite sex. In such cases, the external sex organs of the boy partially resemble those of a girl, or the reverse.

Pseudohermaphrodism exists when the internal and external sex glands and organs only resemble those of the opposite sex. True hermaphrodism exists when organs of both sexes are present in the same child. However, these organs are usually incomplete or deformed.

The *true hermaphrodite* is, technically, a person who is born with some of the reproductive organs of both sexes, usually an ovary, testicle, and perhaps an imperfect uterus or vagina. These are accompanied by either an undersized penis or an oversized clitoris.

The hermaphrodite is seldom able to copulate satisfactorily, and reproduction is practically impossible. Usually, he has been raised either as a boy or as a girl, and therefore when the problem is finally discovered by a doctor, the decision usually rests with the patient as to which organs should be removed and what alterations are to be made. True hermaphrodites are extremely rare. Most sexual anomalies of this nature occur in pseudohermaphrodites.

Doctors are rarely mistaken in making a correct diagnosis of sex in a newborn baby. Fortunately, some correction is often possible. However, plastic surgery and retraining are not always accepted by these unfortunate patients; and their management requires the combined efforts of several specialists—endocrinologist, urologist, surgeon and psychiatrist. Thereafter some type of counseling may be required for years.

Your child is entitled to know that there is no danger that a healthy person will develop a spontaneous change in his sex. Like alopecia (baldness), a sudden "loss of manhood" or of female hormones from anxiety, illness, or injury is always possible; but certainly not from masturbation. Tumors and disease are another matter.

Mixed Sex Hormones

Long before puberty, the child's sexual chemicals or hormones are normally at work. Boys and girls each possess glands which have similar influences on their secondary sex characteristics, but boys and girls both develop male as well as female hormones. This is normal and it explains why some girls' voices are lower pitched than others and why they often have a little hair on their faces and bodies. It also explains timidity in boys and some bosom development (gynecomastia); and it probably has something to do with acne and other dermatological problems.[10]

There are many males who envy and desire the female form, her symbolic bosom, her ability to attract and influence or seduce men, her important reproductive role in life, and her relative safety in the home, away from the commercial and industrial jungle. There are also just as many females who covet the convenience and symbolic aggressive authority of the male anatomy, his freedom from menstruation and pregnancy, his social and economic advantages, and his assumption of the double standard of morals.

Fortunately, mutilating operations are few; although self-mutilation by accident or design is more common than is realized. Where plastic surgery and hormones fail to take over, other attempts may be made to change or minimize one's sex differences. These are seen in the choice of clothing, hair styles, costume jewelry and current dance steps in which both partners are equally independent and there is neither leader nor follower.

Castration Anxiety Accentuated at Puberty

Preoccupation with genitals is accentuated by natural changes at puberty, and by guilty handling.

> If thy right hand offend thee, cut it off,
> Or thy right eye . . . pluck it out.
> (Matt. 5:29, 30)

We no longer preach this philosophy to our children, but the average child still gets the idea that something drastic will happen to his hands or to his penis or even to his mind if he persists in playing with himself. This is especially prominent at puberty because of orgasm, emissions, and other genital fluids.

The fear of genital injury is no light matter. A glance into any maternity ward shows that some male genitals take quite a beating during delivery. Careless diapering and the later design of male trousers add to the discomfort. Little girls who watch boys urinate may resent the lack of a similar convenience in themselves. Here is a common reminiscence from E., a married R.N.

> We used to stand in front of the toilet and imitate my brothers making wee-wee. It was a mixture of disgust and envy. They'd compete to see who could urinate the highest and the farthest. And I always thought it was unfair that we had to go all the way back to the house. Nice girls and all that stuff. Whereas, if we'd been boys . . .

Little boys are also at a loss to account for the missing appendage. They invent explanations when none are offered. Three-year-old Mark, to his girl playmate of the same age, was over-heard by his mother to say, "Come on, Mawylin; let's go out in the woods and look for your lost peanut."

Little boys can innocently upset and goad adults into making rash and ridiculous threats. Hints concerning sin, amputation, insanity, or weakness are often carried as unconscious heavy-weights far into adult life.

Testes are also sensitive. They do not have the abdominal protection that is accorded to the ovaries, and they are constantly exposed to trauma. When they are late in descending both the boy and family may be disturbed and conclude that the child is abnormal. The boy himself will feel different. It could affect him in the same way that a flat chest would affect a girl.

Unfortunately, an education in nursing or medicine does little to correct these anxieties. Too many medics still carry this fear, according to Lief in a 1959 survey of the graduates and faculties of five medical schools in Philadelphia. He found that half of the students and a fifth of the faculty believed that mental illness was frequently caused by masturbation.[12]

Regardless of the influence of medics, however, many a child develops and retains a deep and lasting fear of handling his own genitals. The fear of sin and punishment often mushrooms into a general anxiety which can affect both sexes at all ages. This may drive the teenster into religious preoccupation, or ob-sessions about cleanliness, or prolonged frigidity or impotence.

Overconcern for the safety of one's genitals is usually reen-forced by accidental injury, genital assaults, physical intimida-tions or infection, and by some of the emotional reactions de-scribed above. The concern is universal, however, and lest we conclude erroneously that "castration complex" is just another figment of freudian imagination, we might review some of the mutilating atrocities committed during some of our famous (or rather infamous) wars; and the practice of some hunters who still cut off the testes of a bull moose and nail them to a tree.

Circumcision as a token amputation has psychological aggres-sive features (puberty rituals) as well as sanitary and religious aspects. A man's sons are competitive, and the word "virile" has many challenging connotations. Circumcision is mostly confined to males; but whether for religious or health reasons such as phimosis (tight foreskin), a boy's attitude is largely determined by the attitude of his associates.

Competition between males continues to be the way of life and has not yet abated in our civilization. Mayhem, in the form of castration (removal of testicles), has even been condoned by some religious orders in order to retain boy soprano singers. It was also ordered by potentates to produce eunuchs to guard their harems.

The elimination of sex differences is indicated by changes in manners and mannerisms, by the choice of profession or occupation, and by the invasion of both sexes into formerly restricted areas. No one is immune from such unconscious emotional conflicts. Some authorities believe that the tendency of young people to mimimize the sexual differences at puberty by stressing similarities of hair styles, clothing and mannerisms is an attempt to cling to their childhood intimacy and dependency and to postpone the inevitable separation and growing up just as long as possible.

SOME PRACTICAL FACTS OF SEX

Menstruation

Menstruation is a normal function of the adolescent girl and should be treated as such without pampering or special emphasis.[6, 8, 10, 16] Like the growth of the breasts during puberty, the regular monthly flow is a sign of womanhood and a badge of femininity of which your daughter should be very proud. So if you hear her referring to menstruation as "the curse" or some other inelegant or disparaging term, you may want to reexamine your own past attitude on the subject. Perhaps your Junior Miss has had other indoctrination that may have neutralized her own casual acceptance of normal puberty. The use of terms like "the curse," "falling off the roof," and "monthly sickness" to describe the occurrence of menstruation are better replaced by such expressions as monthly period, menses, menstrual flow or just plain menstruation. Another common term for menstruation is "my boyfriend" which suggests a gesture of pleasurable welcome rather than a rejection.

Only a few of the disturbances of the mentrual cycle are the result of physical or organic difficulties. These are strictly medical or surgical problems. The vast majority of menstrual disorders, however, are expressions of emotional tensions which can usually be prevented.

Strong emotional crises and anxieties can delay or speed up the various steps in the menstrual cycle: an expected dance, an important date, the receipt of bad or special news, or competion as in the case of Deborah.

Deborah's Premenstrual Tensions

Deborah was a white pregnant housewife of twenty-five who came in for hypnotic relaxation training for her third pregnancy. Intake interview disclosed the following relevant data:

> I didn't menstruate 'till I was fourteen. Most of my girl friends did when they were twelve; some of them ten or eleven. I couldn't buy the clothes they wore. Nothing would fit. I didn't have the waistline, or curves. I was like a stick. I still looked like a kid. And I hated it. Hated all the ghetto type kids we were. I still resent Jews, and my parents. I still get terrific premenstrual tension; still can't sleep, get water-logged, bloated, put on seven pounds.

> I never told my mother. We could never tell her anything. Oh she said it would happen, but that's about all. Said she never started 'till she was fifteen. I learned everything from the kids at school.

> I didn't want to be top heavy—too sexy. Glad I'm not flat like my mother. Sister's full breasted, too, like me. Overnight I blossomed; but I didn't have a really nice figure 'till I was eighteen, almost twenty.

> The only time I'm happy is when I'm pregnant, like now. Same thing happened twice before with my other kids.

I suggested that now she did not need to fear that menstruation would never come; that she had already caught up with, and perhaps surpassed, the other girls who were ahead of her at puberty; and that now that she had uncovered one of the connections between menstruation and anxiety, it would hardly be necessary to be so tense before future periods.

At the close of the session she herself suggested,

> And I suppose I was jealous of my brother. Maybe I
> held back that first menstruation because I wanted to
> have his boyish figure—unconsciously, I mean?
> I told her it was quite possible, especially since mother obviously
> preferred boys.

Prevention of menstrual tension is best accomplished by teaching the child to accept her sex from the moment she is born. As has been repeatedly stated, a girl can be proud of being a female only if her parents are also proud to have her as a girl first and then to accept her as a woman. This question of how a girl feels about herself does not make much sense to most parents until they reflect on some of their own kidding references to girls as God's "second choice" or "inferior merchandise" during their daughter's earlier years.

Kitty's Father Prescribes Manure

> I know I'll never get larger breasts, and I know why, too. When I was fourteen I was still flat. My cousin already needed a bra. One day my father was admiring her in a bathing suit. "Too bad about Kitty," he said. "Have to go over to the barn, next door and get some manure to make her grow. Hah. Hah!" Some joke. I'll never forget it.

Parents who favor boys can hardly avoid the tendency to encourage their daughter's leanings toward the tomboy type, but their preference for boys can produce much more physical protest than most people realize as with Deborah above. When a daughter feels accepted as a girl in her own home, her menstruation will usually be uncomplicated. The vast quantities of anticramp medicines that are being used today suggest that much improvement is needed in this area of parent-child relationships.

For many girls, menstrual anxieties are monitored by the calendar. Keeping a record of the periods not only helps to prevent these worries but also aids in planning future social events. The record is also valuable when the doctor needs a medical history during sickness from other sources or at the annual physical examination. Your daughter should be taught that many innocent sources of delay may interrupt the regular menstrual schedule. Chief of these causes for menstrual tardiness are exposure to cold, sickness, worry over exams or dating, and excitement from other expectations such as awaiting an important message.

Self-punishment, if not wishful thinking, may also delay a menstrual period, as in the following case of Lulu.

Lulu's Anxiety Delays Menses

At seventeen Lulu was accustomed to menstruating every seven weeks, so when she was one week late, she became convinced that she must be pregnant. Unable to sleep or eat she finally told her mother who became hysterical with horror. Mother then told her to pack her clothes because in the morning she would have to tell father who would order her to leave the house. After awhile she questioned Lulu and learned that the extent of the girl's indiscretion had consisted of manual touching by the girl's steady beau several weeks earlier. Whereupon she laughed hysterically and scornfully exclaimed, "You foolish kid—go to bed."

The next day the girl reported that her menstrual period had suddenly arrived, and mother warned, "Now look—you wait until you are married—you *have* to do it then. Even I have to, because if I didn't, your father would go to someone else."

Lulu and her mother never referred to the subject again. She married the same boy, four years later, but sadly reports, "I've never allowed myself to enjoy sex. There is always the fear that I'll get caught in this terrible act."

Vicarious menstruation may occur in the form of epistaxis (nosebleeds) and occasionally as mild anal bleeding. Astringent suppositories take care of the latter, but nasal cauterization may be required for the epistaxis which can also be precipitated by compulsive nose-picking. However, emotional tensions from other sources are usually involved and should be investigated.

Other Genital Fluids in the Girl

Other genital fluids in the girl include several excretions in addition to the menstrual flow. Some of these are the result of infection (gonorrhea or trichomoniasis) that has been innocently acquired, although public toilet seats are a more common source of the crab louse than of infection. The use of paper seat covers helps to reduce this common source of anxiety by avoiding direct contact but is not as effective as avoiding direct contact by the use of a squatting position for elimination.

In the normal healthy girl there is a colorless sticky lubricant that is usually associated with sexual excitement. Normally it is restricted to the vulva or external genital organs and is scarcely

enough to soil the underclothing, but occasionally, erotic stimulation may bring on a liberal amount of discharge. At times this
may be thin and watery like the discharge from a running nose,
and it may spread onto the inner side of the thighs. This does
not necessarily mean that the girl has been indulging in heavy
petting or other sexual mischief. The stimulation may come during sleep, while daydreaming, or from reading an exciting novel
or watching a passionate love scene on the screen. Ordinary
cleansing and your own reassurance are all that are needed at
such times.

Leucorrhea is a common source of annoyance. It is a whitish
genital discharge which results from tension and overstimulation
(as in masturbation or petting), or from worry. Leucorrhea can
also result from infection. Usually it comes from the cervix or
neck of the uterus, and disappears spontaneously like a running
nose. Frequently it is associated with menstruation in which case
it is not even noticed. For these and other annoyances like itching, rashes, or offensive odors, encourage your daughter to confide in you and to consult your doctor; but when a specific disease
has been ruled out, and routine treatment seems to fail, keep in
mind the fact that anxieties in the form of unresolved emotional
conflicts (other than sexual) can also produce some of these discharges.

You might try a simple question like, "I know you've been
worried a lot lately about exams. Is something else troubling
you?" Your girl may not feel like telling you just then, and there
is usually no need to require an immediate answer. Give her time
to respond to your overture. Meanwhile, you have started her
thinking in the right direction. You have shifted the emphasis
away from the physical problem and toward the possibility of
emotional causes. Usually this new approach will cause her to
worry less about her complaints. Lessening of the anxiety will
also hasten the healing. Later you can take steps to work out
the emotional or social problem along the lines suggested in other
sections of this book.

You will want to remember that the distress of a conspicuous
pimple, for example, on your daughter's nose just before an important date is as nothing when compared to the anxiety in a

girl over an unexpected genital discharge or a delayed menstrual period if she cannot come to you for help and has no one else to turn to. Even the family doctor is off limits because he might tell the folks. As a result, the fear of detection of masturbation, or of ordinary genital handling, in the fastidious young lady may lead to some common compulsions about cleanliness.

For instance, a child may have been warned so sternly against genital touching that he forms the habit of repeatedly testing his or her hands for telltale odors. Sometimes a girl may resort to excessive handwashing and bathing; but it is as unreasonable to assume that a drive for cleanliness in your daughter (at any age) denotes guilt or compensation for secret self-love, as it would be to conclude that every hula dance is a vicarious relief for genital tension in the dancer.

Ordinarily one would not even mention the matter of this emphasis on cleanliness and fear of detection, except that much more than modesty is involved. It is one of the reasons why many girls will not touch their genitals at all and in later years will not let anyone else touch them either (physician, nurse, or husband). In consequence, they may remain frigid even to normal marital relations.

It is also a short and simple step from suppressed feelings to disturbed feelings, so that erotic sensation which may be absent at first (frigidity) can easily change to over sensitivity in the form of itching (pruritis) or at times to actual pain. This can occur at any age, and you can understand how any of these disturbances can interfere with a girl's dating schedule and make her afraid to mix with other young people.

Sometimes the physical evidence of a girl's emotional disturbance is displaced to the bladder. This results in urgency and frequency of voiding, but occasionally the anxiety affects other functions such as sleep and digestion. All this does not make for very cheerful reading. However, it may clear up some questions for which you have not been finding any answers.

The Hymen and Defloration

A few statements about the hymen are in order here because it is one of the secret sources of fear that may prevent girls from making a normal social adjustment. Misinformation on this score can cause a girl to refuse to make almost any kind of intimate or personal contacts with boys lest it lead to eventual discovery.

The hymen is usually a thin, flat, perforated, circular membrane which partly closes the outside opening of the vagina. Like the iris, it is about the size and shape of a candy Lifesaver except that it is usually paper-thin. It is also elastic so that the opening can easily be stretched to about the circumference of a tampon. Anything larger than this, or any violent exercise could easily tear it.

Your daughter will want to know that some hymens have wide openings, like the washer on your garden hose, but others are small like the washer on a kitchen faucet. Some are thick and tough while others are thin and delicate. Some will tear easily. Others will even resist sexual intercourse and may not be ruptured until childbirth or by surgical intervention. Girls are also curious about the "tokens of virginity" which means the spots of blood from the tearing of the hymen at defloration, during the first intercourse. Some hymens will bleed very little—only a few drops. Others might require a sanitary pad and, occasionally, an astringent.

It is normal for a girl to wonder about marriage and intercourse. When you plan on an important adventure like college or a journey, you often dwell on some of the details for months or years in advance. She will be anxious about defloration (to de-flower). Does it hurt? It depends upon the circumstances. If she is happy and in love and free from guilt, she probably will not even know when it happens, let alone feel the tear which is very small, usually less than a quarter of an inch. If she has a lot of conflicts and complexes on the subject, then her first intercourse may not only be very painful but even impossible. Counselors and therapists cannot avoid discussing these problems with girls, who have a right to know about the facts of life from you.

Conception

Nature has already informed the menstruating girl that she has graduated from childhood and that she is biologically capable of making babies. Parents and psychotherapists have a duty to inform and remind them when, and how, and under what circumstances our society will accept these babies. There are laws on our statute books and laws in our Bible, and there is the common-law wisdom of experience. Our love for our children must protect them if they are to survive and grow up to be the happy parents of our grandchildren.

As you probably have learned by now, there is no absolutely "safe period" for sexperiments. A strong, active sperm and an eager healthy egg are nature's recipe for new life. The egg is released from its factory, the ovary, at about the middle of the menstrual cycle which is usually ten to fourteen days from the beginning of the previous menstrual period. Strong, healthy sperms have been known to survive for a whole week in the ovarian tube that leads from the ovary to the uterus.

Even when no sexual entrance has been permitted, it is possible, during sex games, for semen to be deposited close enough for sperms to get inside the vulva and to swim up and fertilize the egg. This is unusual, but it can happen; and the knowledge may help to prevent "experimentation" plus a lot of unnecessary worrying ahead of time.

More than this is up to the parents. Some will forbid petting, necking and even dating but will not say for how long. Others will permit their teen-age daughter to make her own decisions on the limits of "no-man's land," just as they trust them to come home at a reasonable hour and to take care of their personal health. A few parents still allow their daughters to grow up with no preparation for menstruation, with the conviction that a kiss means pregnancy or that a boy's "soul kiss" (tongue in mouth) is a sign of perversion.

Some parents concentrate on the things that daughters may not do at parties, rather than emphasizing the things she must learn to do well if she is to pass safely through the pitfalls of normal adolescence.

Helping the youngster to build up a repertoire of skills, sports and other interests will help to make him a better mixer and more popular with the crowd, but one should remember that while music lessons, for example, can bring much satisfaction, they may also restrict one's outlets. An exhibitor and entertainer is not necessarily a happy and well adjusted participant in group activities. In order to develop poise and self-confidence, additional social training is usually required, for instance, dancing lessons and dramatics, and learning to work and to play with others.

Genital Fluids in the Boy

The first discharge of semen often appears during sleep and it may be as disturbing an experience to the boy as the first menstrual flow often is to a girl.[1] Many of the stories he has heard about venereal disease and the mythical dangers of self-abuse now flood his memory and generate unnecessary anxiety. In some cases a parent just does not seem to understand and misses the boat entirely by scolding or by unfair criticism. This is what happened to Dennis.

Dennis' Wet Dreams Threatening to Mother

I was about 14 . . . we used to hang around the back porch of one of the girls on the block . . . All the other kids used to tell dirty stories. I was too dumb to do anything but listen. I'd get wet dreams. Mom used to get mad at me for staining up the sheets . . . I remember her saying, "What's the matter with you? Can't you get to the bathroom in time? Do you have to wet the bed at your age? . . . I suppose she really thought it was urine. I don't think mother was particularly well versed in that area. I couldn't do very much about it, but I've been afraid of erotic stimulation ever since.

[At 37 Dennis is still keeping company and is still afraid to marry.]

It is impossible to say how many grown-ups have had their own reactions conditioned by teen-age rebukes such as the ones given to Dennis, but the occurrence is certainly frequent enough to make us pause and concern ourselves with better methods of management. The general tendency has been for parents to try not to notice the boy's first nocturnal seminal emission, just as they tried to ignore his small-boy erections. Sometimes a worried parent will take this as an opportunity to warn the boy against masturbation or to tell him about the birds and the bees, but they seldom are concerned with the boy's own feelings.

Some variation of the following case of Ralph is by no means rare.

Ralph's First Emission

At thirteen, Ralph had been used to having erections for as long as he could remember. He had been raised in a large family with strong moral repressions, but with rather primitive plumbing facilities. Despite frequent warnings against masturbation, he was surrounded by stimulating incidents every day of his life. This is his account of his first seminal emission.

> I was taking a bath one winter evening in the wooden tub near the stove in the kitchen, when one of my sisters came in to use the sink. We were on the third floor and it was snowing outside. It was a long way to the outhouse. The sink was behind me.
>
> I heard the rustle of skirt and petticoat, and the familiar warning, "Don't look!" Then there was the sound of running water, and the next thing I knew, I was staring in horror at the end of my penis.
>
> Suddenly, I remembered what my friends had said about making a baby . . . something about white stuff coming out of the penis, then going back inside. I thought they meant that it went back inside of the penis. I didn't sleep well for months afterward. I had no one to talk to . . . my chums and misinformants had all moved away into better neighborhoods. [Ralph is still resentful over his family's negligence and unfairness.] Wouldn't you think that somebody would have given me something I could use besides warnings?

Puberty is the time for reassurance rather than preachments. Semen is a legitimate source of pride, and a badge of manhood; but it is personal and its powers should be understood and respected—by girls as well as boys.

Nocturnal emission, "pollutions" or "wet dreams" are seminal emissions which occur during sleep. They result from the same kind of psychological and physical stimulation that arise from other sexual experiences. After the first reassurances, they can be taken in stride by the average boy. They do not have the regular periodicity of menstruation, and their absence is no cause for alarm; nor do they necessarily imply that the youth has been indulging in heavy petting or reading salacious literature, although both of these are usually provocative of sexual excitation. If the youth recognizes and remembers the dream characters, he may feel sinful or guilty until he can be reassured, but he will not always talk about it.

In the sexually stimulated boy, there is also a thin, colorless, sticky discharge from the penis. Its function is lubrication, and it contains no sperms. A similar discharge in girls is also normal and has been described above.

Parents may unwittingly stimulate their children and should therefore develop a sense of humor. This is what happened when Marvin "bugged" the house for company.

> Marvin, a precocious fifteen-year-old whose hobby was electronics, planted microphones all over his big, old house. One evening his parents were entertaining selected guests for a game of cards. After a few drinks, the "special company" began telling off-color stories. During one of the lulls, they were at first mystified to hear tittering and giggling coming from the upper floor, but they soon traced it to the receiving end of a microphone that had been placed in the unused fireplace in the living room. Home chemistry sets are not the only gifts that can "blow up."

Rectal Discharges

Rectal bleeding of a minor degree is not uncommon in both sexes, especially in boys. Hemorrhoids may be responsible, but rectal stimulation and congestion can occur from other sources. Constipation, a rough stool, or menstruation may explain the phenomena in some cases, where proctoscopy reveals negative findings. The bleeding is usually very slight and disappears with minimal medical management; but its appearance in boys who are away from home, for instance at camp, is a source of anxiety which should not be neglected by the school or camp nurse and physician.

Mucous discharges that cause pruritis (itching) may be a forerunner of a more serious disorder (mucous colitis); but the appearance of strands of mucous on the stool or a few loose stools with flecks of blood can also be a first indication of anxiety over masturbation or other sexual indiscretions. Stools that are gray, black, grossly bloody or putrid require prompt medical attention.

Pelvic Pain

Pelvic pain and "backache" may vary from a dull ache in the testes, groin, lower abdomen or back, to sharp colic. A transient ache or pain is often as common as a temporary itch; but persistent or severe distress is no case for psychotherapy until after clearance with the family physician. Causes include back injury, tumor, infection and overstimulation.

Therapists should remember that family attitudes often compel the youngster to conceal or deny such problems so that several indirect inquiries may be required during the intake history.*

Several other important sources of teen-age tensions occur at puberty. They are both sexual and nonsexual, and they are also vital areas which affect family life as well as the teenster himself. For instance, school dropouts, undesirable companionship, the usage of alcohol, drugs and tobacco, and other delinquencies often start around puberty. They express belated and frustrated attempts to win acceptance. Failures can also be indicated by truancies, running away from home, an increase in the incidence of some form of epilepsy and other more serious breakdowns of the total personality.

REFERENCES AND READINGS

1. BENDER, L., and GRUGETT, A. E., JR.: A follow-up report on children who had atypical sexual experience. *Amer J Orthopsychiat, XXII*: 825 (with excellent bibliography on p. 827) Oct. 1952.
2. CAMPBELL, A. A.; and COWHIG, J. D.: The incidence of illegitimacy. *US Welfare in Review*, 5:4, 1967. (Quoted in Chaskel, R.: Changing patterns of services for unmarried parents. *Social Casework*, 49:3, 1968)
3. CORNER, G. W.: *Attaining Manhood*. New York, Harper, 1938, 1952.
4. CORNER, G. W.: *Attaining Womanhood*. New York, Harper, 1939, 1952.
5. DUVAL, E. M.: *Facts of Life and Love for Teen-agers*. New York, Assn. Pr., 1956.
6. GUYTON, A. C.: *Textbook of Medical Physiology*. Philadelphia, Saunders, 1961.
7. Human Growth (16 mm. color-sound). Brown Trust, Portland, U. of Oregon Med. School.
8. Human Reproduction (16 mm. black/white-sound). New York, McGraw, N.Y.U. Film Libr., 26 Washington Pl., N.Y., 10003.
9. KOLB, L. C.: Personality disorders. In *Cecil Loeb Textbook of Medicine*, Philadelphia, Saunders, 1963, p. 1727.

* Venereal disease, syphilis and gonorrhea are discussed in Chapter 10.

10. KUPPERMAN, H. S.: *Human Endocrinology.* Philadelphia, Davis, 1963, 3 vols.
11. LENNOX, W. G.: *Epilepsy and Related Disorders.* Boston, Little, 1960.
12. LIEF, H. J.: Quoted in *Physician's Panorama,* 3:23, Mar. 1965.
13. MEADE, M.: *Sex and Temperament in Three Primitive Societies.* New York, New Am. Lib., 1950 (1935).
14. OTTO, U.: Suicidal attempts by 1727 children in Sweden. *Acta Paediat Scand,* 55:64-72, 1966. (Reported in *Psychiat Dig,* Sept. 1966, p. 14)
15. RATHBONE, J. L.: *Recreation in Total Rehabilitation.* Springfield, Thomas, 1959.
16. RICHARDSON, G. S.: Ovarian physiology (plasma testosterone rises with menstrual cycle). *New Eng J Med,* 274:1183-1194, 1966.
17. THORN, G. W.: Androgenic function. (In *Cecil Loeb Textbook of Medicine,* 11th ed). Philadelphia, Saunders, 1963, p. 1392.
18. WOLLMAN, L.: The role of hypnosis in the treatment of infertility. *Brit J Med Hypn,* 11:3-11, 1960.
19. WOLLMAN, L.: Transvestism and hypnotism. *Brit J Med Hypn,* 15:2-4, 1964.

Chapter 8

TEEN-AGE TENSIONS

UNCHANGING VALUES

Teen-age tensions are a normal state of affairs. Teen-agers are a perpetual challenge to their elders, a source of admiration and envy to children, and, quite often, a provocative mystery to themselves.

Teen-age tensions result in part from accumulated and unresolved problems of childhood and puberty. Confrontation with the responsibilities of maturity accentuates the conflict; but, despite global unrest and the highly publicized growing revolt of modern youth, the basic problems and values are unchanged.

Unchanging values are expressed by the following answers to the question, What do you consider to be the greatest problem of adolescence? The comments were written spontaneously and were turned in anonymously at my various lectures to high school seniors, college freshmen, and nursing students. From them I have selected these typical replies.

> The period of adolescence opens doors to the independent pathways of life. We must live our own lives; have our own experiences and learn to be responsible for what mental equipment nature has endowed us with. During this period comes the desire for bigger and better things in life . . . Problems which were left unsolved throughout the earlier years of life now come with the constant urge to do and for self-expression which is now nearing its goal—a choice of a vocation, career, graduation, the making of friends, or going away from home for the first time . . . The eternal question of sex creeps out and the laws of convention form the barrier that cannot be crossed unless one bars himself from accepted public standards . . . Adolescence is the age when one is no longer a child but begins to feel that he must assume a little responsibility and plan for the future—naturally some take this much more seriously than others . . . At this age the problems of life seem to become more difficult.

Of equal interest were replies to a second question, What do you consider to be the greatest thing in the world? These answers are characteristically influenced by the sex of the student. Thus, among the young ladies, "love," "creation," "reproduction," "life," "faith," "religion," "successful marriage," "happy home," and "motherhood" are the usual answers; while from the boys come such choices as "reputation," "character," "financial success," and "a career."

It is clear from these answers that while community and parental controls may be less effective, contemporary ideals and objectives are unchanged. Many things other than sex occupy the interest and attention of the adolescent. The following discussion is slanted to meet the needs of the adolescent himself and is based upon his ability to accept and understand the advice which you give him in the counseling situation.

Adolescence Means Growth

The term comes from the Latin "adolescere," meaning "to grow" or "to mature." In most of the standard references on adolescence one finds accounts of special rights and initiation ceremonies among primitive tribes—forerunners of our modern ceremony of confirmation. There were tests of skill and endurance against pain and privation. Weeks of semi-starvation on bread and water were followed by ceremonious beatings or mutilations, such as knocking out some teeth, inflicting wounds or scars by branding with red hot coals or irons, tattooing, deforming the nose or mouth, and circumcision in both sexes.

Sometimes a new name was given in order to signify the birth of a new personage at puberty. The Roman youth at fourteen years put on the "toga virilis," while the English Page ceased to associate with the ladies and became a Squire in the company of Knights and other men of the court. At thirteen years the Hebrew boy becomes eligible to membership in the temple or synagogue, with full rights of manhood through the ceremony of *"Bar Mitzvah"* (son or heir of the sacred covenant with God). A similar ceremony is also available for the modern Jewish daughter (*Bas Mitzvah*). Early marriage was expected but in western society, despite the fact of biological maturity, the legal age for consent to cohabitation outside of marriage is still fourteen to sixteen years.

It was the purpose of the primitive initiation rites to teach observance of customs and laws, obedience and loyalty to the community and tribal chiefs, independence of maternal control, feats of skill, strength, endurance and bravery.

An Automatic Declaration of War

A parent no longer brings his wayward, stubborn, gluttonous and alcoholic son before the elders to pass sentence of stoning to death (Deut. 21:18). Instead he passes on the responsibility to juvenile courts, probation officers, psychologists, social workers, counselors, military and other training schools, and various other specialists.

Psychological and economic warfare has been a perpetual state of affairs between the younger and older generation from time immemorial. It is the same as between older and younger brothers and sisters. Each group is inclined to the erroneous belief that the world belongs to the other. The older generation never ceases to marvel at the boundless energy, imagination, idealism, opportunities, boldness and enthusiasm of youth; while the young folks continually covet the property, wealth, authority, comfort, prestige and experience of seniority.

And an Uncertain Legacy

Contemporary news of the day has been reporting widespread unrest of global proportions. This has been a chronic state of affairs for over half a century. It is also a constant reminder to youth of the failures of their elders to solve the continuing social, moral and economic inequities of the human race. Furthermore, all generations have reason to be apprehensive and pessimistic about mounting national debts, unstable currencies, multiple and recurrent wars, dishonesty, inefficiency, corruption and judicial inequities at every level. Truly it is an uncertain legacy which we hand on to our successors.

It is small consolation that adults have done no worse than most of their forebears in all ages of history. Nevertheless, most responsible people are alarmed by screaming headlines and telecasts of violence, campus revolts, beach orgies, sex murders, atrocities, pornography and underinhibited "entertainers." Combined with commercials that are designed to sell merchandise, alcohol, drugs and tobacco, they provided an almost constant barrage of aggressive and erotic stimulation, persuasive discontent and rebellion. Where these sources leave off, eager disciples of the beatnik and hippie generation take over. Drugs, alcohol, drive-ins, and love-ins compete openly with "old-fashioned" recreation, supervised dating, dancing, sports and other youth activity programs.

Meanwhile bickering and argument over reasonable hours and the responsibility of the individual to keep his family informed of his whereabouts continue to wage a losing battle as teen-agers take over decisions which parents are unable or unwilling to make: financial responsibility, premarital sex, contraception, abortions and experiments with alcohol and drugs.

CHANGING FACTS OF CONTEMPORARY LIFE

For the counseling and guidance expert on teen-agers and their tensions, here are some facts that need periodic review and timely updating.

1. Population in the United States had increased only 8 per cent between 1960 and 1965, yet FBI reports show nearly a 50 per cent rise in crime, especially burglary, larceny and auto theft.

2. Referring to this decade as the "Raging Sixties," Mc-Murry notes that outbreaks of violence have also taken place in areas where there are no slums or ghettos such as Fort Lauderdale, Florida and Nyack, New York. Many of the rioters are whites from middle class homes where they were probably overindulged rather than underprivileged. Rioters and looters involved less than 5 per cent of the Negro population (Roper) in such areas as Watts, Detroit, Newark and Chicago, but almost all of the rioters were young people, of both sexes and between eleven and twenty-five years of age.[5, 9]

   The national figures for 1966 show that children between eleven and seventeen years constitute only 13 per

cent of the population. Yet most of the arrests and 50
per cent of all convictions for burglary, car theft and related crimes were offenders in this pubo-adolescent range.
McMurry calls them "trouble seekers" attracted by the
opportunities for violence, murder, arson, rape, looting
and vandalism. They are also sparked by paid represen-
tatives of "hate" groups whose rabble-rousing tactics appeal to antisocial and emotionally immature psychopathic
personalities.

3. Broken homes are on the increase as working mothers
    and moonlighting fathers rely more and more on un-
    trained baby-sitters and television to amuse and instruct
    their children. The advertised importance of tobacco, beer,
    cosmetics, detergents, and dubious advice on health are
    in constant competition with weird and unscientific tales
    of almost every description. The few programs which have
    actual merit are often missed or rejected.

4. Fortunately, marriage is the rule for most of our popula-
    tion; but close to a fourth of the marriages in the United
    States now end in divorce. However, about 90 per cent
    of the divorcees remarry—many of them to the same
    spouses and about two thirds of those who remarry stay
    married. Unfortunately, the conflicts and tensions do little
    for family stability where children are involved.

5. Moral upheavals are also reflected in the churches where
    more and more reforms are taking place. More churches
    and homes are being built, but the emphasis is liable to
    be more on opulence and status than on utility and prac-
    tical realities. The term "edifice complex" is apt, but the
    practice is ancient. Even when human sacrifice was the
    rule, religious leaders were no more successful than other
    leaders in keeping their followers in line with universal
    codes of ethics and conduct.

6. Technology, like normal philosophy, is still ahead of
    achievement by the rank and file, as personnel shortages
    mount. Meanwhile, the demand for higher pay, shorter
    hours and increasing conveniences accentuates the prob-
    lems of production and the distribution of material goods.

The spectacle of man's inability to deal effectively with his daily challenges is all but complete as we survey the increasing population explosion in the face of mounting global unrest and the concurrent growing food shortages in significant parts of the world.

THE TEENSTERS' CHALLENGE

As if in bold retaliation for the failures of their forebears, our teensters have taken over in a great big way. According to various statistics [2, 8] our population in this country is more than two and a half times what it was in 1900. Furthermore, 70 per cent of our present population was not alive during World War I; 60 per cent was not alive during the great economic depression of the thirties; and almost half had not been born at the beginning of World War II.

In 1965, 40 per cent of the United States population was under twenty. One in three people, between sixteen and twenty-four years of age, bought a car each year. One in five high school seniors owned an auto; and each year over three million more teen-agers became eligible to drive.

Fifty per cent of the teen-age girls owned hair dryers and spent over a quarter billion dollars a year on half of the phonographic records sold in the United States. They also bought more cosmetics and clothes than their mothers. In short, the average teen-ager, in 1964, spent ten dollars a week, amounting to a total of 11 billion dollars a year, for all teen-agers—a figure that was expected by some statisticians, to reach over twenty billion by 1970.

Two other sobering estimates deserve reflection: (1) the crime rate in the United States is increasing four times as fast as the population, and (2) education pays off in increased earnings. A college graduate's lifetime earnings are worth $386,000, compared with $246,000 for a high school graduate and only $178,000 for a graduate of elementary school.[4]

Statistics keep changing, but regardless of actual figures at any given time, the estimates are impressive and the problems of decision and adjustment grow larger, not smaller.

In brief, the anxieties of normal teen-agers are closely linked with prestige, popularity, independence and self-confidence. There is concern with religion and idealism, a career, and a compelling need to be well informed on almost every subject, including drugs, free love and birth control.

Adolescence is a time when many youngsters compete successfully with parents and family. It is a time when too many families obstinately refuse to loosen apron strings as well as purse strings. It is a time when the impatient and restless teenster must come to grips with the realities of preparation for careers, part-time jobs, seductive and aggressive companions, responsibility for reasonable habits, home chores and such hazards as speeding, drinking, smoking, drugs, interfaith and interracial dating, venereal disease, pregnancy, and earlier marriages.

Health Hazards

Health hazards at this stage of life are similar to those of puberty as already described in the previous chapter. They include skin diseases, especially on the face, a rise in the incidence curve of anxiety, nightmares, various seizures and major disorders of personality, especially those that are marked by withdrawal or by overaggressiveness.

Adolescence is a critical time for emotional depression and nostalgia and for their innumerable depressive equivalents, such as conversion phenomena, eyestrain, headaches, asthma, digestive upsets, constipation or diarrhea, hemorrhoids, backache and pelvic congestion. Virus infection, hepatitis, and mononucleosis and seizures seem to flourish at this stage, especially when one is away from home for the first time.

Early Signs of Schizophrenia

Adolescence is conspicuously a time for the emergence of frank withdrawal, isolation, emotional detachment, fantasy, rejection of responsibility and other easily recognizable signs of schizophrenia, such as uncontrolled breaks with reality, responding to delusions and hallucinations, inappropriate laughter or crying spells, unconcern with time or personal hygiene and morals, inability to hold onto jobs or friends and unconventional behavior.

Adolescence is a time for rebellion, emancipation and leaving home. It is a time for experimenting. Tobacco, alcohol, drugs and sex are indulged partly for status and partly in an attempt at self-treatment for anxiety and depression. They serve as tranquilizers and psychoenergizers for the inevitable consequences of broken homes, abdicating parents and disturbed personalities. Adolescence is also a time for suicide.

Suicide

Suicide ranks third as a cause of death in the fifteen to nineteen year age group although it accounts for only one tenth of the total deaths in the United States. It is traceable in part to family and social pressures for academic achievement and is highest prior to final exams and especially during the spring months, possibly from unrequited love.* Some attempts are actually vicarious efforts to prove one's invulnerability.† Others are mere gestures to draw attention—but have backfired from miscalculation.

There are eight attempts for each successful suicide. Attempts that are not intended to succeed are known as "suicidal gestures." Three times as many males succeed, but three times as many females try it. The incidence is higher in whites, the aged, and the unmarried. Some suicide prevention centers with twenty-four-hour telephone coverage are available in various parts of the country; but the supply of trained parapsychiatric personnel to man these projects continues to be woefully inadequate.‡

In a study of attempted suicide by adolescents between the ages of fourteen and eighteen years at the Los Angeles County Hospital, Dr. J. B. Teicher and his associates reported a longstanding history of continuing childhood problems of behavior and personality. There was also a high ratio of changing addresses and schools, along with loss of friendships, homes and parents either through death or divorce and remarriage. Previous sui-

---

* Psychiatric disorders in students. *PD Therapeutic Notes*, 74:142, Nov.-Dec., 1967.

† Kubie, L. S.: Self-extinction may not be goal of self-injury. Quoted in Roche Report: *Frontiers of Clinical Psychiatry*, 5 (12):6-8, June 15, 1968.

‡ *Newsweek*, April 1, 1968, p. 97.

cidal attempts had been made by nearly half of them. Total isolation from friends was found to be the critical point. With the contemporary changing status and trend from rural to urban and suburban residency, a comparable rise has been noted in Negro suicides, especially in large cities.[10]

Management depends on the circumstances. When the situation seems urgent, best procedure is to notify local police. However, when it does not *seem* urgent, it often is closer than you would like to believe. Some experts believe that direct confrontation is indicated. "Well, what's stopping you?" Others prefer a more subtle and indirect approach. In effect, the counselor *listens a lot* and says little. When he does talk he tells the patient that lots of people would agree with him, that he is perfectly justified in feeling the way he does, that it would serve everyone just right for him to proceed with his plans, and so on.

But then, there is obviously no compelling urgency to do it right now. Since there has been time for a telephone call or a conference, there is apparently a need to share something with someone else. Whom does he want to be informed, and why? To threaten, warn or punish? To provoke them into doing something to stop him? To test their loyalty? Or, just to temporize and put things off for a while longer.

The informing type obviously needs an audience. Find other ways of nourishing his ego, and your problem is temporarily solved. Have him do you a favor. Make him feel important. Offer him an opportunity to win approval. Yet do not plead with him. Do not belittle him. Make another appointment for him to see you or at least telephone you within an hour. This will give him something to look forward to.

Some therapists who know their patients well have succeeded with a psychological gimmick

> I want you to call me up at six o'clock tomorrow morning to tell me just what time it was that you committed suicide (!)

I usually invite the patient to write me a letter, take a long walk, get with company to avoid being alone, and to start cleaning house so that everything will be in shipshape when they come for the body. If this gets a smile or a giggle, I usually do not have to worry. If it does not, I am liable to think in terms of electric sleep treatments and psychoenergizing drugs. One visit or call is seldom enough. Prolonged counseling supervision is indicated.

The New Look

The new look in hair, clothing, and discotheque is more than a gesture of defiance. It is also an attempt to establish equality and to reduce barriers between the sexes. Transvestism (wearing clothes of the opposite sex) is technically illegal; but girls and women started the trend with overalls at work. They continued with tight bras and short skirts in the twenties, slacks and short hair during the thirties, and then the bobby sox of the forties. The males are not very far behind, at least with color if not with full styling. Some of them also seem to be recapturing some of the hairdos of former centuries, as well as their own infancy.

Many an adolescent is unhappy over the size or shape of various parts of his or her anatomy. The more teasing he has to endure on these real or fantasied shortcomings, the more anxious and defensive are his attempts to deny or to compensate. Secret practices, reading stimulating books, weight lifting and indulging in various body manipulations may result from attempts to make up some of his deficiencies. Unfortunately, when parents consult the family doctor, they are often told not to worry because "he'll grow out of it."

Sometimes this is true, but it is no consolation to the underdeveloped fifteen-year-old who may not menstruate for another year or two. Yet she is often compared to, and has to compete with, a precocious twelve- or thirteen-year-old who is practically bursting out of her 36B bra and loving every inch of it. The girl who avoids gymnastics and sports may be ashamed to be seen in the shower room or in a bathing costume. Her subsequent avoidance of dates and sex may pass for virtue or prudishness, whereas her real fear is that she will be rejected because of her size or shape, or perhaps because of her name, religion or color, or because of her father's occupation, a certain type of illness her mother had or because her brother was sent to reform school.

Similar crises face the boy. For instance, a tall boy without the self-confidence that one would expect from his size and the increasing use of a razor may resist your efforts to guide him into basketball. He may feel too self-conscious. Others resist athletics because they fear unfavorable comparisons of genital size or shape in the locker room. A large, strong boy may still be afraid of physical harm, as an emotional leftover from previous bullying during his earlier years.

Any of these factors may accumulate and, along with continuing parental rejection, can result in suicide as well as schizoid withdrawal or psychopathic compensations.

Complaints Often Disguise Problems

In general, the complaint that is presented to the counselor is seldom the real cause of the youth's anxiety. Disappointment with the important people in one's life, whatever the reason, is often concealed by neglect of studies, truancy, preoccupation with alcohol or drugs, watching sports, or concern over sex in its various forms. On the other hand, problems that appear to be sexual in origin often have a very different significance.

Unsatisfactory interpersonal relations and the choice of careers are often related. For instance, selection of a career may be designed to protect one from the necessity of competition or close relations with the opposite sex. Occasionally, the teenster's solution of his conflict may be sought by concentrating on books or by plunging right into the first available heterosexual relationship. Sometimes a homosexual attraction appears safer as a temporary refuge from family rejection and consequent self-dissatisfaction. In many such cases of disturbed interpersonal relations, eyestrain, headache, backache, and bowel or skin trouble may be the chief complaint.

THE WITHDRAWN TEENSTER

The normal teen-ager wants to be associated with desirable and eligible friends. Yet in some cases he permits himself to get stuck with almost any available date or companions. Occasionally he will cling obstinately to undesirable acquaintances, despite all opposition. He does this in order to compensate for feelings of inadequacy over schoolwork, as an escape from quarrels at home, or as rebellion against restrictions. For many a girl the price of acceptance in terms of sex, alcohol, drugs or delinquency may seem cheap because she is convinced that she is so unattractive that there is no other way to feel wanted. Without even these friends of dubious value, why else would she care to go on living?

It is far more important for the teenster to choose the "right" crowd of young people and then try to become desirable to them by working to meet *their* terms than to brood in isolation while waiting for someone or some group to accept him as he is and on his own terms. The group may be an exclusive sorority or fraternity, yet it may have no substantial value to the youth because, of course, there are also cliques within the group. By the time such an unhappy youth comes to the attention of parent or counselor, most of the emotional damage has already been done, and he has already withdrawn from social competition. As mentioned above, suicide and schizoid states should be kept in mind.

The withdrawn teenster mirrors the defects of his family. Few parents want to wait until their child has a reputation for being fast, bold or unreliable; and still fewer parents can accept responsibility for their own share in helping to produce the reverse of such a situation.

Ordinarily the rule is that even a bad home is better than no home. The obvious exception is the home with the "battered child syndrome" with emotionally deprived, immature and unstable parents who literally beat their children to death. The following case of Marion may seem extreme, yet the mistakes of Marion's family are by no means rare.

When A Bad Home Isn't Much Better Than None

Marion at seventeen was doing all the things she was not supposed to be doing outside her home and balking at every chore inside the home. Her European parents believed all that was said of her by outsiders but would not believe Marion's own report which also implicated her older brother. Even when the brother admitted his indiscretions, they sided with him by putting all the blame on Marion. They were shocked, but they refused to believe her accusation that he was taking beer from his friends in exchange for her sexual favors or that he had ever been drunk and had often beaten her into submission.

When a three-months' pregnancy could no longer be concealed from mother's "watchful" eyes, they finally consulted a specialist to whom the parents solemnly promised, "We'll do anything you say. Just tell us what to do."

Many parents make such promises. Apparently they want to keep them; but they cannot or will not, and they do not. Marion's parents were no exception. They did not follow through. They themselves feel displaced and therefore cannot acclimate themselves completely or comfortably to the new culture. They still cannot break completely with the customs and traditions of their own parents regarding early hours and restricted dating; and they cannot sympathize enough with their children to accept the changing tempo of modern social activities; nor will they admit that sexual cravings are normal and more demanding at puberty.

When such parents do identify with the teenster they have to suppress their own earlier rebellious attitudes against the strict training by which they themselves were raised. This alliance can arouse guilt as well as compensations, and guilt must be dealt with. Unfortunately, however, instead of recognizing their own earlier rebellion when it appears in their own children, most parents reject and deny it. Instead, they identify with a "good" child—that is to say, with an obedient teenster—the kind of child they themselves believe that they should have been and would like to be if they could have a second chance.

This prejudiced favoritism is their "second chance" to live over again the unhappy friction-packed years of their own youth. Consequently, they often become even more strict and despotic than were their own parents. Like Marion's parents, they do not even know why they themselves react so violently; so, of course, they have difficulty in understanding their own children.

It is not an easy task to get people to accept the psychological implications of dating and family tensions. As is usual in such cases, Marion's parents discontinued their visits to the specialist just as soon as the crisis was over. Their inability to follow through with guidance persisted even when Marion's brother, their fair-haired "boy," finally decided that he too needed help.

Marion herself continued with the treatment conferences long after Mother Nature came to her rescue in the form of a spontaneous and uncomplicated miscarriage. Two years later the rejected girl found her future husband with whom she is happily continuing her emotional reeducation.

COMPLICATIONS OF "MAKING OUT"

Idealism Versus Realism

Teen-agers are great idealists. In moments of exaltation they may let their imaginations run away with them as they plan to reform the world. Their discussions on free love, birth control, and eugenic babies are just as serious to them as their talks on religion and great social reforms. Many of them can use their brains for study and research, yet they may rationalize on morals.

Teen-agers differ widely in their interpretation of "petting" and "making out." To some young folks, petting may be as innocent as holding hands at the movies, while for others "making out" may range from wrestling above the waist to various degrees of exploration, stimulation and release, or "going all the way." Some popular songs boldly proclaim, "It's no good unless somebody loves you all the way," and "I wanna be thrilled to desperation (with) every kind of intimate sensation. . . ."

According to a *Newsweek* report, the Kinsey Institute for Sex Research at Indiana University finds that coeds who do indulge in premarital sex are enjoying their first coitus more than before the current trend toward sexual equality. This is partly related to increased protection from "the pill" and partly from more liberal attitudes. *They are not, however, becoming more promiscuous.* They still place love as a first requirement; *and they have not abandoned the single standard.* Boys have become less dependent on prostitutes for their first intercourse, but otherwise they are about the same.*

Most girls and boys are much more conservative in these matters than is generally supposed. Girls usually encourage boys to take the initiative in making overtures, especially when they are ovulating (about half way in their menstrual cycle), but they

---

* *Newsweek*, Jan. 15, 1968, p. 70.

are expected to reserve for themselves the privilege of setting limits on the degree of familiarity which they will permit. Generally speaking, if they show that they mean whatever they say, the average boy will accept other restrictions in his life. Boys also know about the dangers of unrestricted intimacies, but they still want to experiment with the boundaries, not only to prove virility but also in response to the instinct for conquest.

Just how liberal and unsafe some of these boundaries between safety and status can be is indicated by the figures on unmarried mothers whose *average* age for first babies is well under seventeen years. In many parts of the country, and in some larger cities, the average age for unwed mothers is only fifteen years.

In one group of eighty-three unwed mothers, alcohol or drugs were a factor in a few cases, but most of them were unpopular and consistently failed to use contraception.

Ruth Chaskel reminds us that although 8 per cent of live births in the United States in 1965 were illegitimate, the rate of increase of "out-of-wedlock children" is only about 1 per cent a year. However, the rate is greater in the fifteen to nineteen year age bracket because there are more teen-agers than older women, giving birth to illegitimate babies.[1, 3, 7]

If girls are given reasonable opportunity they may learn for themselves when to apply the brakes; that petting is fun only when it can be kept under control; that safety lies in dating in groups and not in going steady too soon; and to place definite restrictions on privileges. Sounds terribly old-fashioned, of course, but so are vaccination, insect control, pasteurization, sterilization and even soap and water.

For better or worse, adolescent marriages are increasing. Usually this is the result of premarital pregnancy; but many of our grandmothers can remember when teen-age marriage was an accepted fact of life. At that time large families were common and early deaths more frequent.

COUNSELING THE UNWED MOTHER AND THE UNWED FATHER

Statistics keep changing, but it is a generally accepted fact that the age of unwed mothers ranges between eleven and fifty years in this country, with most of them between sixteen and twenty-four years. A first fling at sex in the older age group often results from increased androgens (male sex hormones) that are normally produced each month at the time of ovulation. This makes the woman more aggressive and more receptive to masculine advances. It is also the time of greatest liability to pregnancy. Younger girls often resort to intimacies in defiance of parents, to keep a boyfriend, or in the hopes of pregnancy as a preliminary to marriage.

The National Center for Health Statistics report that illegitimate births have tripled from less than ninety thousand in 1940 to a total of nearly three million in 1965. Also, the number of white women bearing a child within eight months of marriage has doubled from 8 to 16 per cent between 1945 and 1965. Nonwhites in the same category stands at 41 per cent. Factors include a decline of induced abortions and a reduction in sterility caused by venereal disease.*

Rowan also points out that large-scale migrations from southern farms to industrial cities in various parts of the country have contributed to the dissolution of family ties and overcrowding in substandard housing.

Approved social agencies are equipped to furnish necessary advice on procedure and referral to suitable homes and clinics for prenatal care.

Therapeutic abortions, when agreed upon, should be performed by competent specialists after suitable study (in most states, by two qualified psychiatrists) and only to protect the mother from suicide or other serious breakdown. Occasionally the probability of a deformed baby is legitimate cause for emptying the pregnant uterus during the earliest months. In either case, the hazards of surgery increase after the third month of pregnancy when a different, and often more complicated, technique must be employed.

Counselors should remember that false pregnancies from wishful thinking are fairly common and that while most laboratory tests for pregnancy are fairly reliable, they are not necessarily 100 per cent dependable.

---

* Reported by Rowan, C. T., in *Springfield Daily News*, March 25, 1968, p. 14.

Psychological and social alibis for pregnancy are common:

> *"It was the only way to get our parents to consent to our marriage." "I didn't know he was married." "We were going to be married as soon as he got his divorce." "I'm not ashamed, because I love him."* [For most women, and many men, "love" justifies everything.]

Unmarried fathers come from all walks of life; but, in modern times they seem less concerned about their moral responsibilities. Like their own parents and even the judges who preside at bastardy hearings, some are indulgent while others are overly strict. Many compensate for personal frustrations by severity, harshness, or escape by taking off. According to Kinsey and others, a very large percentage of normal women have premarital intercourse with the man whom they eventually marry, so that the date of pregnancy is merely a technicality. On the other hand, some girls are not averse to making the most recent partner a convenient scapegoat. Thus both parents are liable to take it out on the child eventually.

Honesty is not a consistent trait in either of the participants. Many a young teenster conceals her pregnancy from all parties until her marriage is a *fait accompli*.

> Helga's plan included something extra, but it backfired. She withheld the significant fact that her first sexual partner was not only married but also of a different color and religion. *After* the somewhat hasty marriage, she claimed that she had confided in her young husband and that he had agreed to the marriage on condition that she give up the baby without even seeing it. By so doing, they could start afresh with their own baby a year or two later.
>
> Helga's desire to prove she was grown-up and to punish her hostile and gossipy parents permitted no alteration in her plans. These did not include the peace of mind of either her husband or her parents whom she intended to saddle with her baby regardless of its origin or color.
>
> Something unforeseen happened, however. During the latter months of the pregnancy Helga fell in love with her husband. Unbeknown to her family, she saw the Negro baby, told everyone it had died at birth, and then gave it up for adoption to a childless Negro couple that did not care what colors it might eventually develop.

Guilt and Suicide

When a first baby is aborted, born deformed or dies, the mother is usually burdened with a depressing sense of guilt. Suicide is comparatively rare in such cases, but compensatory resort to alcohol, drugs, promiscuity and other rebellious defiances may complicate the picture.

There is an adage taught to medical students which teaches that the Lord is good to the pregnant woman and saves her from many of the medical complications that would otherwise harm her if she were not pregnant. This seems to run true for the unmarried mother who may indeed commit suicide, but not because she is pregnant. She usually tries to take her life *because of despondency over rejection by the man she loved.* Refusal to marry or to contribute to costs is a reaction of males that is much more common than most girls care to admit. Incidentally the costs of abortions may easily reach several thousand dollars in addition to hospital expenses, even with the help of medical insurance.

REFERENCES AND READINGS

1. CHASKEL, RUTH: Changing pattern of services for unmarried parents. *Social Case Work, XLIX:*3-10, Jan. 1968.
2. *Information Please Almanac.* Atlas Yearbook, 21st ed., New York, S. and S., 1967.
3. KRAVITZ, H., *et al.:* Unwed mothers: practical and theoretical considerations. *J Canad Psych Assoc,* 2:456-464, 1966. (Reported in *Psychiat News Med Dig, 1:*2, April-June 1967.
4. LIVINGSTON, J. A.: Mirror of America. In *U.S. Book of Facts, Statistics and Information for 1967.* New York, S. and S., 1966, pp. xv-xviii.
5. McMURRY, R. N.: Permissiveness and the riot-prone. *Psychiat Opinion,* 5:10-18, June 1968.
6. MENNINGER, K.: *The Vital Balance.* New York, Viking, 1963.
7. National Center for Health Statistics, Pub. Health Service, U.S. Dept. H.E.W., Washington, D.C.
8. New York Life Insurance Co.: *Guide to Career Information.* New York, Harper, 1957.
9. ROPER, E.: Beyond the riots. *Sat. Rev,* Oct. 7, 1967, pp. 24-26. (quoted by McMurry, above)
10. TEICHER, J. D.; JACOBS, J., and MARGOLIN, N. L.: Adolescents who attempted suicide. Report to Amer. Orthopsychiat. Assoc., San Francisco, 1966. *Psychiat Progr, 1:*3, May 1966.

Chapter 9

CRUSHES AND SEXPERIMENTS

CRUSHES, EXPERIMENTS AND MISTAKES IN SEX BEHAVIOR are often the result of disappointments and frustrations in other areas. When people are rejected by the opposite sex, it is natural for them to turn for comfort to friends and companions of the same sex. Early in puberty this is the normal pattern, but the average "crush" is no cause for alarm unless such an entanglement develops into a frank and repeated homosexual intimacy. The youngsters will usually outgrow the attachment if there is someone to talk to and adequate guidance, but the continued lack of emotional acceptance at home makes an ultimate heterosexual adjustment more difficult.

SEX AND CHANGING SOCIAL RELATIONS

At puberty and adolescence, changing social relationships involve the obligation to shift from homosexual to heterosexual interests. On this new challenge, here are some facts that are not too well known.

As Dr. Kubie reminds us, most parents teach their little boys that it is more offensive to touch a little girl's genitals than to touch another little boy's. In group bathing he learns that other little boys are just like himself and that there is no harm in looking at their genitals. Therefore, investigating and touching another boy's genitals in childhood is seldom cause for alarm, whereas the same behavior with the genitals of girls usually arouses some anxiety in grown-ups. For the child it is often a worse offense to touch or play with his own genitals than to touch another child. This is something which nice little boys and girls are not supposed to do.[4]

At puberty, however, this attitude is reversed. In our zeal to get the boy to make a normal heterosexual adjustment we are inclined to overstress the importance of playing with girls and to denounce the same sexual play with boys as perverse. According to Kinsey, this attitude depends on the social level of the parents. For instance, among the lower classes, homosexuality is considered to be much more serious and abnormal than heterosexuality, whereas homosexuality is regarded with much more tolerance in the upper social levels.

From puberty on it becomes less threatening and less abnormal for the boy to play with girls sexually than to play with other boys, but at the same time it also becomes dangerous, for he is obviously too young to marry, yet not too young to fertilize. This is another reason why self-love through genital masturbation becomes more active at puberty and during the teens.

It is something like giving the youth a brand new gun and ammunition but no license to hunt and not even an opportunity for target practice. When the gun goes off "accidentally" for the first time he has no experience on which to base his conduct and no opportunity to develop judgment for future procedure or behavior.

Natural fatigue will normally prevent excesses of masturbation, and each one must learn for himself what his own limits are; but for compulsive excesses, a tranquilizer may be indicated along with dynamic displacement and reconditioning.

Ordinarily, in the counseling situation the boy will be seeking information on safety limits as to the frequency of indulgence in masturbation although he will not ask about it in these terms. Instead, he will be "interested" in knowing about the frequency of normal intercourse, whether there are dangers in coitus interruptus (withdrawal) and how safe are birth control pills. He may even pretend to have no interest at all, but he has a right to be informed on these additional facts of life.

There are no *safety limits* on the frequency of self-love *or* of coitus. "Normal" frequency may vary from as little as once a month or less to as often as three or more times a day. The greatest urge for sexual expression often occurs during late adolescence, but it may start as early as eleven or twelve years. Potency and virility may continue past the age of ninety. Sexual excesses, at any age, will usually result in natural fatigue, the same as with any other physical activity. Whenever such excesses produce fatigue and anxiety, the boy or girl will recognize it by the usual physical signs; but his accompanying feelings of guilt may produce much more tension and exhaustion than is normally expected from other physical activities.

In addition to listlessness or irritability, there are conversion reactions which usually include abdominal cramps, digestive disturbances, headache, backache, aching testes, or ovaries, flushing, perspiration, awareness of heart beating rapidly, impaired appetite and sleeplessness. Almost any other symptom which the body may choose as its outlet for expressing emotional pressure may make its first appearance as an accompaniment of such erotic anxiety. Yet you may be doing your child an injustice if you conclude that his first attack of asthma, for instance, is necessarily related to sexual worries. Rejection by a parent or playmate is a more likely cause.

Even normal sexual intercourse, under legitimate conditions in marriage, will produce some of these same signs of fatigue and frustration if it is interrupted, rushed, or incomplete; or if it is preceded by an argument or quarrel, or followed by recrimination or some unfairness.

MASTURBATION

Masturbation at any age is a common and normal defense against helplessness, rejection, and boredom. The desire for self-love is liable to become most urgent when the boy or girl is left alone, has been punished, feels rejected, or is anxious for other reasons. The comfort it gives serves to build up self-confidence. It makes him feel important when all other ego supports fail him. It also usually produces feelings of guilt and more anxiety than it relieves.

Petting and "heavy" necking, especially prolonged "soul" (tongue) kissing, may accomplish the same results for both the girl and the boy. There is usually a great deal of speculation as to whether early sex play may influence their growth and health, but whether it is the groundless fear of losing their minds or the guilty recollections of previous sex experiences in earlier years, such anxieties may overshadow an entire lifetime, as in the following case.

Old Enough To Know Better?

A few years ago a timid lady of sixty-eight years telephoned to ask, "Are you the sex doctor?" When she was informed that I was a nerve specialist and was also considered to be an experienced counselor on sex problems, she made an appointment to see me.

The consultation was about herself, and the problem on which she wanted reassurance was masturbation. She had worried about it since the age of eleven, had never dared confide in anyone and was just now beginning to wonder whether her failing memory could be the result of her secret practice rather than from natural aging and hardening of her arteries as her family doctor had told her.

Examination was normal and I was able to reassure her. As a result, her health and memory began to improve immediately.

"Mental masturbation" is even more widespread than physical masturbation. This is commonly achieved by voyeurism, using foul language, telling dirty stories, passing obscene pictures or suggestive literature, wearing clothes of the opposite sex ("transvestism"), using words with double meanings, trying to embarrass others, censoring other people's morals, postural tensions, squatting, certain forms of dancing, and daydreaming.

As with homosexuality, attitudes vary with culture and economic levels. For example, Kinsey found masturbation acceptable in the middle classes, while it was considered perverse by the lower classes. Just the opposite attitude exists regarding coitus, which is considered normal among unmarried people and young folks among the lower classes but is not acceptable in the middle classes.

These are some of the reasons why statistics may vary with your own experience.

Genital tension and relief through masturbation are often stimulated by preoccupation with excretory and bladder function. Children are expected to repress such erotic desires, but they differ in their ability to do so. This is one of the reasons why the urinary functions of other people and of animals often interest and excite even grown-ups.

While telling me her dreams of being chased by horses, Janet, a high-school girl, was reminded of seeing a horse performing his natural functions.

I was about six, and no one else was watching so I

didn't have to feel self-conscious or anything like that. I had seen male horses before but this was the first time I'd seen one go to the bathroom in the street. I wasn't the least bit excited (sexually) but I was impressed by the tremendous power of the stream.

The idea of a horse "going to the bathroom" is no longer amusing to a teen-age girl whose reluctance to learn the correct pronunciation—she called it "yoonirate" instead of urinate—suggests an obsessive complex with bathroom activities.

Masturbation by compressing the thighs and other non-manual manipulation can take place during a dance and other close embraces. It brings on the same kind of flushed and moist skin, dilated pupils, rapid pulse, excitement, ecstasy and relief, or guilt and anxiety, as with boys. There may also be some wetting of the labia from a small amount of cervical or vaginal and vulval discharge. Such a wetting can be copious enough to run down the groin and thighs, especially during erotic dreams or in sex play.

Masturbation in the girl differs in several ways. Unlike males there is no concentrated ejaculation at the point of orgasm. However, some excess of moisture is usual. The need for some form of blotting or wiping especially after voiding requires some repetitious touching. Touching frequently contaminates the hands, which cannot always be washed immediately. Vicarious smelling of the hands for telltale odors is easily noticeable. In certain institutional wards where girls and women are often left undressed for many hours, especially after their showers, the masturbation is open and unabashed. So, too, is the practice of making nongenital overtures of love to each other, usually via embracing and oral kissing.

One of the chief differences is that most girls and women almost never talk about masturbation in any detail, not even to their therapists. They will confide almost everything else but are reluctant to pursue the subject even when given an opening cue. They have obviously been brainwashed even more thoroughly than boys on the "awfulness" of the practice of self-love for release of tension. In their attempt to repress or exile the pleasurable sensation as a form of self-punishment, frigidity is a common consequence.

Counseling management calls for verbalizing suggestions of various possible causes for the anxiety or other other presenting problems and casually including mention of various practices of self-love as a need to relieve tension. In children the habit can be compared with rubbing or scratching an itch, the cause of which is often quite unknown. In older patients, the theme of someone getting under their skin is something which they can usually understand and ponder during subsequent weeks. Reassurance against danger, mental and physical illness should be given, but if there seems to be causal connection, e.g. with leucorrhea, then this should be mentioned along with other possible factors. Medical clearance is usually indicated before assuming that the case is essentially a psychosomatic problem.

Cultural variations in mores, patterns and individual differences must be kept in mind constantly, if the counselor is to avoid the traps from his own restricted experiences. Here are two cases illustrating this need for an open mind.

Alex, a young man of thirty, while discussing this subject with me recently, blushingly reported, "I was almost twenty before I found out that you didn't have intercourse with a woman through her belly button . . . I sometimes get two or three wet dreams in a row, and they stimulate me into wanting intercourse. I feel guilty and selfish about masturbating . . . I guess that's where my superego takes a beating . . . How is it with an insane person?"

I told him that in the insane, it is the referee, or ego, that takes the beating and lets the superego, or conscience, and the id, the natural unrepressed instinct, fight it out with each other. Having answered his last question first, I was then in a better position to discuss the rest of his problem with him.

The following case of Marvin is self-explanatory.

I was born in "X" in the mid-South—the unhappy result of extramarital relations. I never saw my father. When I was four, my mother married a minister and moved to "Y." She was referred to as "Sis," and I grew up with several other illegitimate children of her sisters, all of whom looked on our grandmother as "Mother." I was ten when I discovered the truth, that my "big sister" was really my mother. I grew to hate Dotty, the illegitimate offspring of another "sister," because she was an intrusion into my private world and later because she

was a constant reminder of what I myself was—a
bastard.

My first attempt at sex relations occurred at nine or
ten years with Flo who lived across the street and who
was two years younger than I. I got an infection, could
not wear pants, and had to go about the house in a dress.
The humiliation kept me "virtuous" until I was fifteen
when my sexual partner was a girl of eighteen who
knew what it was all about.

As a child, I never masturbated although it seemed
a rather ordinary thing among boys of my own age.
Somehow it never occurred to me as a means of sexual
gratification. It used to make me very angry because
none of the fellows believed that I never "hit my fist"
or "beat my meat" as some of them called it. I had
always resented homosexuality as being ineffective and
degrading. I had always felt that opposite sexes were
created for their mutual satisfaction. I wanted children
so that I could rear them properly and give them advantages I felt I should have had—a mother and a
father, a home, and an education. I was determined to
be a success because, in my estimation, my father had
not been. I would show him and the world that I was
a superior man . . . I met Liz . . . We had several dates
and believed that we were in love with each other; but
one night when we attempted sexual relations, suddenly
and without apparent reason, I found myself impotent.
I could not have an erection. I was just turning seventeen.

Psychotherapy for Marvin was neither short nor easy, but it
was eventually successful.

HOMOSEXUAL PROBLEMS

Homosexual alliances are often well established during adolescence, but the problem of homosexuality is as old as life itself.
Prohibition against sodomy is specified in Deuteronomy 23:17;
so, too, is transvestism (the practice of dressing to impersonate
the opposite sex) in Deuteronomy 22:5.

It is well known that many mammals indulge in various erotic
activities between members of the same sex, especially when frustrated or in heat. Our children can see it daily in dogs on the

street or in their homes, and in cows on farms while riding along the highway.

Most adults can also remember some form of sex curiosity and also sex play, with one or both sexes, during their early childhood. Handsome boys are frequently offered bribes of candy, toys or money to play with older boys or men who do not dare risk rejection by an older partner. These are usually isolated experiments and do not leave emotional scars unless the child is unable to confide in someone he can rely upon. When the seducer is an unstable parent, especially with his or her own child, abuses are liable to follow. Psychopathic lying is more common in the adult, and child beating is a potential hazard.

Crushes to the point of some form of physical expression are the rule rather than the exception during puberty and early adolescence.

Ellis, quoting Kinsey and other reports, concludes an incidence of homosexuality amounting to between 3 and 4 per cent in the population of most nations and tribes in the world.* Kinsey's study included males who, for three or more years at some time in their lives, have been exclusively or mainly homosexual. He estimated an incidence of 8 per cent male "homos" in the United States, plus about half as many females. Kubie's comments on Kinsey are sobering, however, and should be studied by researchers.

None of this is surprising when we remember that the male adrenals and testes normally produce the hormones of both sexes, estrogens as well as androgens, and that the female adrenals also produce androgens. Androgens are increased during ovulation, making the normal female slightly more aggressive and sexually responsive at about the halfway mark in her menstrual cycle. The therapist who deals with the homosexual patient must therefore make exhaustive inquiry into the physical, endocrine and emotional endowment of his patient. He should also be well informed concerning the personality of other members of the patient's family. Most homosexuals come to treatment via the courts. In some states the overt practice of homosexuality

---

* Ellis, A.: *The Folklore of Sex.* New York, Institute of Rational Living (45 E. 65th St.), 1961.

is only a misdemeanor, while in others it is a most serious felony punishable by twenty years to life imprisonment. Treatment may be sought independently by the patient as a result of the threatened loss of his job or of a marital breakup. Many "homos" are also bisexual and most of them tend to discontinue their treatment just as soon as the legal, domestic or other pressure is released. They often rationalize their relationship as "the only true and understanding experience" in their lives or they shrug their shoulders—"I can't help it. It's a habit I'm unable to break."

Concurrent alcoholism or dependency on drugs is common in the sexual deviate because the "homo" is primarily a character or personality disorder like any other addict.

Effeminacy in earliest childhood is a strong predictor of future homosexuality; but counselors soon learn that sounding the alarm for such families is not always appreciated. Unconscious conflicts reinforce conscious rejection. Consequently the counselor has his work cut out for him and his best efforts are liable to be sabotaged.

Promiscuity and school dropouts are common in the "homo." So, too, are mothers who prolong their son's wearing of dresses and curls, saddle him with a girl's name and "protect" him from associating with normal boys who are "too rough." Parents who keep teasing with "too bad you weren't a girl" or who proudly encourage their daughters to be "tomboys" are psychologically just as destructive and may be equally unaware of their own unconscious conflicts. Yet their own complexes are often quite apparent to others.

Kolb confirms this principle with the reminder that homosexual patterns are seldom the result of biological failure. They usually develop when the child fails to acquire a wholesome identification with the parent of the same sex. Common causes include seduction, separation, and loss of inhibitions as a result of alcohol.[3]

Female homosexuals have a disturbed relationship with their mothers, but their relationship with their fathers is even worse.

In many countries all homosexual practices are considered to be illegal. In Britain, however, a recent act of Parliament no longer makes it an offense when homosexual acts are carried out in private between consenting adults. A similar change in attitude is beginning to take place in this country; but it is not yet a reality.

In the United States, homosexual offenders in institutions show higher education levels and better work histories among men than in women. According to Bluestone almost all female homosexuals (in institutions) show a triad of prostitution, addiction to narcotics, and homosexuality.[1] Female offenders typically show no motivation for change and very little anxiety or guilt. They therefore show little promise for treatment.

Best treatment is still prevention; and this holds true for both males and females. Counselors of parents can play an important role in these areas, especially because of the tendency of youngsters to rationalize their own weaknesses.

Here is one of my cases in which parental rejection produced a devotee of "the third sex."

Case of Earl

Mother told me she'd seen headlines in the local newspapers about my being fined for lewdness. The first thing she said when I got home was, "It's a good thing that not many people around here know my last name." She referred to the men and women at the factory where she works. They all call her "Joe."

I was stunned but I shouldn't have been and I said to myself, To heck with her. She's always been more worried about herself than she has been about me. That's probably why I turned to the boys in the first place. There never was any sex education for me or for my sister. Mother always liked to have people call her "Joe."

As for my father, he wasn't any better. The only time he even mentioned the subject was once when he found me in the bathroom. I was about twelve and all he said was that he'd never masturbated in his whole life. Nearly all the books I've read since then said it wasn't abnormal. Of course, I didn't believe him even then, but I feel awful to think he'd lie about a thing like that.

I told Earl that his father may have been telling the truth; but the youth insisted that it was purely a technicality and didn't matter anyway.

What I did with that boy may have been lewdness,

but when he put his arms around me and spoke my
name softly as though he thought it was a wonderful
name and kissed me, I just felt warm and happy all
over. My father never did that, and if Mother ever did,
it happened so long ago that I've completely forgotten it.

Many parents are ashamed to show affection for their children. A pleasant smile, a warm friendly greeting and a pat on
the back, or a handshake may be just as effective as a hug or a
kiss, if it is sincere, but should not be forced on him if it em-
barrasses him.

The case of Earl throws a lot of light on the so-called third
sex and how they get that way. As you have probably surmised,
homosexuals are made—they are not born that way. Hormones
may have something to do with the problem in some cases but
usually "gay" boys (and girls) are the result of parents who
reject their children as well as their children's sex. Such behavior
on the part of parents is usually a carry-over of their own complexes from previous generations. Consequently, psychotherapy
at this stage usually stands very little chance of success except
in peer groups and where legal pressures offer some degree of
motivation.

MANAGEMENT OF THE HOMOSEXUAL

Many specialists are reluctant to attempt counseling or
psychotherapy for the sexual aberrations because of discouraging resistance or because of their own aversions and anxieties,
but intensive long-range supervision can bring satisfactory results. Hypnosis *per se* is not necessarily contraindicated because
even without hypnosis both the homosexual and the heterosexual subjects can develop erotic fantasies involving their
therapist.

The counseling therapist should discuss these possibilities,
either in advance or as they arise. He should not promise too
much. He should also put less emphasis on the physical and
erotic aspects of the patient's problem. Instead he should em-
phasize the emotional transferences of the situation in terms of
dependency versus self-confidence. He strives for self-realization
by the patient as an acceptable person. When the word "homo-

sexual" intimidates the latent homosexual, a better approach to the subject is to refer to the universal and natural need for acceptance and *approval* by members of the same sex, as well as by members of the opposite sex.

Dangers to the counselor from predictable paranoid patients and potential lawsuits by unpredictable patients with character disorders are no greater with the homosexual as long as the operator keeps within the realms of his own field of competency. He must also recognize his own prejudices and fallibility.

Here are a few pointers to keep in mind concerning psychodynamics and psychotherapy for the homosexual patient. According to Oversey, *et al.*, the homosexual is lonely. He feels rejected at home and ostracized by society.[7] He therefore seeks his own kind, not only for sexual gratification but also for acceptance and dependency as well as for power.

Homosexuality may also be a symptom of a neurotic defense against a chronic castration anxiety. Fears of competing with father are mixed with fears of punitive rejection by mother. Homosexuality (in the male) weakens the patient's masculine identification. Recovery is indicated when he is pleased to discover that a female can make him feel like a man again.

Hadden reports voluntary efforts at heterosexuality after intensive group psychotherapy in peer groups.[2] However, some "homos" have been rendered impotent by overaggressive females and have turned to males for solace. Many of them are better off when they have studied their total situation and made peace with their families and themselves.

When they are contented with their chosen lot and are economically useful to society and when they no longer provoke gross indiscretions, a more realistic therapeutic program is indicated. This can be confined to supportive therapy with symptomatic relief of compensatory or displacement phenomena. The patient concentrates on learning to handle situational stress tensions as they arise, but a permanent change to heterosexuality may not be possible for a long time to come, especially in older patients.

One explanation for the psychological preferences of the male "homo" is the simple fact that the active fellator pays symbolic and literal homage to another male father figure or brother figure every time he gets down on his knees for a "blow" job. At the same time, the passive partner gets a psychological boost to his ego via reassurance of his virility. One of my patients used to brag about having a steady "clientele" of allegedly successful business executives stretching from coast to coast.

Looked at from another viewpoint, however, each participant is also playing a dual role. On the one hand, the fellator is now in a position of power. He can ruin his patron or customer by a single bite. On the other hand, the "powerful executive" is entrusting his penis, which should be a prized possession to the discretion of his hired lover, yet at the same time unconsciously daring him to do his worst. One must draw his own conclusions as to the mixture of emotions in both participants to the art of fellatio.*

Similarly with the lady who felt it necessary to tell me, "I want you to know I'm a Lesbian." She then qualified her statement with "but I'm strictly a fan-waver." This meant that she permitted only passive cunnilinctus while she pretended to be bored and waved a fan before her face. Since she had already told me of her resentment against her mother for allegedly driving her father to other women and drink, I merely asked whether she could think of any method that would be more effective in order to thumb her nose at women (meaning a mother figure) than to invite them to kiss her perineum, her vulva, and perhaps also her anus.

She promptly burst into laughter, "Why I just never thought of it in that way before . . ."

The therapy then proceeded to concentrate on her other disguises of emotional depression, of which her alleged frigidity and Lesbian leanings were only part of the presenting symptom complex, addiction to drugs, alcohol and compulsive smoking being the others.

The "homo" does not do well in mixed groups with non-"homos", but *group psychotherapy* for sexual deviates has been

---

* Analysts equate penis with nipple and semen with milk. Some degree of fellatio, like cunnilinctus, is also a natural part of normal love making in humans as well as animals.

found to be effective when using dual directors. When a male and female therapist work actively with such groups, some patients have been able to alter their ego ideals and to develop ego strength. Persistent and adequate motivation have paid off in terms of producing altered patterns and wholesome heterosexual adjustments in as many as 50 per cent of the younger patients. The series is small but offers promising possibilities for a heretofore pessimistic personality disorder.[2, 7]

SEDUCTION WORKS BOTH WAYS

Young people often seduce their elders. Too many parents believe that children and even teensters cannot be trusted with very much knowledge on the facts of sexual life. While it is perfectly true that some degree of overstimulation and preoccupation is unavoidable in sex education, it should also be kept in mind that lack of adequate knowledge may expose a child or teenster to mischievous or malicious playmates. Youngsters often make up stories and promote situations for the sake of gaining attention and prestige with their gangs or to forestall punishment for being out too late. While it is not commonly realized, it is also true that occasionally these unhappy children are the actual seducers of older people. Usually they conceal the truth so well in court that their pathological lies have sent innocent people, especially older men, to prison for crimes which were never committed. This is what happened to Richard.

Wendy Accuses Richard

Richard was a happily married young man who had given a lift to Wendy, an attractive girl of fifteen. He had seen her around town for several years and she seemed to know who he was. Furthermore, it was raining. The hour was rather late and the bus service infrequent. The delay from a flat tire did not help matters.

Wendy's father had reason to mistrust her in the past so she knew that he would not believe her story. Fearing that he would carry out his oft-repeated threats to send her to a reformatory as a "stubborn child," Wendy told her father that Richard had "molested" her. Actually, it was she who had tried to seduce him.

As her father confronted her with many questions, she amplified the accusation; and in court the jury believed her. Even after her father had died, the fear of punishment for perjury kept the girl from exonerating Richard who is now on probation but who has become suspicious and hostile even to his own nieces.

From your history books, you will recall more serious consequences in Salem Village, Massachusetts, a couple of hundred years ago when several young girls accused innocent people of bewitching them into hysteria. As already pointed out in a previous chapter, the warped personality of the seductive child can be recognized and must be handled in conjunction with intensive family therapy, especially with the parents.

Pornography is a substitute stimulus for those who are less bold in their efforts at seduction. Here is a common situation that you may run into.

Steve's drawings

Steve, a young junior high school student, drew a sketch of a nude man and woman having intercourse. He drew the man without a head, which may have eased his conscience. This sort of behavior often brings out a stormy response in parents and sometimes harsh accusations and dire threats are made. However, Steve's mother noticed that on the other side of the paper he had also drawn a sketch of a police car. Mother concluded that this indicated that Steve was aware of not doing the proper thing. She decided not to say anything to the boy, although she did report to her husband that she had found the picture in the boy's wastebasket. Father had been used to talking things over with Steve, so this time it was easy.

The boy promptly agreed that he had intended the drawings to be found, that he no longer needed to show off his superior knowledge, and that there were more acceptable subjects on which to practice his artistic talents.

As long as people will buy pornographic material the business will flourish. Surprisingly enough, too many adults leave such material around where young folks can have access to it. Unconscious seduction as well as rationalized negligence is a greater factor than most people care to admit. Careful and repeated inquiry into these areas by the counselor may elicit such practices as logical explanations for disturbing youthful preoccupations.

REFERENCES AND READINGS

1. BLUESTONE, H., *et al.*: Homosexuals in prison. *Psych J Soc Therapy,* 12:13-24, 1966. (Quoted in *Psychiat Dig,* Sept. 1966, p. 13)

2. HADDEN, S. B.: Male homosexuality: observations on its psychogenesis and treatment by group psychotherapy. *International Handbook of Group Psychotherapy.* Moreno, J. L., *et al.* (Eds.), New York, Philosophical Lib., 1966.

3. KOLB, L. C.: The psychoneuroses—personality disorders. In *Cecil Loeb Textbook of Medicine,* 11th ed. Philadelphia, Saunders, 1963, p. 1727.

4. KUBIE, L. S.: Influence of symbolic processes on the role of instincts in human behavior. *Psychosom Med, XVIII*:189-208, 1956.

5. KUBIE, L. S.: *Practical and Theoretical Aspects of Psychoanalysis.* New York, Int. Univs., 1950.

6. NOYES, A. P., and KOLB, L. C.: *Modern Clinical Psychiatry.* Philadelphia and London, Saunders, 1963.

7. OVERSEY, L.; GAYLIN, W., and HENDIN, H.: Psychotherapy of male homosexuality. *Arch Gen Psychiat,* 9:19-31, July 1963.

8. Frequency of suicide in U.S., *Roche Clinical Frontiers,* 5:2, 1968.

Chapter 10

SEX, VENEREAL DISEASE AND DRUGS

Does one have to be a physician in order to recognize the possible existence of venereal disease and to take proper steps toward treatment and prevention? The question practically answers itself, for even in biblical times the conditions were well known and prevention via bathing, isolation, and abstention were frequent admonitions (Levit. 15).

Since this is a book on counseling rather than medicine the dedicated counselor is referred to some of the texts listed at the end of this chapter, as well as to his family physician, dermatologist, urologist, or gynecologist for more specific questions and answers on the signs, pathology and management of venereal disease.

Some elementary and basic data on what was once politely called the "social disease" should be at the command of everyone who attempts to give personal and marriage counseling.

For instance, one should know that syphilis is caused by a microscopic spirochete, through a break in skin or mucous membrane, while gonorrhea comes from the gonococcus and attacks mucous surfaces including genitalia and eyes. Both are highly contagious, and both organisms travel in the bloodstream and affect other parts of the body.

Veneral disease is increasing on a global basis. It is also the most widespread adult communicable ailment reported in the United States. According to one report recent statistics reveal that venereal diseases infect more than a quarter of a million young Americans each year. Gonorrhea alone is fifty times more prevalent than polio. Legalized birth control information is now available to fifteen-year-olds in Denmark. It is also gaining ground all over the world in a belated effort to stem the population explosion.[1] Yet such birth control measures do not diminish the danger of venereal disease from unclean partners.

According to Trythall, by 1964, only thirty-seven states required premarital physical examinations as well as blood tests for both applicants. "Bootleg" marriage certificates, evading the law, are in widespread use.[13]

Visitors to Las Vegas are confronted with illuminated store front sidewalk "Chapels" and reminders that churches are open twenty-four hours a day for "complete" quickie marriages at bargain prices that include license, clerygman, organ, bouquet and witnesses and even a gift for the bride, all at an hour's notice.

WHAT TEEN-AGERS SHOULD KNOW ABOUT V.D.

V.D. is the medical designation for venereal disease, especially syphilis and gonorrhea. Unfortunately, technical details are not always easy to learn and are also too easily forgotten. Consequently, even physicians, pharmacists and nurses who once passed final exams on such matters usually need to refresh their memories from time to time.

Syphilis and gonorrhea are generally considered by medics to be the most common diseases affecting the sex organs, but there are other conditions which provoke anxiety and are not even reported to the family doctor. Among these are unsightly warts, trichomona vaginalis, pruritis (itching), crab louse (from contaminated clothing or toilet seats), furuncles, abrasions, and impetigo.

Some of these conditions are more obvious and are often self-treated with patent medicines. Some may exist without the patient's knowledge. Others, especially impetigo, gonorrhea and early syphilis ("Lues") are highly contagious. They also heal slowly and require special care.

Syphilitic sores (sometimes called "luetic") appear on the genitals between ten and forty days after exposure. They can also appear on other parts of the body, especially the lips from kissing an infected partner or on a finger through a crack or cut in the skin.

Untreated syphilis and gonorrhea can lead to serious mental and physical illness including blindness, mental disease, sterility, bone and joint deformity, and death from a damaged brain or heart.

Negative blood tests are not a full guarantee of immunity. Home remedies and self-treatment, even with the advice of a druggist, can be dangerous as well as inadequate for the problem.

When in doubt, consult your family physician first and then your dermatologist whose board of examiners certifies him as a specialist in both dermatology and syphilology—a fact which even medics frequently forget.

In gonorrhea the symptoms of "running-nose" type of genital discharge may appear within twenty-four hours following sexual contact. The maximum incubation period is two weeks, but the discharge usually appears between the third and fifth day in males.

Symptoms of gonorrhea, sometimes politely referred to as "gram-negative" or "Neisserian infection," also include urethral discomfort, urinary burning and frequency. Symptoms are generally less severe in the female and do not affect the vagina, but they do involve the urethra, introitus, cervix and ovarian tubes with consequent pelvic inflammatory disease.

Complications of gonorrhea include disease of the reproductive tubes (salpingitis and epididymitis), joints (arthritis), and eyes (conjunctivitis and iritis).

Diagnosis is not easy, even for the expert, but treatment can be simple if it is given promptly. One to three injections of penicillin (e.g. procaine penicillin G.) in aqueous suspension, intramuscularly (6 million U.) are usually sufficient, but in patients who are sensitive to penicillin, there are still the sulfanilamides, erythromycin, and streptomycin.

Only a few decades ago, none of these drugs were available. Instead, patients had to undergo long months to years of treatment. These were painful and the results were often unpredictable. Still newer drugs are in the making and may be available by the time you read this. Yet, despite the ease of modern treatment, the incidence of the disease is rising. Along with other emotional and behavioral problems and the exploding population, the courting of venereal disease is another complication of teen-age rebellion.

Follow-up care and repeated negative smears of urethral secretion are important before the patient can hope for dismissal as cured. However, inasmuch as negligence is a common accompaniment of irresponsible people, too many patients follow the rule, "out of sight—out of mind." They consequently stop treatment too soon; and most state laws are still inadequate to compel them to do otherwise.

It is easier to detect a gonorrheal infection in males, and with modern antibiotics it is also easier to treat. Natural discharges in the female may mask a coexisting gonorrhea which may then progress internally and result in salpingitis (infection of the fallopian tubes). Some cases of salpingitis can resemble appendicitis or a diseased ovary. Consequently, if untreated, sterility, a complicating peritonitis, and even death, are also possible risks.

Syphilis is not much easier as a diagnostic problem. Routine blood tests for syphilis are often neglected in doctors' offices and even in the larger hospitals. Tests for congenital syphilis may be overlooked until too late. Unfortunately, there is less diligence among too many clinics and specialists in seeking possible or latent gonorrhea and syphilis in the average woman than in taking smears for the detection of early cancer. Widespread publicity and popular education campaigns are responsible for the greater emphasis on cancer than on venereal disease—which again accentuates the need for each new generation to relearn the lessons of its predecessors.

General guides for laymen and therapists alike include the following:

1. Syphilis may mimic any disease and can easily mislead one. When in doubt, refer to a specialist.
2. Unlike the years before penicillin (World War II), treatment for both "Neisserian infection" (gonorrhea) and "Lues" (syphilis), at least in their early stages, is simple, inexpensive and brief.
3. Neglected syphilis can cause damaged bones, joints,

heart, and brains, as well as syphilitic offspring, and even death. Other signs may include a skin rash like the dermatitis of German measles, swollen lymph glands, sore throat, aches and weakness, symptoms resembling virus infection or the "flu," and sometimes patches of baldness. These secondary symptoms of syphilis also vanish, like the chancre, and they seldom reappear; but the untreated blood remains contagious.

4. The first syphilitic sore, chancre, or ulcer, which appears as early as several days and as late as several weeks after exposure, often heals without treatment—but healing does not mean that the disease has been cured.

5. The third, or latent, stage of syphilis may take as long as twenty years before the appearance of such signs of "tertiary syphilis" as optic neuritis and blindness, encephalitis and meningitis, syphilitic brain tumor, disease of the aorta, spinal cord, bones, joints and skin.

These are some of the dangers of inadequate treatment. Furthermore, a congenitally syphilitic child may appear to be normal and healthy for several years only to develop intellectual retardation, deformed teeth or nose, and defective hearing before his teens.

THE LURE OF DRUGS

People of all ages have been taking stimulants and tranquilizers since the beginning of time. Even our animal forebears have had long experience with roots and herbs and fermented fruits. Within the memory of your grandfather, people have resorted to aspirin, bromides, Jamaica ginger, vanilla extract, cough syrups, barbiturates, ephedrine, ether, alcohol, chloroform, liniments, paregoric, morphine, codeine, and many more remedies for common ills. They have also used them to produce varying degrees of overstimulation and euphoria for their depressions and to slow down excitement and agitation. Wine, in particular, has long been used by the ancients. In small doses it exhilarates and excites, while in large doses it stupefies and anesthetizes.

The teenster is attracted by drugs as a status symbol, or for profits, or by reports of being "turned on" and alerted to "hidden secrets" whereby he can share in "forbidden pleasures" including heterosexual and homosexual relations. To him there is no crime except in getting caught. He is quite right in claiming that one who has not had a "trip" (with LSD) or smoked "grass" (marijuana) cannot possibly share his experience; but to claim that one cannot possibly understand, or be justified in trying to suppress his use of drugs, is tantamount to saying that a physician who has not experienced delirium tremens has no business treating an alcoholic who is having an attack of D.T.'s.

The colloquial terminology of the drug users varies somewhat but, in general, "speed" refers to Methedrine®; "Bennies" to benzedrine (amphetamine stimulants); "hash" means hashish; "reefer," "stick" and "joint" refer to "grass" or "pot" (marijuana); "acid" and a "trip" refer to LSD; "smash" refers to heroin. From smoking cornsilk and banana skins to tobacco and opium is often a matter of a span of only a few years. Christometh and D.N.T., morning glory seeds and many more crowd the scene. Complications are the rule. Inert substitutes and dangerous dilutants are constant temptation to profiteers. Hustlers and prostitutes who start on marijuana soon graduate to some expensive drugs. The use of drugs was legal in India for two thousand years, until 1929, and only became generally outlawed by international agreement among sixty nations at about the middle of this century. However, a black market still exists in many parts of the world.

Chief dangers are the loss of normal, rational control, release of latent tendencies towards violence, homosexuality, indiscriminate heterosexual liberties as well as venereal disease, illegitimate pregnancies and suicidal behavior. If one feels he can fly, why worry about a window or porch being on the tenth floor? If one feels invincible, why be concerned over a mere truck or train that gets in his way? Physical and physiological needs are neglected. Loss of weight occurs because of loss of appetite and failure to eat properly. The need for money leads to concealment and dishonesty. Preoccupation with the growing habit leads to neglect of ordinary responsible pursuits. Use of impure diluted preparations leads to poison, sickness, neglect of health and death.

Treatment of drug addicts is difficult once the habit is underway. Court action is usually needed for confinement and supervision. Hospitals and clinics have a high rate of recidivism (repeaters). Early users can be reached by group therapy with their peers, the same as with homosexuals. They can also be taught to turn themselves on and off again by autohypnosis without any drug at all. Unfortunately, some of them already do this spontaneously from overdoses of drugs and are unable to control their reactions. With hypnotic techniques however, they are taught to remember previous hallucinogens; to derive psychedelic stimulation and fantasy within a controlled atmosphere; and to retain self-control at all times. General medical and nutritional care is, of course, indicated and encouraging results have been reported from methadone as an unconditioning agent for withdrawal, but the best treatment is prevention.

Prevention of addiction is also difficult. It becomes more so when parents abdicate their responsibility and have inadequate controls or minimal influence upon their children. When such a problem reaches the counselor he needs the full cooperation of the entire family, neighbors and community. The best preventive is the cultivation of a strong character and a well-rounded personality. When more satisfying outlets are available and there are also strong family ties, the lure of drugs becomes no more enticing than the lure of prostitution, chronic alcoholism, or a life of crime. Most of us think twice before seriously contemplating any of these dubious attractions.

The usual intensive recreational and other activities of a well-run boys' and girls' club or community center can go a long way to prevent most of the delinquencies of youth, provided they have concurrent parental and community support. Some churches and other organizations have been conducting activity groups for decades; but they seldom cover the crucial adolescent years adequately. This is partly the result of overemphasis on religious rituals and partly the result of young people leaving home, moving to other areas, and just plain rebellion against too many restraints and dull programs.

COUNSELING THE FAMILIES OF DRUG USERS

Reminders to parents need reinforcement and frequent repetition.

1. *Hallucinogens are not a new discovery.* People have been using drugs to stimulate, sedate and tranquilize for many thousands of years. Psychedelic reactions and other signs of drunkenness from fermented fruits and grains have been observed even in animals. Man's experiences with wine are also a matter of biblical record. Children experiment with aspirin, plastic bags, mock hangings, glue sniffing and cough syrups; and it is by no means rare for patients of all ages to prolong sickness that rewards them with paregoric, codeine, barbiturates, bromides, whiskey and even ether jags from frequent surgery for obscure pains.

2. *Rebellion is ancient history.* Recourse to drugs is only one of many expressions of the age-old conflict between adults and the teen-age generation. Other problems that seem to have been crowded off the front pages continue to be just as important. They include smoking, alcoholism, unmarried mothers, venereal disease, school dropouts, runaways, changes of name and religion, and other activities in defiance of laws and customs such as love-ins and mixed marriages.

3. *The entire family is involved.* The probability of successful management is enhanced when the entire family is involved. It diminishes sharply when only one or two take the trouble to do something about the problem. Family therapy is not a new innovation, except for some of the more specialized forms of psychotherapy. Family therapy goes back to ancient times where the entire council of elders, all blood relatives, and even the entire village community were very much involved. Saving face and acceptance by group and family proved to be magical incentives to conforming to standards and regulations. Sanctions, taboos, and exile or death were powerful therapeutic deterrents.

4. *Hospitality and integrity are priceless ingredients.* Houses must be made into homes. Parents must secure training in the arts of family living. This should have begun in their infancy; but it can be started now with adequate group activities where dynamics and remedies can be worked out with their peers.

5. *Responsibility must be shared.* Good direction is not enough. Families must share responsibility with the counselor as well as with the disturbed youth. Remedies must be adequate, promptly invoked, and firmly upheld. Since most of these youngsters are developing character disorders, an authoritarian approach with direct confrontation, and no nonsense tolerated, offers the best chance for success.

6. *Long continued therapy is usually indicated.* Therapy is usually needed for several years, although it is usually resisted by the patient.

7. *Prevention.* Prevention consists of careful attention to developing wholesome recreational opportunities and skills as early as possible in childhood.

REFERENCES AND READINGS

1. AYD, F. J., JR.: Contraceptives for teenagers? *Med Sci, 18*:20, Sept. 1967.
2. BARNOUW, E., and CLARK, E. J.: *Syphilis: The Invader.* New York, Public Affairs Pamphlets No. 24A, Columbia, 1955.
3. COLEMAN, J. S., *et al.*: *The Adolescent Society: The Social Life of the Teen-ager and Its Impact on Education.* New York, Free Press of Glencoe, 1965.
4. DUVAL, E. M.: *Facts of Life and Love for Teen-agers.* New York, Assn. Pr., 1956.
5. ELLIS, A.: *The Folklore of Sex.* New York, Institute of Rational Living, 45 E. 65th St., 1961.
6. HADDEN, S. B.: Male homosexuality: observations on its psychogenesis and treatment by group psychotherapy. In *International Handbook of Group Psychotherapy.* Moreno, J. L., *et al.* (Eds.), New York, Philosophical Lib., 1966.
7. HOLMES, D. J.: *Adolescent in Psychotherapy.* Boston, Little, 1964.
8. JACOBZINER, H.: *Attempted Suicides in Adolescence. JAMA, 191*:7-11, Jan. 4, 1965.

9. KIRBY, W. M. M.: Gonococcal disease. In *Cecil Loeb Textbook of Medicine*, 11th ed., Philadelphia, Saunders, 1963, pp. 196-200.

10. KOLB, L. C.: The psychoneuroses—personality disorders. In *Cecil Loeb Textbook of Medicine*, 11th ed., Philadelphia, Saunders, 1963, p. 1727.

11. MARIHUANA AND SOCIETY. Council on Mental Health. *JAMA*, *204*:1181-1182, 1968.

12. McDERMOTT, W.: Spirochetal infections. In *Cecil Loeb Textbook of Medicine*, 11th ed., Philadelphia, Saunders, 1963, pp. 349-362.

13. TRYTHALL, S. W.: The premarital law—history and survey of its effectiveness in Michigan. *JAMA*, *187*:900-903, 1964.

Chapter 11

DANCING AND OTHER ANTIDOTES
FOR TEEN-AGE TENSIONS

SOCIAL ASSETS OF DANCING

WHOLESOME FUN FROM DANCING AND PARTY GAMES is just as welcome to teensters today as when grandma was a girl. Boys and girls still use the dance to increase their social circulation, to be seen, to try out new dates and to show off their latest finery, new steps or other acquisitions.

What they most need and want are socialization, respect, and acceptance by their peers, with relative privacy, minimal restriction, popular music and simple refreshments. It is only when tensions are heightened by unreasonable controls or by parental indifference or social and scholastic rejections that the needs arise for tobacco, alcohol, drugs, sexual promiscuity and other misbehavior.

Many girls and boys may find close dancing too stimulating. They become extremely self-conscious. Perfumes, physical contact and rhythm may be too novel an experience for them. Erotic arousal is common; embarrassing as well as exciting. Consequently they may adopt protective devices such as refusing to dance or date at all. Keep this in mind when you hear people, especially young folks, expressing a dislike for dancing.

You might remind the self-conscious youth that his partner probably feels just as self-conscious as he does, not necessarily about sex but about the new experience, or about her clothes, or about her steps. You can then encourage less intimate dance routines for letting off steam, such as folk or square dancing or discotheque until self-confidence and controls have been developed.

Some girls discover that close dancing often gives rise to an urgency to visit the powder room. Such a displacement of sexual emotion to the bladder is normal, and the urinary urgency or frequency is no cause for alarm. Genital lubricants may be stimulated in both sexes, as a result of close physical contacts. These have been described above. They are normal but they may become relatively profuse and embarrassing. Counseling calls for a change of pace along with adequate information and reassurance.

The dance is also a place where many weaknesses other than the lack of terpischorean know-how will show up, such as fear of rejection, and habitually asking girls who will most likely refuse him.

Ricardo's Remembered Rejection

A nineteen-year-old youth was being taught autorelaxation to discover the causes for his self-consciousness and also as a remedy for recurrent seizures. At his second visit he was allowing his fingernails to grow and reported that he is using autorelaxation quite a bit to relieve his tensions. Ditto with his guitar.

> I'm really enthused since we started cutting down
> the medicine. I agree with you there's something disturb-
> ing me. I'm timid around people—afraid of them—don't
> know why.
> Q. How long?
> A. All my life I guess.
> Always shy—very self-conscious. Playing in the band
> is a tremendous outlet for me.

On probing the past via the clenched fist displacement technique, he first closed his left fist, indicating recall of an unhappy event. His eyes filled with tears, and then he squeezed his dominant fist as a neutralizer and antidote. He smiled and shook his head in mystified disbelief.

> It's something that happened a long time ago. Kind
> of bugs me whenever I think of it. There was this school
> dance—7th or 8th grade in the War I Memorial Hall.
> A record hop. There was one girl I liked very much—
> Liza. It's pretty ridiculous. I thought she liked me—but
> she really didn't care for me too much. Liza had this
> girlfriend, Pat—nice but fat. Pat came over and said,
> "Look, I want you to go over and ask Liza to dance.
> She's dying to dance with you and she's crazy about
> you." It was what I wanted to hear so I believed it.
> Pat talked me into going over; and then Liza *in
> front of everyone* said, "I hate your guts." I walked out
> —but it bothered me quite a bit.

He heaved a deep sigh but remained in a light trance. I suggested that it was Liza who had cold feet, otherwise she would not have gotten Pat to betray him; that it was Liza who was envious of him and had no guts; that she had used "hate" with ambivalence because she feared *love*; and that "guts" means confidence and strength which she coveted, but which he obviously had and still has, since he was now dating more successfully. He was advised to reevaluate Liza's insecurity and Pat's perfidy.

Now, three years later, he is engaged to marry someone he understands; and his seizures are under control with minimal medication.

The counselor should remind the insecure teenster that he may be much more acceptable to girls who are less attractive. Teach him to look for more desirable qualities in a girl than a pretty face, stunning gown, or a bold display of bosom or other makeup artistry. Encourage him to rely on other means of building up his own prestige and self-confidence than by parading an attractive date before his friends. The right kind of girl is not necessarily the best looking nor the most popular.

The plainer looking girls are often a better choice because they have had to learn how to be dependable as well as talented and gracious. The pretty girl, like the handsome boy, usually receives much more adoration than she can use—just by doing nothing more than spending a lot of time on her appearance.

Although many beautiful girls are also gentle and hospitable and can say "no" without hurting a boy's feelings, there are many more who are still in the learning stages. They just do not know how to refuse graciously.

LEARNING SOCIAL GRACES

What does one say when a girl becomes very much upset because a boy has made an offensive pass? Here is how one parent was able to reduce resentment, resolve hostility and cultivate a more wholesome attitude in her teen-age daughter.

Elementary, but universal psychotherapeutic procedures were used. First, mother listened attentively, then she asked for more information, then she encouraged her daughter to express how she felt about the situation, and, lastly, she explored the situation for some other explanation that might fit the facts. In this way, the whole problem got a suitable airing and the girl's ruffled feelings got an opportunity to become unruffled and soothed. It all boils down to whether a pass from a special boyfriend should be interpreted as an insult or a compliment.

Case of Annette

"Well, Annette, how do you feel about Tommy now?"

Annette's snort of disgust was expressive, if not elegant. Mother persists and spars for an opening. "But he did take you to the prom."

"Are you taking sides with him against me?" [The girl is defensive.]

"Certainly not, dear, but haven't you wondered why he did it?"

"Well, it couldn't have been because he liked me. Or are you hinting that I should have let him paw me all over? If so, I must say I'm very much surprised at your change of attitude." [Projection.]

"That's not what I'm saying at all, and you know it." [This rebuke had been deliberately solicited by Annette in order to appease her conscience, but Mother avoids the trap and tries to hold her temper.]

"Well, then, why are you taking sides with him?" [Annette is being obtuse in order to cover up her own ambivalence.]

"I merely asked whether you've given any thought to his feelings, but if you'd rather not discuss it now, let's just drop it." [Strategic offer to retreat]

"Oh, all right, I didn't mean to blow up, and I'm sorry if I sounded fresh, but believe me, it's an experience I don't want to go through again in a hurry, I can tell you that!" [The ice is broken and the girl yields a little. Mother honors the concession with moral support by agreeing with her.]

"I don't blame you in the least, dear, and that's exactly why I thought we might discuss the incident, if it's agreeable to you, that is." [Mother also has offered an out, for the present.]

"Okay, Mom. Shoot."

[Mother now tries an indirect approach.] "Well, let's suppose he had asked Jenny to the prom instead of you."

"That big fat slob?"

Mother ignored Annette's indignation and continued, "But *suppose* he had asked her instead of you."

"Well?"

"Well, would you have felt complimented or insulted?"

"What a question! Insulted, of course!"

"Now suppose you and Jenny were both at a party, and all the others were playing post office."

"Kid's stuff." [Annette's expression was eloquent.]

"But just suppose."

"All right, I'm supposing." [The contrast with Jenny has boosted her ego and she can now afford to be a little indulgent with mother.]

"Now suppose Tommy kept calling for Jenny's number and never called for yours at all."

Annette could not think of an answer to that one, so her mother continued, "Would you then feel complimented or insulted?"

"You mean when a boy wants to make a pass at a girl he's doing her a favor?" [Annette has already gotten her mother's message but is not yet ready to admit it.]

"No. Not at all. But would a boy want to make a pass at a girl for whom he didn't care the least bit?" [Deepening insight shows in the answer.]

"Well, I've wanted boys to kiss me, if that's what you mean, but . . ."

"But you've been smart enough not to show it?"

"Something like that."

"Girls are usually wiser and more mature in such matters, and boys are inclined to be somewhat impetuous."

"You can say that again, Mom."

"I was only trying to point out that his desire to make a pass at you suggests that he likes you much more than you thought possible."

"Humph. Well . . . maybe you're right, but that doesn't excuse the rest of his behavior, does it?"

"No, it certainly doesn't My point is that on first impulse you don't really know how the boy feels about you. Furthermore, he was confused too; and he needs time to think things over. And I'm sure that when he gets a chance, he'll probably apologize for it."

"Oh, he's already done that. I forgot to tell you. But . . ."

"But you slapped him down again?" [Mother now knows why the girl is so upset. Annette is angry with herself even more than with Tommy.]

"Sort of. I was still mad and I hung up on him."

Mother kept silent as she let the girl's thoughts reshape themselves. A few minutes later she asked, "How do you think you'd handle the situation now?"

"Tell him nothing doing, he's got the wrong girl for that sort of thing? Right, Mom?"

"Well, that's one way of handling it, but how would that make him feel?" The girl pondered the question, then she brightened up.

"Oh, I see what you mean. Still a slap, huh?" Mother smiled.

"Okay, Mom, tell me how you would handle it."

Mother resorts to acting out her answer. "All right, dear, I'll try, although it's been a long time since I was your age. Now let's pretend I'm you and you're Tommy. Now you do to me just what he did to you." Annette was startled and embarrassed.

"But, Mother! I couldn't!"

"Well, then, just start to do it . . . and you can put your hand on my shoulder instead." [The substitution of shoulder for bosom proved reassuring, inasmuch as a growing girl must also learn to put aside childish desires for the breast and to substitute arms and an embrace for the more intimate routine of a hungry baby at feeding time.] As Annette tried to steal a kiss, Mother deftly turned her head so that the girl's lips touched her cheek instead of her lips. Then as one hand reached toward the woman's shoulder she seized it firmly in her own hand and gently lowered it to her waist. Still holding on to the girl's hand, Mother whispered softly into Annette's ear, "Please, Tommy, don't."

Annette looked at her mother incredulously. "You mean to say that just holding onto his hand would do it?"

"That and placing his hand on your waist."

"But would that keep him in check?"

"I think so. Perhaps you might try it next time and see."

Annette showed open disbelief in her face but could find no words.

Mother smiled and asked, "Do you feel like experimenting with me further?"

"Well, no, but . . . but shouldn't I resent his taking such a liberty with me?"

"Yes, if you think he really wanted to embarrass you."

"Well, I don't think he dislikes me that much, but . . ."

"Don't you see, honey, he's used to holding you about the waist during dancing. So by holding onto his hand you not only restrain him, but you can also direct it to a less intimate part of your body. When he dances with you he has you in his arms. You know, you aren't the only one who can daydream during a situation like that."

Annette was very thoughtful as her mother continued to talk.

"Also, by keeping his hand against you, you show him that you still accept him, that you still like him, and that while you do not play in the way he wants to, you are not offended. You have saved his face and avoided hurting his pride. The slap could have been avoided, and he would have admired and respected you all the more for not humiliating him."

"He looked as though he could have killed me!" said Annette, smiling ruefully.

"Isn't that the way they used to challenge someone to a duel?"

"Why, yes! Insult them by slapping the face with a glove! Well, what do you know!"

Mother said no more but was deep in her own reminiscences as Annette ran out of the room and called back, "Quite the psychologist, aren't you?"

A moment later Mother heard her daughter telephoning to Tommy and heaved a sigh of relief. It had been something of an ordeal for her, too, but she is gradually becoming more accustomed to this method of dealing with her daughter's social and personal problems.

Breasts Are Symbolic

The bosom is a universal symbol of mother and food. But to the small child, feeding time is also loving time. Loving time means strong arms and a warm embrace, hugs and kisses, pleasant talk and sounds and relief not only from hunger but also from boredom. Boys are not the only creatures who never seem to have had enough of this great emotional and physical comfort. Girls too may have been given the short end of the deal, especially when their mothers have refused breast feeding, have been ill, or have gone out to work, or died far too soon.

The result of too early deprivation of the mother relationship causes the child to overvalue the bosom in his future relations with girls and women although at times he may suppress this interest quite successfully. This suppression is also what our respectable daughters are expected to accomplish lest they be accused of having homosexual leanings. Consequently, the girl often does to the breasts (others as well as her own) what she has already learned to do with the dangerous attraction of male genitals. She represses her natural interests. She rejects them as necessary but unattractive embellishments which must be tolerated but not encouraged. She may subsequently become sterile as well as frigid; homosexual as well as alcoholic or a drug addict. She will require a good many years of happy marriage before she learns to overcome this attitude. Even then, she will repeat her mother's pattern—preferring sons and neglecting daughters.

Meanwhile, painful leftovers from her own teens may cause, in some mothers, a feeling of unrest and discomfort. Perhaps there was a similar experience and the unexpressed wish that she had handled the situation differently. Sometimes she can talk the matter over with her husband and in this way recover her self-confidence. Still we must keep in mind that the mere mention of the word "sex" as well as the subject itself can be provocative of anxiety in a listener or reader. Much reflection and discussion will help to overcome the discomfort or resentment that often arises when one is exposed to a study of intimate problems.

Other Defense Measures

For the obstreperous youth who cannot take no for an answer, firmer measures are obviously necessary. Boys are expected to learn to fight their own battles. Our modern girl should also be taught how to defend herself. A girl's wrestling, judo or even karate class is very much in order. It may well serve her better than tennis or basketball. Her best asset, however, is the reputation which she builds for *meaning "no"* when she says "no," and for refusing to date unknowns or to go out with boys who have "fast" reputations. Flattery, expensive gifts, beer, cocktails and heavy petting are well-known forerunners to trouble which girls should be taught to discourage.

Instead, encourage your girl to be a leader in personal matters. Teach her how to say "no" graciously but show her also how to be a competent hostess, how to organize a party, how to have fun in a crowd, how to protect herself, how to relax, how to avoid single dates, and how to make good use of her spare time when she does not have a date.

In order to prevent disturbingly close contacts, young folks may become seclusive and difficult to manage. As already mentioned, they avoid dates, concentrate on studies, or overdo at work, sports, reading, television, or music. Sometimes they pick a quarrel with close friends or family, and they often show hostility to their teachers and even to the counselor to whom they have come for help.

INSIGHT AND SELF-REMEDIES FOR TEEN-AGE ILLS

The following collection of recommendations from anonymous adolescents, whom I have been teaching over the years, tells its own story of positive values to offer comfort to the counselor for teen-age tensions.

> The period of adolescence opens doors to the independent pathways of life. We must live our own experiences and learn to be responsible for what mental equipment nature has endowed us with.
>
> The eternal question of sex creeps out, and the laws of convention form a barrier that cannot be crossed unless one bars himself from accepted public standards.
>
> We want to be heard in discussions of family affairs; and be agreed with, if possible.
>
> We want to choose our own friends and have reasonable privacy to entertain them at home.
>
> We want parents not to be condescending, cross-examining, or keep harping on past mistakes. They must not pry or gossip—especially when we have given them our confidence.
>
> We need a clothes budget and an allowance with freedom to shop.
>
> We need an opportunity to learn for ourselves the value of acquiring reasonable hours, morals and other reasonable habits.
>
> There are many firsts at this time of our lives: choice of career, schools and new friends, going away from home for the first time, first loves and dates, first jobs, and first big mistakes. Some parents, like some judges, should disqualify themselves sometimes, from giving advice, on the grounds of prejudice or conflict of interest.

What adolescents want is simply expressed in the following short and casual prayer written by a girl while waiting for one of her appointments with me. It is a plea for someone to depend on, someone who knows more than she does, and someone to listen.

A Girl's Brief Prayer

Dear God,

I never quite know what to say. It's like I don't know my own feelings.

Firstly, please forgive me for my sins; then guide me. Please, *never leave my side*. I would be forever lost.

Help me not to hurt others in search of my own happiness.

Thanks for listening. I'm worried.

Bonnie

REFERENCES AND READINGS

1. Duval, E. M.: *Facts of Life and Love for Teen-agers*. New York, Assn. Pr., 1956.

Chapter 12

SPECIAL HELP FOR STUDENTS

A KINESTHETIC MEMORIZING TECHNIQUE

THIS IS A MOTION FEELING PROCEDURE which should be learned during early years in grade school. However, it will be found helpful for teensters and adults who have learning conflicts.

It is an extension of the established rule for utilizing as many senses as possible by reading aloud while writing the problem at the same time. The technique is applicable to a lecturer who wants to draw a sketch or diagram accurately and "off the cuff," or for a student who wants to memorize a difficult formula or how to spell a complicated word, or to a field officer who is required to memorize a map. The procedure is simple.

Draw or write the sketch, diagram, or word as accurately as possible and as large as possible. Then trace each line, form, or letter carefully with the index finger of the writing hand using hand, forearm, arm and shoulder in the process. Speak the letter or number aloud each time it is traced. Be sure that the tracing is accurate. "Keep the finger on the chalk track" is what one would say to a child. Trace and speak the letter or number simultaneously, and repeat the procedure at least five times in careful succession. This uses sight, sound, speech, touch and movement of the tracing hand, forearm and arm. It also involves a much larger area of the cerebral cortex, than when trying to memorize by using vision alone.

After sufficient tracings, erase, draw or write in (from memory) the same word, figure or formula, and then compare with the original. If unsatisfactory, repeat the procedure with ten successive tracings. Try it yourself on a simple cartoon. The results will astound you. Here is an example of how it was used on a third grader.

Everett, aged nine, was having difficulty with spelling. The words "picture" and "pitcher" were especially confusing. In fact, he could not even pronounce them correctly. On the blackboard he drew a sketch of each and was coached in their correct pronunciation. The teacher then wrote each word separately in large twelve-inch well-formed letters.

Everett then began to trace each letter of the word carefully with his writing index finger. He spoke the name of the letter aloud each time, and traced the entire word, "pitcher," five times in succession. Next, he was directed to write with chalk over the now nearly obliterated original word and again speak each letter as he wrote. He also had to speak the word before and after each tracing and writing: "Pitcher, p-i-t-c-h-e-r, pitcher."

After five tracings and a sixth writing, he erased the word and wrote it correctly from memory, the eighth recording. Finally, he was ready to turn around and spell the word to the class, correctly and without hesitation. The procedure was repeated for the word "picture." The entire demonstration required less than ten minutes and impressed a score of his classmates as well as several visiting teachers.

Two weeks later, when the lesson was put to a test and the words were again required of him, Everett hesitated in the oral spelling; but, while doing so, his right hand was seen to be involuntarily tracing the proper sequence of the letters. As a result, he quickly corrected himself. However, he showed no hesitancy in *writing* the words correctly; and this time, voluntarily added a very creditable drawing of each article, something he had been practicing on his own.

By tracing one syllable at a time one can learn just as quickly such treacherous combinations as "Mississippi," "Massachusetts," "electroencephalogram," "phenolsulphonephthalein"; complicated formulae in mathematics, chemistry, electronics and physics; historical dates; sketches; and diagrams. Moreover, once learned *by this technique of adding motion feeling to sight and sound,* the lesson seldom requires repetition.

OTHER HINTS FOR STUDY AND EXAMINATIONS

Guidance counselors and teachers are usually well informed on organizing programs and improving study habits. Such procedures as tackling the most difficult assignment first; breaking up study periods with exercise, fresh air and brief recreation; the use of visual aids; elimination of distractions (especially television); checking off accomplishments; and brief reviews before breakfast may not be popular, but they are most effective.

Frequent reviews are fun and possible only when one keeps up with his daily assignments, but too many youngsters consider the job an ordeal rather than a privilege. An occasional reminder that the student is free, after he becomes sixteen, to quit his job and go to work at something else is usually far more effective than constant nagging about neglecting his schoolwork. One also needs to be sure that the anxious parent is not compensating for his own scholastic negligence or inadequacies.

However, here is one more formula which will endear the pupil to his teacher. The orderly sequence of an answer will also simplify the problem for the student.

Three Parts of a Definition

Answers usually come in threes. Whenever a student attempts to answer a question, he will do well to remember the three principal parts of a definition: (1) the *name* of the article or subject to be defined; (2) the *general classification* to which it belongs; and (3) the *distinguishing characteristics* that differentiate that particular article or subject from all others in its group or class. For instance, What is psychology?

> (1) Psychology is [not "It," or "It's"] (2) the scientific study [not "something" or "something to do with"] (3) of the mind, or of mental activities, and/or behavior.

Try the question on your family and discover how many people will answer the question with, "Well, it's got something to do with what's going on in your mind or your head." Such an answer would apply equally well to a neurosurgical problem, or certain x-rays, or psychoanalysis; but it would not clarify the problem for the student.

Similarly, "A chair is something to sit on" might satisfy a young child; but for one who is just learning the English language, one would have to start with "A chair is an article of furniture . . ." and then give the distinguishing characteristics which differentiate the chair from a bench, sofa, box, bed, and so on.

Many years ago a crucial college chemistry examination question called for a discussion of "Eutectics." At first, I had not the vaguest idea; but I did recall something about *eutectic mixtures.* Remembering my high school English teacher's admonition about the three parts of a definition saved the day for me. I guessed that the term referred to the subject of eutectic mixtures and then proceeded to define them in a convincing manner.

The actual definition of eutectics has no relevance here. The important point is that when students are confronted with technical distinctions they can avoid panic by remembering simple rules.

Fortunately, such subjects as the essentials of electronics, molecular physics, chromosomes, outer space nagivation and even techniques of modern surgery are no longer confined to a few. Excellent visual aids on selected television programs have aroused popular interest. Animation and repetition are reaching greater numbers of viewers. The art of teaching and the pleasures and excitement of learning have received a new lease on life. They offer an encouraging balance and powerful antidote to the less desirable attractions; much as good literature has always won out over trashy paperbacks and lurid "comics."

Letter Association Technique

Although listed as "New" by Dengrove[3] this is actually an old but little used variation of the demand bid for the first five letters that come to mind. The school counselor and others can readily make a game of it.

The student is requested to reflect on a particular problem. He is then asked to relate it to the last occasion when he experienced a similar or identical complaint. If he can think of none, he is then asked how far back in his life he does remember. Since most of the answers to our dilemmas are already floating around in our subconscious minds, it is now merely a matter of reconstruction.

The student is invited to ramble on with seemingly irrelevant associations pertinent to the time he does recall. This automatically releases some repressions, even though nothing positive or constructive is apparent at the time. It also temporarily takes the pressure off him for an immediate resolution of the conflict.

The student is then requested to give the first letter that comes to mind; then the second, third, fourth and fifth. He is then invited to make "free" or permissive associations of words with each letter. Usually, this will release some "forgotten" (repressed) material that will furnish clues to the origins of his problem.

This is also a modification of the familiar association formula by which medical and nursing students used to memorize the twelve pairs of cranial nerves:

> *On old Olympus towering tops,*
> *A fat armed girl picked snowy hops.*
> (Olfactor, optic, oculomotor, trochlear, trigeminal, abducens, facial, acoustic, glossopharyngeal, pneumogastric (vagus), spinal accessory, and hypoglossal.)

The technique for a self-made demand bid on the first three or five or more letters that come to mind is readily applicable for students during examinations, especially when the demand is preceded by brief autorelaxation.

WHEN NEGATIVE EMPATHY IS SELF-SERVING

Here is a common blind spot that affects students, teachers and counselors alike.

Empathy is a *feeling relationship* which also implies some degree of sympathy. One may feel sympathetic without any emotional obligation to do anything about it. The counselor and teacher, however, is experiencing empathy only when he understands the student's problem, has his own emotional reactions under control, and still tries to do his best to help even when he does not agree. This is quite an order; and one which most people have difficulty in filling. One effective method for its management is best illustrated in the following case:

Von's Negative Empathy

One of my students had been hung up for several years on a teaching manual which he was preparing for his assistants in a hospital. The particular chapter was tentatively entitled "Empathy in the Physiotherapist." We got nowhere in private conferences, so the problem was put to his regular group.

One member of the group, a professor who was visiting from another department, suggested that Von collect his notes, arrange them by topics, and bring them in for us to hear. Von continued to procrastinate. On several successive meetings Von gave impromptu talks to the group, without his notes; and on each occasion his grasp of the subject and presentation improved; but still no manuscript. I decided that it was time to give him a shove.

V. H. (catalyzer and recorder for the group) asked him point blank whether there has been any time in his life when Von had felt that he needed empathy and did not get it. He said he did not; but he did admit that the past patient with whom he had had difficulty had reminded him somewhat of his wife! This association had been worked out a month earlier* with no apparent change in his blocked manuscript except that he was willing to pursue it in group.

I then suggested a more indirect approach via the calendar. Von was asked how far back he could remember; but all he could think of was a toy rooster, an old piano crate, and crawling under a boxcar to get down to look for his father. His rambling was cut short by a request for specific associations with sickness. It was then discovered that when he was in college he had to be hospitalized with a football injury to his knee. He kept insisting that he did not remember whether his parents came to visit him; but finally he realized that all the other fellows in the college infirmary had visitors, while he had none.

It should be no surprise that when Von's mother became ill he did not make any particular effort to visit her too often. By the end of the two-hour group conference he volunteered the thought that "She didn't give too much sympathy. Maybe I was sort of paying her back."

On the following week Von beamingly reported that he had collected his papers and had a first draft for his manuscript.

N.B. It is well known that counselors are overloaded and, therefore, too busy for any kind of prolonged analysis. What they can do, however, is to make each brief contact count as much as possible in terms of building rapport and suggesting productive introspection on which the student can work in between his conferences.

---

* See Chapter 3. When the counselor is subjectively involved.

HINTS FOR COACHES AND SPECIALISTS

Great Expectations

By definition the athlete is a performer who symbolizes the epitome of physical fitness. He is presumed to possess a sound mind in a healthy body as the basic requirement. The familiar inverted triangle of the Y.M.C.A. is a dramatically symbolic escutcheon. Since faith and morale are equally essential for a mature and stable personality, along with "Mind" and "Body," it is appropriate for the third side of the triangle to be labeled "Spirit."

From ancient times the survival of mankind depended upon the effective combination of physical, intellectual and emotional or spiritual fitness. Primitive tribes sometimes chose leaders for special skills, outstanding spiritual values, or for their intellectual genius or physical prowess (Goliath); but they depended upon those who are well balanced, mature, strong, capable, cunning and wise (David). Then, as now, competent potential leaders were few in number but champions and victors were no less important and popular. Popular idols like other champions, usually demand a great deal of themselves. Like their admirers, they consequently have great expectations.

The Coach

The coach seldom inherits his position. He has to earn it. He is generally a "nice guy" who has the interests of his charges at heart. He has been through the mill. He has also had his innings with other coaches, some of whom were older and wiser, while others were less competent or more difficult. He is usually a good sport, was fairly successful and often popular in school, frequently has had his choice of the prettiest and smartest of the available girls, and, in general, enjoys the emotional security of membership in an elite segment of his society. Because of all this he may have forgotten his own hardship years and be impatient with his athletes, or he may go to the opposite extreme and be like an overindulgent parent—provided his contract is not in constant jeopardy for failure to produce a winning team.

In some schools, the athlete and his coach may feel like the low man on the totem pole. Consequently, when academic courses are stressed, the athlete is faced with extra pressures from all sides. Too frequently his best is not good enough—simply for lack of sufficient hours in the day rather than for lack of intelligence. One of the responsibilities of the coach is to try to balance these pressures without adding to them and without sacrificing the individual for the glory of the team. It is a nice trick but far from easy, especially when accidents, failures, sickness and absenteeism build up parental as well as faculty opposition.

Theoretically, the coach or other specialist expects maximum efficiency from the given capabilities of each of his charges—no more, and no less. Yet the coach is only human, and like any normal human being he usually has favorites without realizing it. Just how objective can one be when he has to deal with a prima donna on the team? Can he be rationalizing when he assigns, for example, fifty extra push-ups for all members of a team "as a warm-up" or perhaps as a penalty for a general letdown of efficiency? The average leader recognizes this failing quite readily when he sees it in others but seldom admits it in himself.

The Parents

Parents often wage a perpetual war between mind and body. This is commonly seen in their efforts at weight control or in pressures they put on youngsters for higher marks or for music lessons. Sometimes a father rationalizes his own failure to continue his schooling or to succeed in athletic activities by concentrating on sports. More often his "interest" is expressed as a vicarious observer or fan, rather than by active participation with his offspring. Whether in sports, scholastics, music or hobbies, a parent frequently tries to live his life over again. He unconsciously identifies with the boy (or girl) and often pushes his hapless offspring into activities that are beyond his capabilities and interests. Friction in the family may also come from an overprotective mother, aunt or grandparent who tend to take sides with the youth. All this adds to the tensions. Accumulating pressures produce divided loyalties in the frustrated youth. Youngsters need understanding and acceptance far more than the direction, regimentation and great expectations with which they are surrounded.

Parental obsessions over racial, religious, social and financial status are often the real stake in their overambitious standards for their children; but these factors may be disguised by rationalizations which lead them to oppose sports as a waste of time, an interference with studies, an excuse to neglect home chores or remunerative jobs, and an activity that is "dangerous." The spectre of a crippling injury may be indelibly imprinted on an adamant and opposing mother and thence onto her children. At the same time, the triumph of an Olympic Decalon may be in the nature of a Holy Grail to an ambitious father whose offspring does not dare to fail. Some teen-agers are thrown into deep depression, and suicide may be chosen in preference to facing a parent, e.g., with nothing worse than a poor report card.

Reasoning and explanation to such a parent gets you nowhere. Inevitable accidents and injuries to others, if not to their own offspring, naturally lend strong support to their arguments. Moral support for the youth, and sometimes joint conferences and talks with both parents may afford some relief; but the coach and the overambitious parent are not likely to become good friends.

Whatever the parental attitudes and reasons, their prejudices, both positive and negative, will inevitably influence the youth himself. If he defies his parents, he may feel more guilt than he cares to admit. Yet even when he obeys them, he can also build up more resentment than he realizes; and the guilt will bother him just the same, for he can hate them for abusing their authority and he can also hate himself for not standing up for what he believes is right. Coaches who are also parents, often have the same problem that other professionals do in trying to understand why their offspring do not follow in their footsteps.

The Athlete

According to the *Encyclopaedia Brittanica** competitive sports go back to pre-Egyptian times. Professional Greek athletes were first introduced at Rome several hundred years B.C. They increased in popularity after Augustus instituted the public games

---

* Eleventh edition, pp. 846-848, 1911.

and finally supplanted the gladiators. Guilds or unions of athletes each had their own temple, treasury and exercise ground. Membership was almost entirely Greek and was recruited from the lower orders as a means of livelihood. Though they ranked above gladiators and actors, they were socially beneath the dignity of a Roman. Nevertheless, in earlier times, Romans of good birth competed for glory without material gain.

To this day there still exists the same social distinction between the "amateur" and the "pro"; but collegiate participation in regular athletic sports dates back only to the beginning of the nineteenth century in England while in America the revival began only after the Civil War.

Today's athlete, like other performers, both male and female, is essentially a normal person with a normal need for self-fulfillment and normal satisfactions from trying to do what he likes to do. In general, athletes and performers of both sexes are usually more aggressive, enjoy competition, have a need to win, like to exhibit or show off, appreciate approval and applause, and adopt an informal style of dress and haircut.

The athlete, however, has the same inner doubts and anxieties as anyone else. Most of these reflect the misgivings and prejudices of his parents or the important people in his life. In addition he compares the size and shape of his body, the slight prominence of breasts or genitals, or paucity of hair in strategic places, the quality of his voice, and the relative importance of his other assets, both physical and intellectual. In consequence he inevitably builds up a group of defenses and a series of "musts" that may assume compulsive proportions. This is especially true for the tall girl who has limited social opportunities and has to overcompensate in other ways.

In such compulsive cases, efforts of the coach or others to slow him down or to diversify his activities from muscle building and weight lifting, for example, to such skillful arts as wrestling and to such teamwork activities as baseball, may prove futile. The short boy may feel a need to prove himself at least the strongest if not the biggest. The tall one may not even try to excel in anything.

General Procedure

The management of problems of athletes, entertainers and specialists follows conventional outlines for counseling, guidance, psychotherapy, suggestion, group discussions, psychodrama and relaxation techniques. Most coaches use nearly all of these techniques at one time or another. Here is one, submitted by one of my students (K.M.) in a summer course I once gave on Psychological Aspects of Physical Training in Athletes. In effect, it consisted of removing pressure to heal a stomachache and neutralize a conflict before a swimming race.

Ruth's Nervousness

Fourteen-year-old Ruth had won many swimming events and was considered the best one hundred yard free styler in her division in the New England area. She was also a worrier, especially just before a meet and even when competition was negligible.

Ruth: Who will I be swimming against?

Coach: Don't think so hard about it. I've gone over the competition with you and we both know that you will be able to "bring home the bacon," for us. [*We're depending on you!*]

Ruth: I hope so.

Coach: Don't let it get at you, Ruth. I know you want to do the job. But if you were to slip off the block, or get a cramp, or miss a turn and come in last you'll find that the sun will still rise tomorrow morning. [*This isn't exactly what she wanted to hear.*]

Of course it will be nice to win; but nobody is going to say she could do a better job. They couldn't anyway.

Ruth: Well, it's just that I'm not feeling good. I think I ate too much. [*She resorts to a familiar medical complaint.*]

Coach: Where does it hurt? [*He wants to be sure it's nothing new.*]

Ruth: Points to area of her abdomen. [*Coach then agrees with her.*]

Coach: It probably is something you ate; but if you feel you can't swim, just let me know and I'll scratch you. [*Definitely the last thing that Ruth wanted him to do.*]

Ruth: Oh! But who would you swim (instead)?

Coach: If you're sick, Ruth, we don't even care who
will take your place. After all, this is but a
grain of sand in your life. Let's put it this way:
You rest up now and see if you don't feel better
by the time the race is called. Be sure you let
me know. [*He has put her welfare ahead of
victory.*]

Nothing more was said; but half an hour later, Ruth entered
the race and won.

Every coach and special teacher can think of many such instances which have responded to similar management. The better
one knows his client, student or patient, the easier it is to apply
negative as well as positive psychological strategies.

NEW WORLD CITIZENS WITH OLD WORLD IDEAS

The teen-ager is a problem chiefly because of unpreparedness
—yours as well as his own. His anxieties should actually be
fewer than those of his childhood because he has many reasons
to feel more secure. His age, size, sexual maturity and intellectual
development are all approaching their prime. Yet his anxieties
continue to reflect the same old boogymen—lack of self-confidence, school difficulties, sexual taboos, uncertainty over counseling and guidance programs, and the inevitable tendency to
rebel against authority. This rebellion is most distressing when
it is directed against parental authority and society in general.
It is best typified by the almost universal conflict in the case of
New World citizens with Old World ideas. Nevertheless, all parents have the same problems, the chief difference being that in
the case of foreign-born parents the child seems to have a better
excuse for resenting them.

You already know why such parents cling to the language
and customs of their native land. It is their way of satisfying the
hunger of their own personal nostalgia. You also know why
native-born children reject the old ways and want to acclimate
their foreign-born parents so that they will not stand out from
the group and cause embarrassment and rejection. Here are some
suggestions for foreign-born parents.

Suggestions for Old World Parents

1. Keep emphasizing the *similarities* rather than the differences between your ways of life and those of the neighbors. When entertaining friends, serve conventional meals and keep your native or favorite dishes for the privacy of the family UNLESS your child (or your guest) ask for them to be served.

2. Keep your focus on those accomplishments of which the child of any age would normally be proud; such as his success in fitting in with the local scene, his acceptance by his group, scouts, ball team, school band and so on. This recommendation also includes your own language and mannerisms. You will not want to admit that you cannot master conversational English and speak just as well as your in-laws. You will want your child to adopt your ideals and some of your customs. This will come of itself when he has succeeded in making a positive identification with you, but let the desire to identify with you come from the child and not from yourself. A child does not mind being told that he looks like mommy or behaves like his father if the parent is popular with his group.

3. Let there be a time and place for everything, your child's needs as well as your own; and when you want his participation in some cultural or religious ceremonial, or family function, see that you mean business. Too much freedom and too much choice may imply that you do not really care particularly one way or the other.

4. Participate in your child's activities as well as your own. You can at least attend P.T.A. meetings, and you should make it your business to attend as many of his school and other activities as possible. This is important whether or not your child is performing. Few dates are more important than going to hear and see your youngster's choral or athletic efforts, or watching him march by in a parade. Your mere presence will be a priceless memory for your child. In later years, it will be the other way around, especially after he has gone away from home. Then it will

be you who want him home for holidays and anniversaries.

5. When frequent family conferences seem to be getting you nowhere, let up on your pressure. Give yourself time to simmer down and give your youngster time to digest the situation. Too much pressure can compel your child to run away, as in the following two cases.

Hilda had been keeping company with a youth of whom her family disapproved. Yet they tolerated him as long as they felt that marriage was not contemplated. When Hilda told them she wanted to marry her sweetheart, they ordered him away from the house and forbade her to see him again. The girl became seriously agitated, fled to her boyfriend's house, and threatened to kill herself unless he married her. The best, and worst, efforts of Hilda's parents could not prevent the wedding which they did not attend. Father disowned her and refused to let her have any of her own clothes including a new fur coat and some jewelry which he had recently given her. Mother threatened to have a nervous breakdown, but she did not. Father eventually let her have her clothes; and several years later, the two were divorced after discovering that pressure does not pay. Obedience and conformity does not necessarily imply *loyalty*.

* * *

Irene at seventeen is an honor student in her senior year at high school, but she finds herself unable to complete her studies because of shaking spells that prevent her from doing any written work. This came on just before college board exams for which she was fully prepared. The high standards set by her mother made it imperative that Irene should attend one of the best colleges. Consequently, her principal's assurance that she could be admitted to most of the other colleges solely on her record, and without college boards, did not help her very much. The conflict was not so much the result of a desire to frustrate her mother's ambition, as it was a fear of adding to her father's financial load. Father's business had not been doing too well of late. Irene's sickness solved the dilemma for her. By being too sick to take the exams she had a legitimate excuse for not getting into the Ivy League colleges. Thus, she avoided a conscious choice between Mother's ambition and Father's unexpressed preference for one of the less expensive colleges. The sickness lasted until the examination period was safely over. Both of Irene's parents had started college, but neither of them had completed requirements for a degree. Both of them insisted that they did not care whether Irene went to college or not, but you can draw your own conclusions.

HOW PARENTS CAN PREVENT SCHOOL ANXIETIES

If your child's program is too ambitious, help him to scale it down to a level which he can handle comfortably. If he has developed some unsatisfactory habits of work and study, you may need help to find out whom he is imitating. Your own habit of keeping late hours at night and encouraging last-minute morning rushes can influence him more effectively than your ambition for him to study music and your emphasis on "good" report cards.

When you have set a good example, when you take time to read his compositions and tests, and to discuss them with him, when you consider his needs and wishes in the matter of time for practice versus time for playing with the kids, when you have decided that he does not have to be the leader in everything he tackles, nor the prize entertainer for your important family gatherings, nor the chief source of your prestige in the community, then you will notice that his tics and grievances, his nightmares and nailbiting, his hasty and finicky eating and his carelessness with your cups and saucers will all begin to disappear. It is not enough for you to keep *telling* him that you are not really interested in high marks. It is necessary for you to *show* him that you mean exactly what you say. Sell yourself on this idea first, and then you will have no trouble in convincing your child. He is an easy customer, and he will be only too happy to buy.*

REFERENCES AND READINGS

1. APTEKAR, H. H.: *The Dynmics of Casework and Counselling.* Cambridge, Riverside, 1955.
2. FINE, BENJAMIN S.: *Profiles of American Colleges.* New York, Barron's 1966.
3. DENGROVE, E.: A new letter-association technique. *Dis Nerv Syst, 23:* 25-26, 1962.
4. HAWES, G. R.: *The New American Guide to Colleges.* New York, New Am. Lib., 1962.
5. KAMENS, D. H.: Fraternity membership and college dropout in different institutional settings. *Sandoz Psychiat Spectator, 4:*7, 1967.

---

* Speech problems and their correction have been discussed in Chapter 6.

6. LIVINGSTON, J. A.: Mirror of America. *U.S. Book of Facts, Statistics and Information.* New York, S. and S., 1965, pp. XV-XVIII.
7. TEICHER, J. D.; JACOBS, J., and MARGOLIN, N. L.: Adolescents who attempted suicide. Reported to Amer Orthopsych Assoc, San Francisco, 1966. *Psychiat Progr, 1*:3, May 1966.
8. USDIN, G. L. (Ed.): *Adolescence: Care and Counselling.* Philadelphia, Lippincott, 1967.

Chapter 13

MARRIAGE AND SOCIETY

HISTORY AND CUSTOMS

The Institution of Marriage

Most people marry. They also stay married or remarry when widowed or divorced. In primitive societies, girls were required to marry at puberty, and bachelorhood for boys was discouraged. The avowed purpose of the marital state was to protect the young and to share responsibilities and duties. This instinct is highly developed in birds although some species mate for only a season. It is not as well developed in the chimpanzee and gorilla, and it is absent in reptiles whose young are born with the ability to care for themselves.

The Forms of Matrimony

Monogamy is of relatively recent origin; but polygamy (one husband for several wives), and polyandry (one wife for several husbands) still exist in certain parts of the Asiatic world. Among certain ducks which are normally monogamic, variations occur as a matter of adaptation to circumstances. When there is an excess of males, polyandry develops with two males in constant and amicable attendance on the female.

In humans, too, whenever a disproportion occurs in the number of males and females, polyandry is the rule. Among the South Pacific Marquesan's the jealousy between primary and secondary husbands was definitely kept at a minimum for obvious reasons. The sex favors were decided by the amount and type of work that was contributed. The night with the wife was granted as a reward for production. It was advantageous both to the wife and the chief husband to keep the men happy and their productivity high since the wealth, prestige and welfare of all depended upon it.

In contemporary life, a small bottle of perfume or inexpensive jewelry and an anniversary remembrance celebrated by dining out can accomplish similar miracles. However, this lesson in elementary psychology is often neglected by wives as well as by spouses. Negligent spouses are liable to use poor judgment in distributing rewards and privileges to the rest of the family as well as to each other.

Group marriage is said to exist among the Urabunna tribe of Central Australia. It is a convenient arrangement by which all men of one class are regarded as actual or potential husbands of the women of another class.

"Communal marriage," a custom requiring a host to offer his wife, sister, or daughter to any male guest, was formerly a proper and moral obligation. Now it is a mere gesture of hospitality which is not to be taken literally except in some remote parts of the world.

Exogamy (marriage outside the culture, group, color or religion) is generally disapproved of by all societies. It was usually punished by exile or death. When it does occur, the couple usually drift towards the stronger family, whatever its race, color or religion may be. However, exogamous or "mixed" marriages are on the increase, all over the world. They are also known to have a divorce mortality up to seven times that of nonmixed marriages. The consensus among the experts is that marriages are mixed enough even when the partners are of the same race and religion. The mixture, of course, includes age, education, temperament, background and family. Much of the hostility of the community is believed to be based on the fear of dilution of the breed and the breakdown of their culture. Still the natural attraction for partners who are different continues to excite and entice people of all levels. Part of this is based on the theory that the differences accentuate potential sexual excitability, but much of this theory is based on a rebellious defiance of parents and family traditions. Religious leaders who deal with intermarriage confirm what psychiatrists have long recognized—those who marry outside of their own religion are generally hostile to all religions, even though they often overcompensate by becoming zealous converts to their partner's professed faith.

Other customs included the *"jus prima noctis,"* or right of a landowner, lord, or high priest to cohabit with every maiden on her first bridal night. It is still the custom of some marriage officiates to take the first kiss from the bride.

In some groups prenuptial chastity has been discouraged; and a girl must demonstrate her ability to produce a baby before she can hope to attract a husband.

Some societies still approve of harems, concubines, mistresses, "sacred prostitutes," virile male priests who oblige barren wives, child marriages, the lending of wives, and divorce for failure to produce a male heir.

While few cases of this sort of liberal interpretation of contemporary morals reach our newspapers, any marriage counselor could tell of similar incidents in the lives of people who would otherwise pass for normal in their community. For instance here are a few from my own practice: a wife who persuaded her unmarried sister to be a substitute for coitus which she found distasteful; a husband who scolded his wife for falling asleep in her lover's car outside of her home instead of bringing him indoors and who later suggested that thereafter each be allowed the freedom of the house to carry on their affairs in privacy; couples who openly exchange boudoir partners, especially after they have had a few drinks; numerous incestuous relations between father and daughter, brother and sister, and even mother and son; and, of course, the triangles and philandering experiments of married people for which "love" is the usual excuse.

MARRIAGE, PERSONALITY AND CAREERS

Personality and marital careers are intimately related. The home is a nucleus for the culture and training of the family. It furnishes protection for father as well as mother and children. Since procreation is a wifely function, it naturally followed that most of the responsibility for support and protection fell upon the male. This division of labor and responsibility is being shared with greater equality on many levels. It not only serves the best interests of the majority but it also balances the equation between male and female.

The Industrial Revolution has brought millions of women into the commercial and industrial wage-earning class with increased recognition and freedom. It may be that it has displaced some of them too abruptly and upset their psychological stability by seeming to ignore their biological role. It may also be that elevated respect, which economic independence inevitably commands, has spoiled some of them for their role of homemaker.

In her war for equality between the sexes, the modern wife sometimes overlooks the biological origin of her dependency upon her mate. Moreover, since childbearing utilizes some of the best years of a woman's life, she has been enjoying considerable legal protection from desertion and divorce. However, some recent decisions on alimony for divorced males with genuine hardship are beginning to put the shoe on the other foot.

Both parents bring to the marriage not only the physical companionship that changes a house into a home but also those cultural contributions that serve to make the home a true cradle of happiness and character formation. Such contributions by both partners make it possible for all members of the family to develop their potential for creative activities and other wholesome productivity. The home can be a tense and crowded factory with a stereotyped product (the child) that is generally modelled after the dominant parental figure, or it can be a thriving research laboratory that is filled with thrilling and rewarding surprises.

Changes in personality, careers and recreational hobbies need not be for the worse. All partners in the household can continue to explore new horizons of achievement. Novelty of interests and activities should be combined with the habit of utilizing time and energy with reasonable economy—these are the seeds from which spring the blossoms and fruits of well-rounded personalities and rewarding careers.

LOVE WITHOUT MARRIAGE

Love-ins, without benefit of clergy, are not new in the history of the human race. According to Havelock Ellis, the absence of formal marriage tends to give increased security to women. Their men are more considerate and more faithful. Quoting Booth from "Life and Labor of the People," Ellis reports that the rough laborers of nineteenth century London behaved best when not married to the women with whom they live . . . "if they marry it always seems to lead to blows and rows." (p. 388)[2] Allegedly the women work better in the house when they are not legally married; and the men are more faithful.

The same tendency was prevalent in Jamaica where the population was largely colored and 60 per cent of births were illegitimate. Ellis concluded that legal illegitimacy has ceased to be immoral and has become the recognized custom of the majority of the inhabitants. A comparable situation is reported to exist in several contemporary South American countries, according to recent studies.

Quoting W. P. Livingston in "Black Jamaica" (1899) Ellis (p. 210) reports "the people recognize that faithful living together constitutes marriage; they say they are "married but not parsoned." They are also disinclined to incur the expense of legal marriage. This excuse is offered for a similarly large incidence of illegitimacy in Venezuela, Abyssinia, and in other places where an official marriage ceremony is usually postponed until old age or until legal complications of property rights arise, or until the marriage is well established in fact and compatability.

Ellis associates this custom with the superiority of women who refuse to bind themselves to a man who may turn out to be a burden instead of a help and protection. So long as the unions are free they stand a better chance of becoming permanent. When they are made legal, they are liable to become intolerable and provoke desertion. The habitual practice of mutual kindness and forebearance becomes necessary. It also establishes a condition that is the best insurance for permanency.

It is much this same absence of legal compulsion which makes the average host more hospitable to his voluntary guests than to his own family. His wife and children cannot readily walk out on him when he forgets his "company manners," but if his guests object to inadequate refreshments or unreasonable demands, they may take offense and become his enemies. So, too, with courtship in our own culture where many more privileges and allowances are made before than after marriage, each partner is perpetually on his best behavior for fear of offending and losing the other.

Similar psychological factors are observed in those penal institutions where the locks have been removed. The percentage of escapees is astonishingly small. Even psychiatric hospitals are discovering less and less need for locked wards. Furthermore, all disciplinarians know that it is much more effective to use "may" rather than "must" and "please" or "How would you like to . . .?" or "Shall we try this?" etc., rather than "Hey, you—do what I tell you and be quick about it."

Westermarck points out that there is a general absence of celibacy among savage and barbarous people.[3] It was rare for a woman over sixteen not to have a husband prior to the coming of the whites and the breakdown of aboriginal customs. "But in all the richer, more energetic, and progressive countries . . . marriage is late . . . (as a result) a certain proportion of men, and a still larger proportion of women (who exceed the men in the general population) never marry at all." (Ellis IV, p. 390.) In other words, there is a growing proportion of adult unmarried women whose sexual activities are recognized neither by society nor (officially) by the state. These observations were made over half a century ago, yet they are still valid, today.

MATRIARCHAL AND PATRIARCHAL PATTERNS

Historians and sociologists are not in agreement as to which came first, the patriarchal state which places women under the protection of the men or the matriarchal state which existed among the ancient Lycia of Asia Minor, as well as in Sumatra and other primitive cultures. Our contemporary clients choose the kind of marriage they can live with. They may bewail their unhappy lot, especially about in-laws, but they are not in a hurry to change them.

Many a modern marriage duplicates the matriarchy in all but name. The male goes to live with the female or with his own family who contributes much of his support. He often transfers his affection to his wife's mother, or he may keep his own mother, sister or favorite aunt foremost in his heart. He then wonders why his wife objects to the competition and why she has a continuing fear of impermanency and abandonment.

Be sure to inquire as to where the couple lived during the

first years of marriage. Sharing quarters with families may have saved dollars; but it usually leaves deep and lasting emotional scars.

According to Ardry, Ellis and others, the male stakes out a claim on property or territory which he is willing to protect. The greater his domain, the more it will attract the best females. Mating is a secondary consideration. The male may have to fight for the mate he wants, as with lions, while she watches the conflict and contentedly trots off with the victor, or he may have to purchase his privileges, as with prostitute apes.

If he is an aggressive newcomer or late arrival he may just move in on the leading dominant male and oust him from both mate and nest, if he can. Otherwise he will just have to be satisfied with the low girl on the totem pole. When that happens, she promptly changes from an abused and dejected outcast to another position in the "pecking order" of the group—taking whatever rank her mate is cast in.

Jealousy, coquetry, desertion, exile and broken hearts are uncommon, but they have been observed, especially in birds and apes. Adultery and loose behavior by the "wife" or "wives" is liable to severe punishment by the "husband," unless the philandering male is victor in the challenging combat. Unlike the breeding harems of herds of mammals, most birds are sentimental and monogamous.[1]

THE THREAT OF ABANDONMENT

The threat of abandonment or desertion is present from birth. It stalks us all our lives and is one of the greatest hazards of any partnership. The threat of abandonment can occur at any age. It causes children to run away, teensters to become ill or attempt suicide, men to fall down on their jobs, women to lose interest in their homes, and both partners to fail in their sexual and other shared relationships.

Just doing things together, however unpleasant, with each one carrying his share, can serve as insurance against this threat; but when one partner sloughs off reasonable responsibility, neglects to help and leaves the other to carry on alone, few excuses can be adequate to heal the hurt that threatens to break up their relationship. The poorer the excuse the greater the wound; because the real reasons can be guessed at, however thinly they may be disguised.

Divorces in the late nineteen sixties are leveling off to about one in four marriages; and newlyweds now have a marriage expectancy of about thirty-two years. Nevertheless, close to seven hundred children commit murder in the United States each year, and two thirds of their victims are members of their own families. Few people live who have never felt a desire to destroy someone very close to them whenever they have felt betrayed. Anger, a feeling of futility and impotence and depression are common reactions. One sure way to escape this intolerable state is by self-destruction.

In the eyes of the emotionally depressed patient, suicide seems a much safer procedure than continuing to live with the risk of betrayal, desertion or abandonment by someone important. Suicidal preoccupation serves also as a vicarious punishment for the survivors, a punishment which is calculated to fit the crime. By self-destruction, the depressed person also deserts and *leaves them*—preferably *before they can leave him.* At the same time, the suicide serves as self-punishment for not having earned the acceptance that was so desperately needed.

The clause in the marriage contract, "for better or worse," is a futile attempt to insure the participant against such abandonment. It is made of the same idealistic but wishful thinking as the Tenth Commandment which forbids covetousness. It is comparable to the noble injunctions to turn the other cheek and to love those who are our enemies. Yet every marriage counselor is obligated to investigate the disguises for possible and probable threats of abandonment and rejection.

Disguised Threats of Abandonment

These appear in the guise of philandering, absenteeism, sickness, alcoholism and comparable addictions, extravagance, untidiness, captious criticism, unbridled tempers, gross discourtesies, cruelty and abuse, and subtle or outright rejection as in the following account by a professional woman of fifty.

The first time my brother came home on military

leave my mother tried to get him and his wife to sleep
in separate bedrooms.

There was other evidence that this abandonment of decency
and adult responsibility by mother was following an old pattern.
The same informant confided the following:

> I was twelve when my brother was born and I didn't
> know anything about it. I said, "I don't believe it!"
> Mother had been staying in the house because she was
> ashamed to walk the streets while pregnant, but I
> thought it was something else and I'd been worrying
> about her health. She wanted all her boys to be priests
> and all her girls to be nuns. *Any girl who became a
> nun she'd call a beautiful girl.*
>
> My husband was no better off. He was nearly thir-
> teen years old when a schoolmate told him that his
> mother and father made a baby through intercourse.
> He was so furious that he beat up the kid for insulting
> his parents.

Less apparent threats of abandonment of responsibility appear
in other forms such as ignoring children, spouse, or important
guests via a conversational marathon, keeping one's nose in a
newspaper or eyes glued to television or a book, habitual gossip
via telephone marathons or tavern companionship, overattention
to business, working long hours, unnecessary moonlighting, preference for night shifts and overloading oneself with organizational, recreational or church responsibilities so that there is
practically no time left for the family.

Working wives may not start out with the idea of abandon-
ing their husbands or children, but it would be unreasonable to
deny them the right to equal emotions and opportunities comparable to those of the major breadwinner. They, too, are
tempted to indulge in sexperiments. As a result they may discover greener pastures and this often affords them good reason
to reevaluate the merits of the double standard and to reappraise
their total domestic and personal situation.

It is often a matter of simple arithmetic. Courtship hours that
were previously given the highest priority are now restricted to
little more than the few hours available for dining, bathing, bed
and sleep. Girls who had to do their own hair, or earn money for
permanents and party dresses, developed a sense of dignity and

importance when their premarital jobs, or husband's income, provided for these and similar luxuries of comfortable living. Such wives will make appropriate sacrifices only as long as their partners reciprocate by carrying a fair share of the domestic load, but when one spouse starts indulging himself, letting down the bars and polishing apples for some friend or relative, then the abandonment of their joint ideals becomes an intolerable injustice to which the other partner inevitably retaliates. The punishment takes various forms including neglect of housework and meals. Common outlets for hostility include rudeness to the partner's family or friends, tardiness with appointments, and rejection or indifference toward sex.

In fairness to the males, it is sometimes the girl who has failed to break loose from her premarital ties. When she insists on continuing to be the errand girl for an inconsiderate, dependent and demanding family, tries to win them over with gifts and services, and subordinates her personal and domestic life to their beck and call, it is the male who retaliates by nagging, tightening the purse strings, drinking, keeping late hours, philandering or even resorting to physical abuse.

Since actions speak louder than the reiteration of declarations of love, the marriage counselor must avoid subjective involvement and personal prejudices. Confrontation of the partners with facts may be a painful remedy, yet it is often the most effective. As a rule, such partners cannot face up to such a confrontation. Usually they will not even come together for an interview; but even when they fail to return, you will have provided them with something to think about. By confrontation, the counselor starts them on the road to reappraisal and reformation.

REFERENCES

1. ARDREY, R.: *African Genesis,* New York, Dell, 1961.
2. ELLIS, HAVELOCK: *Psychology of Sex.* New York, Modern Lib., 1936, Vol. I-IV.
3. WESTERMARCK, E. A.: *History of Marriage.* New York, Macmillan, 1930.

Chapter 14

DATES AND MATES

BEAUTY IS STILL IN THE EYE OF THE BEHOLDER

THE MOST WONDERFUL GUY OR DOLL in one's own, small, private world is the person who possesses certain particular individual differences and requirements. These are the qualities that just happen to fill the needs of the beholder in whose eyes the beauty is apparent. When the guy or doll does not actually have the desired qualities but is clever enough to suggest or cultivate most of them, the net result may be just as satisfactory. This is commonplace and universal because when one is ready for love, he is also an easy prey to self-deception and artful illusion, and he fills in the missing details by such normal compensations as wishful imagination, rationalization, projection, repression or denial.

Time dims one's memory, but first impressions are longlasting. Tribal customs still require scars, tattoos, pierced noses, huge buttocks and other oddities, not only as individual differences but also as marks of acceptable and desirable beauty. In family counseling, the child who resembles a favored relative on one side of the family may be one parent's favorite. However, he may also turn out to be an abhorrent reminder of a disliked in-law. It depends on which spouse is trying to rationalize his rejection or favoritism.

UNCONSCIOUS SELECTION OF DATES AND MATES

Idealized Self-Image

A youth normally patterns himself after his mother's favorite male or males. These usually include her father, a grandfather, favorite uncle, brother, or friend of the family. Their opinions and examples are important. The boy tries to become what these

Note: All reference numbers in Chapters 14 through 17 refer to list at end of Chapter 17.

V.I.P.'s expect of him because they are important to his mother—
who is usually his first and greatest love. When mother dies or
deserts then the loyalty is often tranferred to the woman who
raised the child and was kind to him in her fashion. He then
strives to become the embodiment of her ideal male or males.

The boy's father, in normal family life, represents a composite of his mother's favorite males; but he is also a compromise
and a Johnny-come-lately. Father, therefore, cannot be the first
important male in her life, but he can qualify as the first important male in the lives of his children, if he works at it.

Similarly, a girl's ego-ideal or self-image is patterned after
her father's favorite female or females. She soon learns that what
his mother thought or what his favorite grandmother, aunt or
sister preferred are important to him. She therefore molds herself unconsciously in order to fit their standards. Since her mother
is usually a *composite* of father's favorite females and is often
also his "best girl," at least consciously, the daughter eventually
tends to follow more of her mother's patterns of personality and
behavior.

After all, the daughter usually has much more intimate contact with her mother. She may consciously reject a great many
of mother's ideals, standards and habits during her earlier years,
but she tends to adopt more and more of them as she grows
older. The more she becomes like her mother, the more acceptable she would be to her mother's favorites. *Being like mother
is, therefore, a means of becoming more liked by her mother
and by mother's V.I.P.'s.* The boy often does the same with father.
He may reject all of father's standards while young, yet adopt
more and more of father's habits and prejudices as he grows
older.

Idealized Mate

The standards which a boy sets up for his ideal mate have
to be met by a girl who meets many or most of the qualifications
of his father's favorite female. This is not always the girl "who
married dear old dad." The youth may never have seen his
father's favorite female, but investigation will eventually reveal
her identity—probably in the form of a deceased grandmother,

favorite sister, or an indulged niece who lives at a considerable distance.

Perhaps the one who most loved the boy was a revered aunt by marriage—someone who made life bearable for him in an otherwise unsympathetic world. Nevertheless her identity will often show up in father's remarks about his wife's cooking or housekeeping.

> "Aunt Abbey used to say, 'Waste not, want not'; may her soul rest in peace." Or, "as your Grandmother always said, 'Tomorrow is another day.'" Or "Cousin Mary made the most wonderful pies and she was always so fat and jolly. . . ."

In like manner, the girl's ideal boyfriend will have to meet many of the standards that have been established by mother's favorite males. Occasionally, these may not be as ideal as could be desired.

> "Well, your great-uncle Joe used to drink some, and he never could hold on to a job; but he was always very generous—he'd give you the shirt off his back. I remember he was the only one who ever took me to the circus."

And this dubious eulogy:

> "I must say my father wasn't very athletic, but he sure knew how to go places and get money, even if he did gamble a little." Or, "You'll grow out of it in time. Mother and I both wet the bed until after we were married."

Facial and physical characteristics which resemble the V.I.P.'s in one's life may create the instant illusion of love at first sight, but these may not prove to be very durable. The impressions may last but they often do not stand up well with familiarity and wear. This is especially true where so much time has to be spent on makeup and hairdos that there is little left for cultivating deeper and more lasting values and qualities.

Family patterns are inevitably dominated by parental prejudices and frustrations. If children cannot always have the advantages which were denied to the parents, neither can they have the privileges. For instance, parents often sublimate their own negligence and frustrations by being overzealous or restrictive about their children's lessons, practice, early hours, conservative dress, and religious duties, social amenities—drinking, smoking, dating and morals.

> "Your cousin goes to church every week"; and be
> sure to visit your aunt Henrietta, or we'll never hear
> the end of it."

And this gem from a conservative second generation Irish lady to her married (R.N.) daughter.

> "Even after I was married, I didn't know how
> babies were born. Even when I was in the hospital,
> I thought they were going to cut me open to get
> the baby out." Said the daughter, "That was unfortunate, but such unenlightenment didn't have to
> be perpetuated." To which the mother defensively
> replied, "Well, I didn't know, so why should I tell
> you?"

Unconscious selection of dates and mates is also determined by size, shape, complexion, common interests, shared experiences, similarities of names or features, and mutual desires. Mutual desires and sexplorations are becoming less inhibited among increasing numbers of our younger generation, but most families still retain conservative standards although they may surrender their obligation to enforce them. For instance the practice of *going steady* too soon is a natural stepping stone to encouraging dangerous intimacies, yet parents often lack the courage to be firm.

When parents abandon their responsibilities to be fair as well as firm in the management of family problems, all members suffer. The youngsters tend to seek elsewhere for acceptance and guidance; but in their search for new values and strong leadership, they again run into the fear of rejection and abandonment, if they do not pay the price for admission into the new gang, partnership, or club. Whatever the price may be—sex, alcohol, narcotics, vandalism, or stealing—it will often be paid willingly by any youth who has not been accepted at home. He may sacrifice name, honor, health, and even life itself in order to become important to somebody. The less well endowed he is, mentally, physically, or socially, the greater his need for unconventional companions and devices to lift his self-esteem.

This need also accounts for a handsome youth's "seeing" a vision of loveliness in an older woman or in a plain, homely, or deformed girl who is nevertheless able to make him feel like a king. It also explains why some superior college girls who could easily make the semifinals in a Miss America contest are willing to tie up with an inferior partner. As already mentioned, a desperate need for acceptance, plus the fear and ever imminent threat of abandonment is also one of the strongest psychological and emotional factors which keep such seemingly mismatched couples together.

"I don't love you any more" is often replaced by such wishful inanities as "I'll love you forever and a day." Yet we are also reminded that "it's no good unless you love me all the way" and the more recent theme that says *you can twist, bend or shape me anyway you want. It's perfectly okay as long as you love me*—meaning as long as you cherish me and do not desert me or take me for granted. Of course, whether you are married or not is of secondary importance to the song writers and their eager customers because marriage does not guarantee happiness anyway. "Guaranties" tend to become less important as one grows older and develops more wisdom from the lessons of experience.

GUIDES TO SELECTION

Guides for selection of dates and mates are of little help after one has fallen in love. However, the following suggestions should provoke some parents into long-range planning. They will also help the habitual wallflower and isolated loner to understand what is wrong with their social programing.

1. *Choose the family to which you would like to belong, as early in life as possible.* Consider them as carefully as you would evaluate your doctor, or your bank or college.

Choose them for character, dependability and reputation rather than for status or wealth, or to please your friends. Compare older methods of family selections with the procedure for publishing a book. Publishers now choose the writer for what the public will accept, just as parents used to choose a spouse for suitability to the family as well as to the available mate.

2. *Try to be the kind of girl (or boy) whom that family wants.* Study their requirements. Take the necessary time to prepare to meet those requirements. Put in the energy and effort that is needed to produce results. Years, not months, may be needed.

3. *Once you have been accepted, protect your credit.* Follow the rules. If you feel that a change is indicated, do it through the ballot (discussion and counseling) not the bullet (verbal, fistic, or sexual). But make changes *before* marriage. Changes that are desired after marriage have to be made by *both* partners, else it is too late.

4. *What to avoid:* Do not seek out handsome men or beautiful women; but you do not have to reject them if they seek you out first. Usually this type receives far more adulation than they can digest. They get it with very little effort. They are, therefore, deprived of many normal incentives to be gracious, to be considerate, to develop skills and character. They are often spoiled from infancy. Vanity and consequent jealousies and enmities are liable to be more prevalent. In general, many of the same objections apply to wealthy partners and to people who are prominent.

5. *What to seek:* Stay in your own general class, culture, religion, economic, social and educational levels. *When you and your mate are ready to move into upper levels, do so together,* through night school, congenial work, thrift, reading, travel and social activities, such as volunteering to help with groups and organizations in the social strata to which you aspire. One of you may lead the way, but you should plan to work together from the bottom up to the next rung on the ladder.

6. *Study your models—your idealized self-image and your idealized mate.* They are not 100 per cent pure strains, but they will give you clues to a better understanding of your own unconscious needs and motivations. These have already been described above.

You will have at least four basic personalities that require harmonizing: the male and female models in your own life and the male and female models in your mate's life, but their relative importance changes, and their influences may vary from time to time.

For instance, early in Miriam's life, Miriam's father's favorite females were a rejecting psychotic mother, a reticent but deceased sister who took care of him, a gossipy, high-strung and frugal spinster sister who worked all day and cooked at night, and a warm and friendly elderly unmarried teacher who definitely favored boys. However, in later years, Miriam's father became more reconciled to his wife (Miriam's mother) who also resembled the favorite sister who had died.

Miriam's model for herself is a combination of these women plus her own mother, her mother's sisters and her maternal grandmother. Miriam's personality includes features of all of them. Sometimes one pattern predominates, sometimes another; but more and more of her mother's personality shows through as she grows older. Occasionally, however, one's earliest models resume domination. They then take precedence over later ones. This is especially common in the aged. (Atavistic emotional regression to childhood levels of dependency and identification.)

7. *Knowledge of each other's needs can accomplish more than premarital sexual indulgences.*

My mother wanted a girl. She also was disappointed when my kid brother was born. *My wife's mother wanted a boy when my wife was born, because she already had four girls, but my wife wanted a girl* IN THE WORST WAY.

Family planning calls for more than birth control and spacing of pregnancies. Even if we could deliver whatever sex seems to be desired, we would have to contend with other people's prejudices and preferences. So it is far better to be prepared to accept a child for whatever it is born with and then try to help to improve in those areas that need assistance.

8. *Rejection has different meanings.* One may be rejected because he is too good, as well as because he is not good enough. For example, a girl may turn down a suitor because he is out of her class and she does not want any more schooling to catch up with him. Or a boy may turn down a girl because her tastes are too extravagant for his projected earnings. Application of this principle to the problem of personal rejection throws a different light on the tendency towards self-hatred for failing to win the love of a parent, mate, or friend.

9. *Other conflicts that need consideration*: Girls also need mothering. Boys may decline to step into father's role of responsibility. Thrift, economy, industry, training and ambition should be shared. Planning should include dealing with in-laws and preparations for personal as well as family careers.

10. *Some important questions that need answering before marriage*: Do the prospective partners speak the same language colloquially as well as culturally? Have they many mutual ideals and interests? Are they working and striving for a common goal? Can they read, relax, work, play and sing together as well as they can dance and pet? Are the young people burning up their reservoir of affection by exhausting demands on each other's limited resources of funds, time, energy, generosity, and humor? In other words are they outwearing their welcome in each other's homes and company? Does the correspondence, if any, suffer because of laziness, selfishness, or the irregularities of the postman? Are there obnoxious habits or idiosyncrasies of a personal nature, embarrassing table habits, coarse abuse of diction, habitual profanity, possessiveness, and rudeness or indifference to friends or family? Are the young folks planning their career care-

fully? Have they settled on planned parenthood and birth control? Will the wife work? How about moonlighting? Will the parents of either side help out in case of illness, a confinement, or death? Does either party feel violently opposed to allowing his in-laws-to-be to bring up his child-to-be? What will be its baptismal faith? Is there already a mutual savings account? Is the boy very reluctant to change over the beneficiary of his insurance policies to his bride-to-be? Does he rationalize his failure to economize, habitual tardiness, neglect to attend to his teeth, avoiding home chores, or periodic drinking?

In short, are the young folks mature enough to accept and assume the responsibilities of marriage and parenthood along with the privileges of living together?

Billy's Mismates.

Billy was a girl who willingly paid for her dates with privileges but could not find anyone who wanted something more permanent.

> There was always another girl so we'd break it up. It was the same with the next, and the one after that. Sometimes I wish I was dead. I thought of all ways to commit suicide. In high school I took nine pep pills to study. I wanted to see a psychiatrist but I've been afraid of doctors and needles since I was a child. Mother tried to take poison and I stopped her. Father tried to gas himself. He could never keep a job. Mother would get drunk and abusive. She'd come home at two in the morning and her tears were rolling down on my hair. I'd never hit her back. My brother's with Mother. He's so good(!) I went to live with my aunt. She's not much improvement, and my uncle's worse. But I hate to leave her with all those bills.

Billy's name suggests that she wished she were the favored "good" brother. Her reluctance to leave her aunt indicates that she enjoys playing mother to the dependent and incompetent woman, who has also earned Mother's animosity by favoring Billy.

In private psychodrama between Billy, me, and V.H. who took turns playing the various roles of Mother, aunt and Billy we finally reached a point where V.H. as Billy, goaded Billy (as her mother) into saying "You're a no good bitch and a bastard," whereupon the girl burst into tears.

She was promptly started on psychoenergizing drugs. After a

few more private sessions she was admitted to a group where she had many a row with substitute members of her family and told off a number of would-be dates who made no attempt to conceal what they wanted her for.

Eventually she gained enough courage to leave her aunt; set up her own apartment, for which she received many donations of furnishings from friends she did not even know she had, and she suddenly found that she was having a steady caller. Someone who really cared to date her for herself, without the price of sex, was calling on her every week.

At first she did not even recognize the symptoms of love.

> I'm afraid I'll get hurt. I can't stop thinking about him. I keep waiting for weekends to come. He goes to school too. I get this funny feeling in my chest just talking to him on the telephone . . . (*normal anxiety*).

As long as Billy was under tension from rejections at home she was vulnerable and receptive to anyone who was willing to date her, just to get out of the house. As soon as she had declared her independence, however, the "new look" of self-confidence showed in her expression and appearance. People whom she had not realized even cared about her, began to show their appreciation of her qualities of working conscientiously, expressing interest in other people, and pitching in willingly whenever there was an extra job to be done. A sensible boyfriend is a foregone conclusion, when he is exposed to a woman who has the courage of her convictions and lets go some of her more disabling emotional shackles.

At this writing, six months later, Billy is not only in love with the evening college student but she too is taking evening courses and is also planning a student loan with the aim of completing her own education. Meanwhile, both of them have full daytime jobs.

Counselors of would-be dates and mates need to reassess their own orientation from time to time. For instance, a recent report on eighteen-year-olds show some interesting changes between 1920 and 1968: they are taller, weigh more, marry sooner, and a great many more complete high school. Boys are more than an inch taller and nearly twenty pounds heavier. Girls of today are two inches taller and ten pounds heavier than their eighteen-year-old counterparts of 1920.*

These facts are not confined to the statistician. Parents and teensters are themselves keen observers of the contrast. Pride and envy inevitably go hand in hand, and changing attitudes must keep pace with changing facts.

---

* *Newsweek*, July 29, 1968, p. 53.

Chapter 15

SEX PROBLEMS IN MARRIAGE

THE WAR BETWEEN THE SEXES

Complements Are Competitive But Equal

THE WAR BETWEEN THE SEXES is nature's way of reminding us that competition is the spice of life. Competition is generated by essential differences between male and female—anatomical, emotional and cultural. Differences accentuate the inescapable fact that neither male nor female can be entirely independent. This is another way of emphasizing the point that each one needs the other to compensate for his shortcomings and to make him whole and complete. In short, males and females complement each other.

Continuing friction between the sexes is an attempt to deny this interdependency by accentuating the differences, instead of joining forces in order to strengthen the partnership. Some couples make a game of this competition. They rationalize their denial and also the fact that they have been brainwashed from early childhood into believing that one sex or the other represents second-class citizenship.

Envy is a Two-Way Street

Envy is not limited to females. The thought that wives resent masculine prerogatives often obscures the fact that men also envy females. From boyhood they have envied the important mother role. They are also impressed by the fact that girls mature sooner. They especially admire the faculty of reproduction and the ability of women to attract strong men to protect them.

Where women are no longer considered as property, they have become less passive, less timid, and less envious. During her childbearing age, woman has less need to prove the superiority of her sex. The most creative women, in science, literature and the arts, are said to be either those who have no babies or those who are beyond the childbearing years.

However, as women have become more active and daring and protected by "the pill," they have lost much of their frigidity. This threatens some men and has made them more passive, more conforming and less aggressive in sex. Men have compensated by expressing the biologic urge to create through sublimation in construction, art, music, science and literature.

Feuds Can Be Altered

Unguided couples have an unsatiable need to keep the feud going regardless of costs. "Am I right?" becomes more important than "Am I loved?" They can dish out scornful and cutting wise-cracks, but they are seldom able to take it when they themselves are on the receiving end. Unless they can relieve their tensions in some other way, they remain unhappy and discontented people.

Exchanging roles with the counselor or with each other in a conjoined session is often more effective for letting off steam, than medicinal tranquilizers. Bowling, golf, and gardening or housecleaning and decorating can produce similar results for some people. Others prefer joining a service club, or choral group, or paying a visit to the nearest tavern. In any event, when there is tension and friction, the sexual aspects of the marriage are among the first to suffer; but they are usually the *result* of the frictions, rather than the cause.

As we have already seen parental, familial and cultural prejudices affect all areas of life. However, until recent decades, Western educators have neglected the obvious fact that sexual education is also a continuing procedure. Sexual problems in marriage are usually the result of failure in the early years of development; and sexual adjustments are only one aspect of total marital success. The main objective is the achievement of interpersonal harmony.

SEXUAL ASPECTS OF MARRIAGE

The sexual aspects of marriage are often no more than an accentuation of preexisting problems. Marriage resolves some anxieties but also produces or exposes new ones. Some couples still enter marriage as babes in the woods, their sole physical contact having consisted of holding hands at the movies. Others have had to resort to private masturbation to obtain relief from frustrating and overstimulating situations. Their anxiety and guilt over a "sinful" and longstanding habit can prevent sufficient relaxation to obtain satisfactory relief from normal coitus. Sometimes one partner is afraid to trust himself to the other partner's inept ministrations. According to Masters and Johnson, self-induced orgasm was *more intense* for many women but sexual intercourse proved to be *more satisfying* than masturbation.[34]

There are couples who have remained married despite their inability to complete intercourse, even after surgical defloration. They have a sort of "gentlemen's agreement" never to discuss the subject. Their usual excuse, whenever the matter is brought up by outsiders, is that they both have agreed not to bring children into this uncertain world and besides it would be bad for her health.

Such a woman is usually frigid. She may even experience pain or vaginal spasm on attempts at intercourse. Consequently she desists from all efforts thereafter. Her man has to restrain himself or indulge in gambling, masturbation, philandering, overeating, drinking, or sleeping. He may also sublimate by overwork or by delving into some artistic or other productive activities.

There are many couples to whom most aspects of sex are no novelty at marriage because they have already released their inhibitions premaritally. There are others who have never seen each other's naked bodies or been allowed to manually caress their partner's genitals except momentarily during hasty cohabitation in darkness.

There are husbands who are ignorant of their wive's physiology and wives who still consider the penis as a repulsive, dangerous weapon. Says Carlotta, "My husband jumps me in the bathroom, on the stairs, and even down in the cellar. What kind of a beast is he?" This bride of three months is physically well proportioned but she habitually wears no underclothing. Her novel and carefree exposure in the above situations is such as to arouse her spouse immediately. As might be expected, he is also carefully rationed sexually at all other times. Like other exhibitionists with attractive bodies she is a narcissistic tease who wants to preserve her bait as long as possible. She needs to catch fish without having to feed them (psychological castration). By disparaging her husband's sexual ardor, she justifies her own narcissism, her Victorian purity, and also her relative frigidity.

There are wives who prolong their menstruation or stretch its protection over several weeks in order to avoid coitus; and there are also husbands who refuse to bathe more than once or twice a year. There are partners who insist upon bathing *before* every sexual relationship and others who cannot get to a tub or shower quickly enough *after* intercourse.

There are spouses of both sexes who like to retire early; and others whose compulsion to read or watch television keeps them up late and conveniently out of temptation or danger. Playing possum is a two-handed game. Blaming the other partner for failure in contraception is also a universal practice.

As for premarital pregnancy it is obvious that too many parents never even heard of Kinsey. They keep hounding each other for causing the "one" moral blight on their lives. They keep nagging even after the arrival of grandchildren and when everyone else has forgotten all about their first eight pound "premature" baby that was born exactly seven months after their marriage.

But, in fairness to married sexual partners, there are still too many unanswered questions for which most books are not adequate and still too many counselors and medics who are themselves as uncomfortable as their patients when discussing the sexual aspects of marriage. Anxiety on this provocative subject is easily communicated between patient and therapist, and vice versa.

EMOTIONAL FACTORS IN MARRIED SEX

Sex As a Means to an End

The physical aspects of sex, both in and out of marriage, are largely dependent upon the emotional and psychological foundations which exist in the participants. For some couples, sex continues to be of paramount importance long after the honeymoon. For others, it is important only because it is conveniently available when needed, but for all couples, sexual intercourse often becomes a focal point of tension or dissension upon which to concentrate or displace other emotional outlets. Coitus, as such, may thus be a means to an end, or an end in itself.

For instance, when a man's self-confidence has been threatened by the challenges of other men or women, or by disturbing situations, he often needs sexual outlets in order to relieve tension and to restore confidence or boost his masculine ego. If his legal partner is habitually not available or receptive, he logically seeks other sources of satisfaction. In this way he can use sex aggressively as an outlet for tension, while at the same time he gratefully accepts his new partner's overtures or receptivity as balm to his wounded pride. Satisfactory substitutes which happen to fill his needs of the moment are liable to become endowed with greater values than they actually merit.

In show business and sports many a star is born overnight simply because an eager and capable stand-in was available at the right moment. However, in the biological world, nature still designs males so that they are capable of fertilizing as many females as possible and often with very little preparation. The human female does not have to be in periodic heat in order to accept a mate; but she does require adequate preparation for coitus—a fact which too many males tend to overlook.

Unfortunately, the niceties of courtship are often put aside after marriage, yet many a husband is surprised to find them just as effective with his wife as with a paramour. The difference is that he already knows his wife's reactions and shortcomings, while those of the "new flame" have yet to be discovered. There is always a chance that he may eventually find the "perfect" match—the impossible combination of mother, sweetheart, secretary, assistant and pal all wrapped up in one woman, instead of a harem of multiple partnerships.

When a woman's self-confidence is threatened, she does not immediately turn to sex for compensation. She may obtain temporary relief from her frustrations by having a good cry, getting a new hairdo, going on a spending spree for new clothes or furniture, or engaging in a furious housecleaning. She may also indulge in masturbation, but more women are also turning to swearing, smoking, drinking and philandering.

Like other members of the oldest profession many women make little pretense of rationalizing their sexperiments and collecting payment or gifts for their services. Like men, women often turn to drugs, gambling, and temporary escapes or "taking off" from time to time. Like men, they also explode and vent their hostilities on the nearest available spouse, children, family, friends, or the first appliance repairman to cross their paths.

Like her mate, the emotionally threatened female has a compensatory need to dominate or control. She leads the way, makes decisions and becomes defensive, depressed, withdrawn, or ill when challenged. The frustration need not be a sexual one, and the challenger is often someone other than the spouse. Frequently the frustrating source is someone of the same sex and, often, a close friend or kinfolk.

"AS GOOD AS MARRIED"

Preparation for sex in marriage is usually left to the family doctor, but girls who indulge in premarital intercourse frequently prefer someone less close.[15] Even then, the therapist may step out of his specialty and assume the role of tutor, or turn pastor.

Case of Dixie

For instance, Dixie, at nineteen, insists that she is so passionate that she becomes aroused "at the slightest touch" of her boyfriend. The only problem, according to her, is that "I'm unable to achieve a climax."

Dixie had been referred for hypnotherapy to help overcome her alleged frigidity. After ascertaining that she and her boyfriend were planning to marry within the year, or sooner if she should become pregnant, I suggested that an unconscious fear of pregnancy might be holding back her climax. Dixie did not think so, but the latest reports from Rome on the changing attitudes toward birth control were in the current papers, so with her boyfriend's approval she was sent to Dr. B. who had agreed on the telephone to fit her with an intrauterine coil. However, when she got there he refused to examine her, declined to fit her with anything, or to give her any instructions. Instead, he kept belaboring the point that she was ruining her marriage by having premarital intercourse. He apparently thought that all he needed to do was tell her to stop and presto—all her troubles would vanish.

> He kept me there for three quarters of an hour and all he did was bawl me out. Next time you send me to someone, please explain the full circumstances ahead of time. I'm no tramp and I'm old enough to know what I'm doing. I love my fiance very much and I'll make all my confessions when the time comes. And he's no priest anyhow!

It was after this outburst against both me and Dr. B. that she was able to release some heretofore repressed resentments against her fiance for his limited education and a few other shortcomings. Yet at no time had she made any pretense at birth control nor permitted him to do so either.

Marriage counselors will recognize that Dixie was obviously inviting a pregnancy as an excuse to leave home and not because of love for her fiance; that the religious and legal scruples were secondary to her social rebellion; and that she apparently lacked sufficient self-confidence and drive to go out and compete on other levels for an "eligible" male in a different and more acceptable educational, social and cultural category.

It is also highly probable that she was using frigidity as an excuse to avoid the temptation to try her luck with other men lest she find one whom she would have to marry. Also perhaps, unconsciously, she reasons "no orgasm—no pregnancy." This assumption has no biological foundation, but it may well be a psychological factor in some cases.

Dixie is the type of rebellious woman who manages to get pregnant even when birth control tablets are available free of charge. Irresponsibility is not confined to males. Girls and women can also be carried away with sexual ecstacy and social indifference. For instance, when a girl is anxious to become pregnant, she may thwart or prevent an otherwise successful coitus interruptus by holding on to the male in such a way that withdrawal is all but impossible. In such cases an evaluation of psychological factors in the participants as causes for disharmony is obviously more important than any improvement in coital techniques.

At her sixth conference and in the presence of her fiance, Dixie responded to suggestions for hypnotic relaxation. I used the time to help her to reevaluate that which her boyfriend had insisted on telling me just prior to the trance.

> She told me she'd masturbated until she was ten. She had her first menstrual period when she was ten and it scared the hell out of her. She hasn't masturbated since.

In the light of this revelation, her overzealous attempts to achieve orgasm could be conceived as a vicarious or substitute masturbation with her fiance's penis for which she needed to punish herself by blocking her natural libidinal response. Her fiance also entered trance; and both of them were taught the clenched fist displacement and reconditioning technique.[5] In addition, some appropriate suggestions were made for an enlightened and current attitude toward her parents as well as toward her sexual mores.

At their seventh conference, three weeks later, she wore a little makeup for the first time. She had amnesia for the previous trance but was able to smile, and both of them appeared to be much more relaxed. Only two sexual relationships had been attempted since the previous visit. She was not sure whether or not she had had an orgasm, but she also did not care. The fiance confirmed her report that she had felt much better and was easier to live with.

They relaxed in trance quite readily and she responded to the suggestion that she could recall some significant experience that she might be willing to talk about. She promptly reported a longstanding fear of insects and recalled being stung by a bee, again at the critical age of ten and just about the time of onset of her menstruation when she had also put the brakes on her self-loving genital manipulations.

TECHNIQUES IN NORMAL COITUS

Coition is a natural symbol of affection and acceptance. It expresses multiple feelings, including trusting dependency, tenderness, desire, possessiveness, aggression, and hostility. It arouses and accentuates lust and anxiety and it also releases emotional and physical tensions. Coition accelerates pulse and elevates blood pressure, speeds up respiration and perspiration, loosens inhibitions, starts glands secreting and muscles contracting, produces erection of penis and clitoris, and initates rhythmic contractions of genital muscles and ducts. In humans as well as animals, preliminary sex play that heightens the erotic forepleasure consists of teasing, chasing, protestations, looking, smelling, licking, kissing, caressing, massaging, squeezing, pinching, nipping and, sometimes, biting and scratching.[56]

Other valuable procedures in building up a receptivity for sexual intercourse include subdued magenta or other preferred lighting, soft "favorite" music, exotic perfumes, tender words and caressing, sucking of ear lobes and nipples, and various degrees of stimulation to back, neck, buttocks, groin, bosom, and genitals in approximately that order.

Too many would-be lovers caress the genitals first, instead of last. Too many participants dispense with all or most of the preliminary caresses and rush directly into the last stages of intromission. Failure to build up the female's receptivity leaves her vulva unlubricated, her disposition ruffled and her body unreceptive. Failure to provide artificial lubrication can irritate the organs of both partners. Timing of caresses and stimulation is important, and mutual discussion and exchanges of information regarding progress are useful, especially for beginners.

In older men, or when a young man is not in the mood, he too may require some of the above preliminary procedures to build up his preparation for coitus. He, too, can have other things on his mind or be annoyed with his partner and show impatience.

Couples usually discover each other's needs as they go along. They learn that young and impetuous males often complete their orgasms long before the female is ready but that manual and other stimulation can be substituted until a suitable lapse of time prepares the male for another intromission and a more leisurely series of movements leading to a climax for his partner. Several ejaculations during a single hour are common in young and virile males who may also achieve five or six to a dozen or more orgasms during a twenty-four-hour period.

Older and inhibited males are slower. They can usually wait until the female partner is properly primed. Frequently, they also prefer to wait until she has achieved her orgasm before releasing theirs. This is because a loss of erection may occur rather promptly following the ejaculation of their semen. Continued stimulation after the orgasm may even cause discomfort until after a lapse of several minutes or longer. Mutual achievement of the climax at the same identical moment is not essential, nor is it always possible, especially for beginners.

Some females can experience a series of short but powerful orgasms in rapid succession almost as soon as the penis is inserted or even before insertion during some of the preliminaries. Others, who insist upon coitus interruptus or withdrawal, are unable to achieve any climax until they are certain that the penis has been completely withdrawn and there is little or no danger of semen being deposited within the vagina.

The female climax is not always localized to her genitals. It may at times be diffused and experienced as a generalized feeling of warm and loving security and acceptance during which it becomes most important for her to be held in a snug embrace.

Under ordinary circumstances, some young males will be able to perform three or four successful orgasms within a couple of hours, and some couples, especially newlyweds, can carry on with multiple repeat performances and varying degrees of completion for several days at a time—interrupted only by sleep, food and visits to the bathroom. The younger the participants, the shorter the time required. A minute or less may suffice, if the buildup and preparation have been adequate. Older couples may require fifteen to sixty minutes for completion of a single orgasm, and some couples discover that the efforts can be more exhausting than rewarding. Long periods of preparation in young people usually indicate emotional trouble, but long periods between desired coitus do not necessarily indicate waning love. They may denote sheer physical exhaustion or emotional depression which is a common aftermath in young brides who have moved a long distance from home. Their nostalgia is often translated in terms of sexual indifference as well as loss of appetite and a tendency toward constipation, weeping, or a return of some former psychosomatic or psychovisceral complaint, especially "allergy."

Females secrete more androgens, male sex hormones, during ovulation and are consequently more aggressive and physically receptive at such times. Ovulation normally occurs midway in their menstrual cycle—approximately ten to fourteen days after the first day of menstruation. This is, naturally, her most fertile period. However, when pregnancy is not desired, a woman's conscious receptivity is liable to be greater at the end of menstruation. At such times she naturally feels cleaner as well as safe.

Men can be aroused at almost any time except when depressed, exhausted, or very much intoxicated, or very angry. Women, too, can be aroused at almost any time and may be especially receptive *during* menstruation. At such times, coitus is not contraindicated if both partners are willing, but a bath and preliminary douching are indicated to prevent possible irritation of the glans penis as well as for aesthetic reasons.

Many women prefer to douche as well as bathe daily during their menstruation and to permit no interruption in their regular routine activities. Athletes and show people are especially impatient with women who use menstruation as an excuse for a retreat from responsibilities. They have learned from experience that most menstrual tension is emotional and that it usually responds to keeping actively and happily busy.

Special training and physical preparation for sexual intercourse is mandatory in many primitive tribes. Brides-to-be are mechanically deflowered, taught the art of making love, and carefully bathed and scented. The groom does not even see her until she is ready. In our culture, the groom has to learn quite a lot about his woman in a relatively short time. He learns that she usually keeps some portions of her body covered as long as possible; that she is often modest and self-conscious about lights; that she keeps her thighs close together during most of the preliminary maneuvers of lovemaking; that the pressure of her body against him means that she wants to be embraced and protected but not that she is ready for insertion of his penis. He learns that she is liable to be very shy about touching certain parts of his body and may remain so for a long period of time; that she is apprehensive about sounds, and seems to be forever looking over her shoulder as though mamma or somebody might burst in on them. He also learns that she cannot get her fill of kisses and "I love you's" and that under no circumstances may he comment unfavorably on any of her defects, whatever they may be.

On the contrary, to her lover, a woman must always be the most beautiful and wonderful thing in the world; and he had better keep telling her so and making her believe it, if he wants cooperation. For her part, she usually assumes that he knows that she considers him to be number one man in her life or at least he ought to know it by virtue of the fact that she is giving herself to him. Unfortunately, she may be slow in discovering that he too requires a bit of ego-lifting praise and that active participation on her part is desired by some males, while others prefer to have her remain passive. As already stated, communication and teamwork are essential.

The young groom also learns that, theoretically, he is expected to be virginal; but whether virginal or not, he is expected to know all or most of the answers on how to make love. If his bride is not virginal and knows it, she may simulate ignorance and clumsiness. If she is unaware of not having an intact hymen, she may become even more upset than he when the discovery is apparent. He may not know the difference but if it is important to him, the matter should be discussed long before the bridal night.

Some couples prefer to confess "everything" to each other before marriage. Others are well advised to withhold some details, depending upon the circumstances and the type of personalities involved. Whatever the decision, the nuptial couch is no time for confessions, inquisitions, or irrelevancies.

When the female is ready for entrance, her thighs gradually spread apart, but not so far that the male is not expected to do a little struggling on his own in order to obtain enough room for entrance. By now, the introitus is normally moist; and a self-lubricating oily fluid has also appeared at the meatus or opening of the penis. The entrance should be gentle and gradual. The male should support most of his weight on his hands or elbows when the position warrants it, and each participant should remember that he is a very special guest as well as a host. Undue sensitivity usually indicates anxiety which responds better to reassurance, patience and gentleness than to drugs or coercion.

Photographic studies and observations by Masters and Johnson confirm what has long been known to Van de Velde and other specialists.[34] As the female approaches her orgasm her thighs are brought closer together and her entire body becomes tense. Perineal contractions may occur spontaneously but they can also be cultivated by constricting the urethral and anal sphincters. Locally, in the female, there is a nervous discharge of energy similar to that which occurs in the male, plus rhythmic contractures of uterus and vaginal muscles that facilitate acceptance of the semen. There may be, however, only a limited amount of secretory activity on the part of the introital and cervical glands. In some women there is also very little local excitation. They experience, instead, a high degree of general well-being, comfort, and security that is best expressed by the term "emotional ecstacy." In the uninitiated female the localized genital response must be learned. In the overinhibited partner it may never be learned, and so it is rarely missed.

Consideration for each other's needs and comforts should be paramount. Communication is important and cannot be over-emphasized. Verbal communication is eventually replaced by nonverbal indicators. Corrections should be made as promptly as possible; and errors, once discovered, should not be repeated.

The normal sequence of insertion and partial withdrawal in the form of an accelerated pumping should build up into a crescendo of paroxysmal ecstasy. This culminates with seminal discharge and the simultaneous release of pent-up tension that gradually subsides, first in one partner and then the other. Vaginal and vulval wetting may take place before, during or just after the female climax. Penile wetting in the form of a small amount of sticky lubricating fluid at the meatus usually occurs prior to intromission. Semen may be copious or scanty, thick or watery, milky white, slightly salty and may have a mildly earthy or alkaline odor. Generalized sweating, flushing and rapid breathing are normal accompaniments of intercourse, along with accelerated heartbeat and, occasionally, other visceral activities such as intestinal rumbling or bladder urgency which may also precede the intercourse.

Some partners become drowsy following an orgasm or comfortably relaxed. Others become overstimulated and active. Some girls want to dance. Others often feel ashamed and try to get away as quickly as possible. Some partners become more tender and considerate while others are liable to become irritable and critical. The making of disparaging remarks or wisecracks is peculiar to some participants, representing a self-conscious effort to conceal embarrassment in an otherwise satisfactory sexual relationship. After all, as already mentioned, some people grow up to feel that they do not deserve to be happy or healthy, let alone merit the pleasures of sexual intercourse.

Every couple can add useful pointers from their own personal experiences to the above brief description of preliminaries and techniques in sexual intercourse. For instance, the receipt of good news, the viewing of an exciting movie or stimulating literature, the desire for a baby, the acquisition of a new home or new furniture, especially a new bedroom suite, or a visit with some very important or beloved people—any one of these may spark the desire for cohabitation and can enhance its satisfactions.

Unfortunately, the desire to celebrate does not always affect both parties at the same time. For instance, suppose hubby catches wifey off guard in what, to him, is an exciting state of exposure, as with Carlotta, above. Her embarrassment, added to her state of unreadiness, naturally arouses alarm and indignant rejection, but his impatience does not take kindly to her rebuff. He may nurse resentment for a long time and usually takes it out on her in other ways. Not every incident of sex rejection is preventable, but there are many errors that should not happen. Here are some useful guidelines.

Prevention of Unsatisfactory Intercourse

Variation of Position and Techniques

This is both normal and desirable but may be unaesthetic to one or both participants. Couples learn from others, from books or pictures, or by mutual experimentation, just which variations are most satisfying and acceptable. They also learn that some variations of sexual intercourse are considered to be perversions which reflect the personal needs of the participants. Fellatio, cunnilinctus, pederasty, mutual manual or oral manipulations and even "dry runs" may be tried experimentally and then cast aside for more conventional variations of posture. Some females prefer the dominant superior position, and some males are happier in the passive role. The mischief arises when one partner tries to *insist* on coercing the other into an unaccustomed procedure or persists in demanding repetitions of the new variation long after the other partner has indicated discomfort or displeasure.

Variety prevents monotony. Monotony and sameness of procedures may weaken the strength of an erotic response. Variations can be cultivated in time, place, posture, perfume, lighting, novelty of attire, and in such preliminaries as dining out, dancing, flowers, candy, or some inexpensive but useful "happy unbirthday" gift.

Variation of frequency is usually determined by mutual needs and experience; but attempts to overdo or to ration the sex act are common sources of dissatisfaction with sexual intercourse.

Conflict Over Birth Control Or Unsatisfactory Methods for Contraception

This is a mutual responsibility which each partner is liable to push onto the other, although the contemporary popularity of "the pill" and intrauterine coils has lessened the friction somewhat. The issue is essentially a matter that concerns their moral and religious training, and/or their obstetrician as well as the financial budget and their emotional maturity. When the marriage counselor is consulted, he will also want to consider their families' views on the subject. Current defiance of family standards is often replaced by subsequent regret and reproach.

When withdrawal or the rhythm method are the preferred techniques, one may expect to find a frustrated female with varying degrees of backache, headache, pelvic or abdominal complaints and an equally frustrated male who has developed other outlets for his tensions. Among the target areas for displaced and delayed erotic reactions in the male are painful testes, hydrocoele of the spermatic cord, prostatic, bladder or urethral problems, and even head colds, indigestion or hemorrhoids.

Vicarious outlets such as masturbation can also add temporary hypertension, fatigue and irritability plus a lot of uncomfortable feelings of guilt and resentment. Emphatic denial that sexual maladjustment has anything whatsoever to do with one's marital difficulties or personal health is a fairly safe tip-off that sex is far from satisfactory and that it is also a likely scapegoat for other problems.

Faulty Timing

When intercourse is delayed, prolonged, rushed or interrupted, faulty timing alone can be responsible for a good many physical and emotionally distressing complaints. Faulty timing, like the use of unsatisfactory positions or birth control techniques, can develop into a habitually unconditioning pattern that becomes chronic and is extremely difficult to correct.

Timing is particularly liable to become upset when coitus interruptus is practiced and when avoidable interferences are allowed to take place. For example, failure to insure privacy via locked bedroom and bathroom doors is a common source of negligence. Neglect to attend to elimination, bathing, mouth hygiene, cutting one's toenails, disposal of soiled underwear and socks are also common obstacles to satisfactory intercourse.

Morning erections are usually associated with a full bladder or bowel, or perhaps with an uncompleted erotic dream; but if morning turns out to be the most satisfactory time for at least one of the partners, the need should not be discouraged nor the invitation ignored.

Separate beds, like separate bedrooms, are not conducive to kissing and making up at the end of a day of domestic or personal friction. In cold bedrooms, mutual needs for warmth can quickly transcend special requirements and quickly provide healing balm for hurt feelings. Sex, after a few hours of sleep, or sleep after sex, can be most rewarding both to the giver and the recipient.

Menstruation

Couples need frequent reminders that menstruation is a common cause of unsatisfactory coitus. As already mentioned, the flow may be frightening or offensive for some men, yet it can be sexually exciting for others. Some couples cohabit during menstruation, using both douche and condom.

Some women tend to make a big production of the occasion and wear a pad as long as possible. Others, like most show people and athletes, carry on without interruption and without major discomfiture. Habitually distressing menstruation requires both the gynecologist and the psychotherapist.

Unavoidable Interferences

Babies and children, like guests in the house, represent a third party. Some women become more responsive sexually *after* conception, especially after the birth of their first child. Others are never as interested in coitus as they were before they became mothers.

It is difficult to provide for absolute privacy without any interruptions when there is anyone else in the house. Yet one small cry or cough can spoil the recipe for satisfactory intercourse. This constant threat of interruption is a common reason for paternal resentment, but mothers too can develop impatient annoyance with their own children and not just for interrupted sex. There is also the matter of interrupted sleep.

Parents become deprived of privacy and freedom in many other ways. Budgets become strained. Responsibilities mount. Rest and recreation become more difficult to obtain. On the other hand, some of the challenges of courtship may now become more attractive. For instance, most couples found ways to be alone before they were married, so it is up to them, not the marriage counselor, to prove that their desire for privacy is as important as they say.

MARRIED SEX SHOPPERS

Waning Libido Is Not An Infallible Sign of Fading Love

Married sex is self-adjusting and serves multiple needs, but for some couples, the legality of the relationship may rob the sexual climax of some of its power. For the disenchanted partners, stolen fruits are liable to seem sweeter. The moral issues of the illegal relationship can be temporarily repressed and are often rationalized. This is why so many men and women develop into sex shoppers, who are continually seeking new thrills for old values in temporary fulfillment of a lifelong need for acceptance and comforting.

Some of these disillusioned and dissatisfied philanderers have yet to learn that sex is like any other appetite and that it varies with the state of mind and emotional composure as well as with the circumstances. For instance, sex can indicate confidence and tender affection or, as in profanity, it can express hostile aggression, like a bone-crushing handshake, or a rib-cracking bear hug. Here is an illustrative report.

> "My wife and I had one hell of a big fight. We stopped speaking to each other for nearly two hours while we watched TV. Then she took a bath and I took a shower. As soon as we got into bed and turned out the light, we made a grab for each other and had one of the most vigorous and satisfying intercourses in our three years of married life . . .
>
> The next day was wonderful, and the next night, right after we put the baby to bed, we had the most exquisite and gentle sexual relationship that we've ever had even before we were married."

When both of the disenchanted partners want help, the problem is not insoluble, but when one of them refuses to change or to admit responsibility for any part of the problem, then the marriage counselor has his work cut out for him. Some couples will never consider divorce. Yet most wives, and many husbands, cannot countenance their partner's current mistress or lover. According to some reports, however, more and more married people are sexperimenting—some of them for pay, others for kicks. Still others indulge in extramarital sex as an expression of endearment, or as a convenience, or as a means to an end—the end being to punish the spouse or in expectation of divorce and remarriage with someone "new" and, hopefully, better. Habitual flirtatiousness and increasing dependency on alcohol at social functions are liable to be ominous signs.

Protection Against the Sex Hunter

When more important pursuits are developed by married people, especially in such areas as joint business or professional ventures, music, recreation and other common interests, their emphasis upon sexual satisfactions automatically diminishes.

The same objectives apply in the matter of social activities. New acquaintances offer new interests and new activities to dispel boredom. However, newly met people are often seen at their best. They make it their business to be agreeable, so that it is only after several visits that disenchantment sets in. At such times familiarity may indeed breed contempt. As a result, a couple's social calendar is seldom the same from year to year. Their lists of invitees and greeting card recipients keep changing from time to time as they drop some names and add others in a continual search for ideal friendships.

The marriage counselor has to learn to keep his own morals and opinions as objective as possible. He is expected to help the patient to uncover and to recognize the basic patterns of unfinished emotional business which unduly prolong difficulties. He also needs to recognize the patient's insatiable hunger for reassurance. Married people are supposed to be out of the running; but they never lose the capacity for pleasure at being reminded that they are still desirable, attractive, and important to someone in addition to their mates. They also need to be reminded that people of both sexes are needed to fulfill everyone's childhood dreams for domestic unity and harmony. Without such reminders, they are liable to become easy prey to the sex hunter.

The "Ideal Bachelor"

When the sex hunter is one who deludes himself into maintaining "ideal bachelorhood," the burden of proof is not necessarily on the patient to show cause why any change is indicated. The married partner is deluded into expecting a new and better solution, while the confirmed bachelor of either sex clings to an adjustment of sorts, which he has already made.

The advice of friends and wishes of the families are seldom sufficiently influential, although motivation for change can stem from the influence of other people in peer groups. Unfortunately, the presence of mixed male or female bachelors and married people in groups which accentuate the revelations of marital discord are liable to have a reverse effect on the sex hunter.

The therapist should guide the 'ideal bachelor" toward a more objective and realistic appraisal of his emotional needs and capabilities as well as a reevaluation of his personal limitations. Marriage may turn out to be an unwise prescription that is totally unworkable for many a single man and woman. By the same reasoning, recommendations for divorce should be approached more objectively and realistically, especially when children are involved.

Chapter 16

SPECIAL SEX PROBLEMS

IMPOTENCE

Inability of the male to complete the sex act is generally identified with failure or weakness of erections. Impotence also results from premature ejaculations, no ejaculation at all, as in the eunuch, or from retrograde ejaculation in which the semen is sucked back into the bladder, as in some diabetics. Inability to initiate or to complete a satisfactory sexual intercourse may be partial and temporary, or total and chronic. It may also be organic as well as emotional (functional) and should first be cleared by the urologist.

Psychogenic factors may include unpleasant associations with odors, position, reproaches, guilt or a history of previous coital failures.

A very common cause of impotence is the male's fear of rejection. This can occur when the female has been dissatisfied or when ineptness or negligence has produced discomfort, infection, or irritation in either partner. For instance, an unclean vagina can produce an irritation and discharge that closely resembles gonorrhea. The reverse, of course, is also true because a variety of microscopic organisms are involved. They abound especially under the foreskin of the uncircumcised male. There are also psychogenic factors, such as erotic frustrations and masturbation, that can produce leucorrhea in the female.

Other possible causes of impotence include a history of compulsive masturbation, latent or actual homosexual practices or preferences, alcoholism, drug addiction, self-consciousness over the size or shape of one's penis, or the rest of the body, an overprotective or overpowering mother, sister, aunt or grandmother, a rejecting father, hostile brothers, and a variety of other fears that are usually repressed.

Among these are the male's fear of loss of virility through

dependency upon a female for sexual release, the fear of feminine dominance, unresolved guilt over childhood indiscretions or conflicts, the fear of producing a child who might not win approval, and the fear of some dire punishment resulting from allowing himself to enjoy such a union.

Temporary impotence including inability to ejaculate or to sustain erections can express emotional depression from some personal loss, or threatened danger. It may also indicate resentment against the particular partner. The latter cause is easily eliminated if the male finds himself equally impotent with other partners, in which case the impotence usually represents an emotional depressive equivalent. Treatment in such cases may require anti-depressant medication as well as analytical and reconstructive psychotherapy. Sudden, acute onsets are easier to treat, as in the following case of Adam.

Sudden Impotence as an Indication of Emotional Depression

Adam, a hard working and otherwise healthy thirty-five-year-old electrician from a neighboring state, is happily married and the father of several children. He said that he had been advised to see a urologist but that he had hesitated because he "wondered whether there might be something to do with my nerves." Here is his story.

It was just before the New Year. My wife and I were playing in bed. She responded like she usually does but suddenly I had a feeling like it wasn't going to come up. I started to rush it, but nothing helped. I had an empty feeling in my stomach (points to lower abdomen), kept trying, but I soon got exhausted and my wife fell asleep. After a few hours, I tried it again. This time I only got a little simmer of an erection and a little bit of thin watery discharge. I decided I'd wait till tomorrow—that I was too tired. My wife said, "Are you sure?" and I said, "Sure."

Next night I took a bath and primed myself in usual little ways, but nothing happened. Then she came in. Usually she's kind of bashful, but this time she let me put the light on and look at her while I was playing with her. At first nothing happened. Later something simmered again (partial erection) and then a little bit of discharge.

She said, "You've probably been out with some other woman." I knew damn well I hadn't—not since before

we were married. I told her, "You know better," and
she said, "Well, it ain't never happened before." I said,
"Gimme a few days."

Next morning I didn't even have a "piss hard"—
you know, the kind of erection you get from a full
bladder. She said, "You'd better go see a doctor." But
I didn't.

Three days later we tried it again. It was better, but
not enough. She was trying to help me and it got a little
bit stiff, but after two or three moves it went down. I
tried to concentrate my mind on someone else—pretty
girls, nudes and all that—but nothing happened.

So the next day I got to talking with an old girlfriend. She was sympathetic and agreed to try to help
me out, but it didn't do no good.

I went to see my doctor. He said I was probably
run down and had a cold. He gave me a shot of penicillin. There was just semi-erections and a watery discharge.

After a few days I tried it again, first with my wife
and then with the other girlfriend, but nothing happened. IT FELT LIKE SUMPIN' WAS MISSING IN
MY STOMACH.

Then I saw you, the second week after it started,
and you showed me how to relax the fist. A few days
later I found myself stirred up. It was gradually coming
up. I called my wife in. She was pleased and told me
to go on and relax some more and she'd be back. I
was almost asleep when she came back, but we tried it
and after a few minutes it was just like before, and
we've had no trouble ever since.

(Total duration—three weeks: two before the psychotherapeutic
session of forty minutes and one week following the treatment.)

The second session, lasting one hour, took place three months
later at my request for reevaluation and because of his desire for
help with public speaking at shop meetings. At the beginning, and
without trance, he recited the above history almost word for word
as he had given it the first time. I then signaled him to relax and
invited him to verbalize whatever he could recall of the first therapeutic interview. Here are his recollections.

I remember what you told me—to look directly
ahead and try to relax. As you began to talk and moved
my arm back and forth (kinaesthetic induction) I began
to relax, and you asked me to remember some of the

good things in life—squeeze the right hand—and then think of the bad things and squeeze my left hand and then ease my mind. And think of what had happened to me. Also I would sleep better because I'd thought I had a severe illness and I was wondering what was wrong.

Adam understood that I had reassured him that his watery discharge did not necessarily imply a diseased urethra; that he could still see the urologist if necessary, but that worry could cause both the impotence and the discharge as well as his insomnia and his vague lower abdominal "emptiness." Literal statements, in trance, are often condensed.

Q. That's all you remember?

A. Yes. You told me to continue to practice it.

The trance was deepened by repetition of the induction signal to relax, but this time I avoided touching him. Instead I demonstrated the technique of reversed levitation and suggested that he could remember whatever was important just as soon as his hand touched his knee. There was silence for several minutes before he began to speak softly.

"Well, there was this Potentate in our lodge. He died suddenly in January." (Another long pause which I again did not interrupt.) "Then there was 'D.' He was a very close friend. We worked together . . . He died suddenly . . . about a month later . . . in February."

After a lengthy pause, I prompted him, "Wasn't there a third loss?" At first he could not seem to remember any. Then, "Oh! You mean my Pastor? Yes . . . he died suddenly, too, in March. I went to all three funerals." (Deep sigh.)

Adam was aroused from trance gradually, after I suggested that he need-not-remember-everything; that his impotence had served its purpose and that whenever he felt the need to talk further he would find himself making an appointment for future discussions.

Short-term therapy respects the needs of the patient to proceed at his own pace. Many clues for deeper analysis are evident in his story but, as of this writing (three years later), Adam is functioning satisfactorily and had no return of his impotence even after a fourth loss—this time, the death of one of his brothers.

Retrograde Ejaculation

An unusual form of impotence, known as retrograde ejaculation, occurs when the semen passes back into the bladder instead of out through the urethra of the penis. It has been observed following prostatectomy and also in diabetes and is, apparently, the result of faulty sphincter control. When the urologist passes responsibility to the psychotherapist, some such sequence as the following may be uncovered. The patient is a young, divorced physician.

Case of Dr. B.

Mother considered sex a sin. She knew I masturbated because of the noisy bed. I tried to avoid her furious outbursts by masturbating to the point of orgasm. But I'd hold back the ejaculation by squeezing and compressing everything as if I was holding back a bowel or bladder evacuation. Of course, this must have produced a congestion in my prostate. It's still enlarged and boggy—soft. It interferes with my desire and ability to urinate. I used to sneak up to the maid's room, but some nights my parents came home late and sometimes the girls weren't too cooperative. They'd complain to mother and I'd catch it. Mother would tell father but he'd just pass it off. After all, he was visiting them too. My brothers were the favorites until I got diabetes, and from then on, the impotence has come and gone . . .

The same patient reported the following dream. I dreamed that Shelly was lying naked on the extra cot in my bachelor's bedroom. She was face down and asleep. The buttocks were large and seductive, but there seemed to be unsightly genital hair between the thighs. It was very distasteful.

His associations and self-analysis were as simple as they were obvious:

My ex-wife had large buttocks. We'd use that position for a warmup, especially when I was slow or impotent. She didn't seem to mind. My mother had large buttocks and, especially, my favorite aunts. One of them was very seductive the last time I went home—but nothing happened. As a small boy I remembered playing with other boys in the woods and trying to perform sodomy. It wasn't successful. I don't remember father's body but my brothers and I were all bathed together in the same tub. Mother never wanted boys. She always wished one of us had been a girl.

> Is that one of the reasons for my impotence? I had
> a date last week. She was very responsive but she told
> me I was too soft, too gentle. Like a mother? Am I
> still seeking mothering by showing it?

Premature Ejaculation

This is a form of relative impotence which is usually associated with anxiety and apprehension—for instance, over a possible
pregnancy, or fear of the female partner. By having his orgasm
too soon, the male effectively punishes his partner, as though he
scarcely needs her. He also punishes himself. Reconditioning,
via suggestion and hypnotic time-distortion, is often satisfactory
after the patient has uncovered and expressed his hostilities.
Tranquilizers or hydrotherapy and autohypnotic relaxation can
speed recovery.

Psychological Castration

In males with relatively weak libidos there are many seemingly minor details which may be be responsible for disturbances
in erection or ejaculation. Among them are such factors as avoidable delays, negligent personal hygiene, impatience, and especially an unresponsive, careless or hostile partner, as indicated
by such remarks as these:

> "You go ahead. I'm not in the mood" or "What,
> again? You just had one last week!" or "Oh, all
> right. But hurry it up. I've got an appointment with
> my hairdresser."

Habitual responses of this nature can amount to an accumulated equivalent of a psychological castration which soon leads
to some form of relative impotence or to a search for subsitute
outlets. Amazonian types of mothers are less subtle in their efforts
at psychological castration.

Jessica, in her late thirties, miscarried her sixth pregnancy.
During her convalescence she proclaimed often and loudly for
all to hear, "There'll be no more of this foolishness from now on."
Her husband, several years her junior, soon got the message and
has been impotent ever since. When Jessica herself was asked
about her husband's potency in connection with my treatment of

his accompanying emotional depression she smiled with satisfaction and declared triumphantly, "Oh, he outgrew that foolishness a long time ago." (She deludes herself that he's had a "change of life.")

The so-called *male climacteric,* in an otherwise healthy man, is largely a psychological impotence. Potency may be retained well past seventy, eighty or even ninety or more years, although the frequency and vigor is naturally lessened.

Less subtle results of psychological castration consist of procrastination and alibis that threaten or sabotage the peace of mind or marginal leisure of the male breadwinner. This causes him to skip or gulp his meals, forego or miss appointments, speed or take chances to make up for wasted time, and build up resentments against innocent recipients of preferential treatment, such as his in-laws or even his own children.

On the other hand, and in fairness to the female at any age, one should remember that dominant males are liable to take advantage of weakness, keep their women almost constantly pregnant, overwork them, and shorten their lives.

Even the female lion who does the hunting and killing for food is obliged to sit back and wait for the leavings while her mate fills his belly with the food which she has risked her life to provide. In return, he will fight to the death—both for possession of his mate and the protection of her cubs. Yet when he is challenged by another lion, his mate sits calmly by until the battle is over and then goes off with the victor. Sentiment takes second place to the primitive laws of survival of the fittest, and perhaps we should adjust our own philosophical thinking to long-range planning.

People who will not fight to retain their prized virility, whatever their age, make poor enough parents for tomorrow's generation. From such a viewpoint, castration anxiety becomes another source of impotence since more American couples are having operations to prevent pregnancy, including vasectomy (cutting the spermatic duct).

Contraceptive devices have been known since ancient times. For instance, coitus interruptus (withdrawal or onanism) is described in Genesis 38:9; and according to Southern, for over two thousand years camel drivers in the Middle East have been inserting an intrauterine device into their young female working camels in order to prevent conception.[50]

Adequate sex education is still behind the times. In a Dublin clinic for infertility, an intact hymen was found in one out of every ten women who sought treatment for primary sterility. In contrast, the long-sought secret of prenatal sex identification, is finally yielding to highly accurate predictions from examination of the amniotic fluid.[2]

Here are a few more biological and psychological areas in which the marriage and family counselor must be well informed. When men with anxieties work under pressure, they show an excess of immature sperm cells in their semen. This was especially common among first-year medical students. But plasma testosterone increases with ovulation, making normal females more aggressive about midway during their menstrual cycle.

Emotional tension and unfulfilled sexual activities in the female can interfere with ovulation at any time and can also result in faulty implantation of a fertilized egg.

We have long known that anxiety and frustration can produce backache, pelvic congestion, tension, and pain. It is less well known, however, that sexual frustrations can produce irregular uterine contractions, abdominal cramps, chronic vaginal discharge, delayed, difficult or prolonged menstruation, painful intercourse, and allied disorders of the digestive, dermal, and genito-urinary systems.

STERILITY

Sterility may result from emotional depression or anxiety. Survivors of concentration camps report a loss of sexual desire and even a stoppage of menstruation when hopes were at their lowest. Zoo keepers report an increase in fertility and survival when litters of foxes and other cubs are born in surroundings that most nearly resemble their natural habitat.

Habitual use of contraceptives may alter the mental attitude of the partners and cause delay in conception after discontinuing them.

Some investigators believe that elimination of ovulation also eliminates the natural stimuli which makes a women feminine as well as fertile. When certain pills are used, several months may be required to restore normal hormonal balance in the menstrual cycle.

Sterility from a low sperm count or from indolent sperms can be organic as well as functional. When the urologist and internist have no answers, analytical studies may uncover deep-seated emotional depression along with resistance to paternity, and hostility to the particular partner. The patient may also have a fear of being displaced by a child as he may have been displaced once before by a younger brother or sister.

The same holds true for inorganic or functional sterility in the female, where fear of childbirth and other anxieties are often resolved not only by direct psychotherapy but also indirectly by adoptions or by plans for cesarean deliveries.

Psychotherapy for both impotence and sterility should be aimed at building the patient's self-confidence from nonsexual sources and then reconditioning him. Constructive measures include temporary abstinence, displacement of attention to the nonclimactic phases of the relationship, time distortion and a variety of suggestions designed to alter his overemphasis on the orgasm. Minor alterations and gains that are gradually achieved stand a better chance of success than aiming for a complete correction at one therapeutic session. For example, in premature ejaculation

> Suppose you had no-sperms-at-all—or no-semen —or even-no-orgasm! What if you had to-wait just one-or-five-or even ten-seconds before-letting-go. And the next time you could double-the-delay and then triple-it-to-three-seconds (or 15 seconds or 30).

Meanwhile, in hypnotic relaxation, one could suggest projection and recall of *some possible association* that can come to mind, on a signal—some recollection or idea that might *furnish a clue* as to what might be contributing to the difficulty.

Later, one may also suggest that *something constructive* can pop into mind, on signal or upon returning home.

> Some one-little-change of thought, or behavior,

that you have reason to believe might help-to-improve-matters. Something you'd be willing-to-start, or to stop—beginning this-very-day.

One husband recovered his potency after tracing the onset to his wife's second delivery which, like the first, had endangered her life. Mistrusting contraceptive procedures, his impotence served as insurance against the danger of losing her and also as penance for masculine selfishness (his mother's designation).

It is seldom necessary to inquire as to just what did come to the patient's mind because he will usually be eager to report it on the following visit.

FRIGIDITY

Frigidity, like impotence, may come and go with the mood, or it may be a longlasting chronic pattern. Possible causes include religious and moral conflicts; apprehension regarding contraceptive techniques; conditioning by hostile parents, relatives, or friends; fears of pregnancy and childbirth; resentments over favoritism in the home or among one's associates; self-consciousness over one's body; or previous addiction to masturbatory practices.

The case of Dixie has already been described in which she was unconsciously perpetuating the theme, "My Heart Belongs to Daddy."

The following case of Patricia is much more common although such criticism is liable to include the bosom as well as the hips and thighs.

Case of Patricia

Patricia, at seventeen, eloped with her impetuous lover Charles, who was two years older. They embarked on a sea voyage to the Orient where he expected to land a job. Neither one had ever had any sexual experiences before their first night together. The ocean was calm, their prospects bright, and their spirits high. Nevertheless, on that night, and in the five years which followed, Patricia found herself completely frigid and unresponsive to his embraces. It was only after his accidental death and her subsequent marriage to James that she sought a psychiatrist's help for her continuing frigidity.

A few conferences revealed the following long suppressed episode: Charles had been visiting the bar on the eve of their wedding day. In the bridal chamber he had suddenly put on the lights and with characteristic frankness exclaimed in derisive tones, "Gee! What skinny legs you have, Pat!" Patricia froze up in embarrassment. She remained conditioned against each of several other sexual partners, including her second husband James. This was partly through continued feelings of self-consciousness and partly because of the painful memories of her first coitus, for Charles, with the double handicap of inexperience and alcoholism, had been far from gentle.

Grooms are traditionally altar shy and they, too, can be embarrassed in the nuptial boudoir, but when there is over dependency upon alcohol by either partner at a time of normally psycho-physiological exaltation, the omens indicate stormy times ahead.

The following account by Evelyn, a "bride" for seventeen years, is another example of enduring frigidity that could have been prevented.

Evelyn the "Bride"

> I believe the most unpleasant experiences I have had, have been associated with D's drinking. The night he told me I had "shitty little tits." I will never forget it. It hurt more than anything he has ever said to me. The night he remarked in front of friends that my mother had lived long enough and it was time she died. The night he was working with me hypnotically in preparation for the delivery of our last baby. I had to pretend to be in a trance to keep him from being angry as he was very drunk—he hurt me terribly and that was the end of hypnosis for delivery.
>
> **P.S.** Ordinarily he drinks two or three quarts of vodka a week. That week he had a whole gallon.

Six months have passed since E's report. D's drinking has been voluntarily reduced to less than a pint a week, his abuse has also diminished, and both he and his wife are reporting more satisfactory intercourse. Both of them have also been working at the job of correcting past and current errors, and many hours of psychotherapy have been required.

As of December 1966 they have had a total of seventeen hours in nine visits, the infrequency having been determined by transportation problems and available time. No medication was used, nor were restrictions imposed on the use of alcohol. Instead, they were both taught the clenched fist displacement and reconditioning technique. Both of them were also quite responsive to other hypnoanalytical and hypnotherapeutic suggestive procedures. They also participated in a few sessions of group psychotherapy but soon dropped out because of the relative lateness of the closing hour. As is often the case, the original consultation was for a rebellious teen-age daughter and not for frigidity. A 1968 letter reports "no change."

COITUS INTERRUPTUS

Withdrawal of the penis before ejaculation is a common source of frustration to both parties, but it is especially disturbing to the female. She not only worries about whether her partner withdrew in time, but she is also deprived of the final stages of erotic satisfaction. Accumulated tensions and substitute visceral complaints inevitably build up dissatisfaction in both participants. As time goes on, the sexual relationship becomes less attractive and less satisfying. Eventually, it contributes to some degree of partial impotence as well as to frigidity.

In many males habitual withdrawal results in a chronic congestion of the prostate and urethra that may give all the clinical signs of a nonspecific urethritis similar to gonorrhea. Painful testes are also common, especially in the adolescent male, and from similar frustration. Urethral stricture may complicate the picture. A comparable condition in the female often arises as a result of frustrated coitus or following incompleted sex games which are commonly indulged in during adolescence. This condition is marked by a congested uterus and a heavy sense of pressure and discomfort in the pelvis. The congestion may also be accompanied by a urethral discharge, vaginal leukorrhea, menstrual difficulties, lassitude, fatigue, insomnia, irritability, backache, and various neuroses. Some prevention is possible by adroit use of the hands just prior to the orgasm, but this does not negate the accompanying psychological frustration.

HOMOSEXUAL DISGUISES IN MARRIAGE

It is well known that alcoholism, frigidity and impotence are common accompaniments of, and substitutes for, homosexuality in married people; yet some degree of latent homosexuality exists in all normal people.

Latent Homosexuality has been mentioned as natural and common at puberty (Chapter 9). It exists in all normal people of both sexes and is often concealed by addiction to sports, hard work, habitual gossiping, drugs or alcohol. This does not mean that everyone is on the verge of becoming "gay" but it does mean that everyone is normally endowed with both masculine and feminine sex hormones; that everyone comes from two parents and is normally exposed to an adult of each sex; and that everyone normally needs acceptance and recognition by adults of both sexes. It also means that when one is *unable* to win over the parent of the same sex, he goes out of his way to brown-nose him. He may be willing to pay almost any price for such approval, including repression of all natural interests in the opposite sex. Since he tries very hard to win over other members of the same sex, he is entitled to capitalize on his investment. For example, the more he does for them, the more he has a right to expect from them. This is how ingratiating "homos" often reach high positions of responsibility.

In normal people, ambivalence for members of the same sex assumes multiple disguises but often shows up in one's selection of a career and in the sex of the people whom he chooses to serve and work with.

The ambivalence also shows up in our recreational preferences and, especially, in our language and the type of jokes we prefer. Here is an example of clues in the language of Konrad, a periodic alcoholic, during one of his binges and prior to treatment. Note his preoccupation with buttocks, anus, and his allegedly flat-chested wife. Jealousy of his own teen-age son, who is obviously preferred by his long suffering wife, appears on the surface, but my italicized notes offer some clues to Konrad's own boyhood preoccupations. The tirade took place between pints, some of it apparently directed to himself.

Case of Konrad

> Him and his seductive mother! [*Why doesn't she seduce me?* or *Why can't you be as seductive as she?*]
> And I have to put up with you and your short tits. [*Flat-chested wife, like a boy or man?*]
> I can't wait for him to go into the army. [*To make*

a man of you, or *maybe get killed in Vietnam?*]

Go to bed, you pisspot. [*He calls the boy a receptacle for a penile output.*]

Your mother stinks. [*Preoccupation with anus or a decaying body? Death wish?*]

I don't want to have breakfast with him tomorrow. [*Juvenile retort, "I'm still mad at him."*]

You are just interested in sitting on your big ass with your penis envy. [*Who is envying whom, and what?*]

The quicker he goes into the service, the better I'll like it, and if he gets killed, I'll go to Arlington Cemetery. [*And be proud of him.* He now turns to a younger son who is also present.]

And don't you marry some stupid ass hole like your mother. [*It's stupid to use a woman for pederasty.*] I'd hate to see my boys tied up with a person like you. [*His wife is desexed. She's a person, not a woman or a man.* He then becomes very childish and repetitious.]

I don't want to have breakfast with him tomorrow. [*You'll have to choose between us.*] If he's up, I'll leave. Beginning tomorrow, I'm not coming home . . .

His wife ends her report with this statement:

This is a rundown of his patter. I took it down in shorthand while he was ranting. I was trying to write a letter, so he thought I was still at it. He'd kill me if he knew I'd told you all this. He was so carried away with his speeches he wasn't interested in what anyone else thought or felt or said. For that matter there wasn't any chance to say anything at all.

I've just read this over. The language is earthy but not nearly as strong as usual. Thank God we have a guest room. Goodnight. Sincerely, G.

G's husband Konrad had an older brother who had neither time nor patience for the small-fry at home. He later died, but the son is a strong reminder of the brother whose affection and interest could not be obtained.

Marriage is no protection against homosexual practices. Frank homosexual activities do occur in some marriages. As a rule, they are not conducive to a harmonious domestic life. In theory each partner allows the other free rein; but in practice, multiple jealousies and abuses arise to complicate the picture. Children, if any, are especially liable to suffer because of distorted values and constant pressure on them for alliances with one or the other parent. Since alcohol or drug usage is a common accompaniment, there is little that conventional marriage counseling can accomplish until one or the other partner becomes ill or gets into serious legal difficulties. Paranoid accusations are common, but even then, a divorce is often strongly resisted. Consequently, where young children are concerned, the intervention of police or the SPCC (Society for Prevention of Cruelty to Children) may be the marriage counselor's only active contribution to the total good and welfare of the family.

PROMISCUITY EXPRESSES ANXIETY AND DISGUISES HOMOSEXUALITY

Sexual differences can produce a denial of anxiety, and an overcompensating reaction in the form of promiscuity as in the following case of Zelda.

Case of Zelda, Call Girl

Zelda, thirty-one, a divorced receptionist and self-styled "call girl", noticed a painful lump in her right breast and menstrual pain in her right lower abdomen. These came on shortly after manhandling by a male "client" or customer for her extracurricular activities.

The family doctor found a negative pelvis and abdomen but advised biopsy for the breast tumor. This she declined because the scar would interfere with her profession. Previous psychotherapy, several years earlier with hypnotic relaxation, had not dissuaded her from supplementing her musical efforts with "call girl" activities, but she hoped that, inasmuch as the pains and tumor *could* be psychosomatic, perhaps hypnotherapy would influence them. She agreed to take her surgeon's advice for biopsy if the hypnotherapy should prove to be ineffective. She also agreed that her problem could be both functional *and* organic.

She entered trance spontaneously but became restless when I suggested that her complaint could be related to some earlier episodes in her life. I also reminded her of previous discussions concerning her earlier conflicts with boys and her dream about the swarm of bees and the rotten shells.

Zelda's recollection of these dreams lightened her trance, so I asked whether she thought she could relax more deeply while exploring this factor. She nodded, but, at the given signal, she squirmed, pressed her right hand on her right lower abdomen, and said, "My head got taut." (Body language indicates abdominal distress, even while her words call attention to her head. Psychotherapists can observe the same common dissociation in nonhypnotized patients.) She could think of no associations.

Here is her own story, written later at home, as a result of a suggestion made during the trance. Her first dream recalls childhood rebellion.

> Wonder what it means to dream of a swarm of bees all over me. Someone killed them; I think it was my brother X.
>
> This actually happened to me when I was around ten years old. We were living in the same place as when I wrote my mother that nasty note and she punished me by not letting me go out for Halloween and making me do the dishes for the first time.
>
> All of that time we lived there was an unhappy time for me. I remember being very unhappy in school—not having any friends. I remember my grandparents (my father's parents) having the grocery store, but their never giving us kids any candy.
>
> I remember being ostracized by the neighborhood kids because I yelled when they pulled my pants down in the tent in the backyard.

Z's second dream is a critical and self-revealing sequence to the above.

> I had another strange dream Saturday night. I was walking down the streets of my hometown—there was a lot of redevelopment going on. Just shells of old buildings were being moved. They were old, ugly, rotten shells and I was glad they were being replaced. The railroad station was being moved and I waved goodbye to passengers on the last train moving out. I woke up disturbed and thought of myself wearing shells, but inside I was rotten and ugly—I thought that's why I attract so many undesirable men—they're eligible, but only because no one wants them. Like R., who is some kind of a foreigner, and F., who is a drip, and D., who is short, and J., who is ugly. I must be in the same category to attract them. I couldn't attract B. who is eligible, but good looking with a good job, the kind of guy I would like—No—instead of being attracted to me, he goes for O. who is my girlfriend and married. And she doesn't have to watch how she behaves or what she says to him,

or where they'll go—he'll do anything she says, and more, just to keep her coming to see him.

It's gotten to the point now where I envy her so much, I can't bear to hear her talk about him and how much he caters to her. She has no idea how I feel so she goes into all kinds of details about their lovemaking, etc. And to top all this, she makes him think that maybe someday she'll leave her husband for him, but actually she has no intention of doing so; she just likes having a boyfriend on the side. In the meantime, I'm sick!

There I was laying on the floor, stretched out doing exercises to keep me in shape. (I was always aware of my figure, since it is so important in my business . . . the business of being a "Call Girl.") All of a sudden I felt a slight pain in my right breast and when I touched the spot, it felt like a hard lump. Immediately, I got scared! I was afraid to touch the spot again; but I did, and each time I became frightened over this lump growing there.

The weeks went by and the lump grew and the pain came and went—then I noticed another lump and was so overcome with fright that I started taking tranquilizers. Then I developed a pain on my right side and told myself it was just gas and would soon go away along with the lumps. But they didn't and I was becoming so depressed, that a doctor friend of mine noticed. I blurted out to him how worried I was about my side and my breast.

He examined me thoroughly and found nothing wrong with my side, but advised me to have my breast operated on to see if the lump was malignant. I immediately answered, "No!" My first thought was that he didn't know that cutting me up would put me out of business!

Along with my fear, the thought kept recurring to me that these physical reactions were the result of mental conflict that I had been going through for a long time. It seemed there was one ray of hope for me before I would even remotely think of an operation—and that was to go see Dr. S. and be hypnotized and melt the lumps. I even tried self-hypnosis and for a while it seemed the lumps diminished in size and the pain on my side subsided, but it didn't last, so I finally made up my mind to see Dr. S.

Once I made the appointment, I felt more confident that everything would be all right.

When Dr. S. questioned me about my pains, I felt that he was chastising me for running the risks of being a prostitute (pregnancy and disease), and it seemed that he was saying I deserved these things that were happening to me. He examined me and confirmed the lumps and their sizes. He felt confident that they were not malignant, and immediately I was relieved.

(This diagnosis was later confirmed by subsequent mammography and drainage.)

Then he told me we would see what we could discover under hypnosis. I wanted this, but yet was afraid; I could feel myself tighten up. Dr. S. took hold of my left arm (hand) and raised it; I knew that if and when I relaxed enough, my arm would fall itself. While we talked, I was very aware of my arm, and was thinking that I didn't want it to fall. But then, I thought why am I letting it stay up; it is so annoying and doesn't feel comfortable—then I dropped it.

Dr. S. asked me to think of a number and I answered "two" immediately and I wondered why I said two. Then he asked me to think of a name, and I immediately thought of "Fred" and knew right away that he would be asking me whose name that was and I would say, "My father's." Then he asked me to think of an emotion or feeling. I immediately thought of "fuck," but hesitated for a moment about saying it, and then thought, why shouldn't I, and answered him.

When Dr. S. asked me what "two" meant, I answered that it brought to mind "number two"—what kids refer to as meaning a bowel movement. Then the word "fuck" was pictured in my mind as being scrawled on the walls of a public toilet.

I don't remember how we then talked of the next scene that came into my mind. But my head felt very taut and I hesitated about saying anything, even though I could see the scene very clearly and I was thinking I had told him about this on a previous visit, so why do I have to go over it again. But somehow it seemed he was insisting that I tell him.

The words spilled out then. I could see the windows of the kitchen when I looked up. I could see through them and see the brick building across the way. I was very young and sitting on my father's lap in the rocking chair by the stove. It was my favorite spot in the house in later years. Dr. S. wanted to know more, but I found it difficult to say what I saw. I could feel myself becoming agitated and I clasped my hands tightly; I was getting scared.

He kept insisting and I finally told him that my mother was standing in the doorway. I could see her so plainly—she looked beautiful to me with her long blonde hair and in her nightgown. But I was scared because she was terribly angry with me. She was angry because my father and I were touching our "private parts," and she had caught us!

My own notes during this hypnotic session indicate that some self-acceptance has taken place since she left the office. Here is how they read:

Patient keeps wringing hands, body squirming, tears streaming unchecked, "I can see the windows—see right through them—brick wall—there's a woman—it's my mother—she's standing in the doorway of bedroom—long blonde hair. She's very angry with me—father is touching me—or I was touching him—his penis—he was telling me to do it—and then she's mad at me"—prolonged sobbing.

Note that the memory, as first recalled in the office, is screened and distorted. It is more acceptable to blame it all on mother and father. Z's writing continues

It seems that whenever someone yells in anger, I can hear her yelling at me. I was crying and I felt young and helpless.

Dr. S. handed me some tissue to wipe my tears and I felt there was someone on my side, someone who would help me. I remember Dr. S. saying more to me, but don't know what it was and when he awakened me, I felt very tired.

My notes on the psychotherapeutic feedback contained suggestions regarding these possibilities: the size of father's hand, reaching from child's right lower abdomen to her breast as it hastily retreated from her genitals when caught by mother; the probable suppression of details; and the inevitable arousal of guilty and ambivalent feelings.

During the pre-arousal summary there was a reminder that the genital pleasure or excitement which she may have derived from touching her father's penis could have been displaced to her right lower abdomen (ovary or tube). The pain could then have replaced her pleasure as belated penance. Or, it may be that father's firm grasp with his large hand could have hurt her little body at the time, but that the hurt was not noticed in the excitement.

Furthermore, the same discovery and reproach by mother could have caused father to grab the child more firmly in order to hide his own genital exposure. At the same time, Zelda's consternation over being caught, and allegedly unjustly accused, could have displaced her attention from the painful pressure on her abdomen in an attempt to deny and rationalize—"it was *father* who was touching me, yet *she* scolded *me*."

She was then told that all of this had happened to a little girl a long time ago. She was specifically and repeatedly reminded that it was definitely not happening now.

"Perhaps the lump has already served its purpose and could begin-to-shrink a-little-at-a-time. (Pause. The patient is left with a new and comforting idea.) "It isn't necessary for you to remember *everything* we've talked about today. You can remember-as-much-as you need-to-remember at-this-time. The rest will all come back to you whenever you're ready for it—a-little at-a-time." (Partial amnesia is suggested before terminating the trance because of the traumatic revelation and in deference to her need for tranquility on her long drive home.)

Zelda aroused herself, smiling, and said, "I feel very relaxed." She ignored the tears that were still streaming down her face. Her writing continues

> The next two weeks were like a vacuum to me. I wanted to think, but yet couldn't. The pain on my side disappeared and the lumps diminished. For one day, it seemed as though they were almost gone. I felt physically better.

> I remembered then Dr. S. asking me to try to recall if I was with a particular person when I first felt the pain. I knew that I could find this out by looking through my diary (I had been keeping a running diary of every day since January). I hesitated for several days, not knowing why I didn't want to look it up. Finally, I did and it was very easy to find. It seemed as though I knew exactly what dates to look under, without really knowing who it was. There was a man who bit me on the breast.

> I couldn't really remember what the man looked like, but I didn't like him. He was drunk that night and I

remember that I didn't like the odor from him (the body odor, that is). The words in my diary to describe him were "cruddy" and "pervert." He had a difficult time in making love to me, that is, he was unable to reach a climax; he wanted me to try all different positions, and none of them did anything for him. He finally tried to bring on a climax himself.

By then, I was tired and disgusted with him; I told him to give me my money and go. He refused to pay me. At first I argued with him about the money, saying that I had spent too much time with him. But he kept insisting on trying again. I finally told him to go without paying me as I was fed up with him. He was very abusive but finally left.

The next day he called and apologized and promised to mail me the money, which he did. I told him I would not see him again.

At her next visit, while I was reading the above account, she reported that she had pain in both breasts when writing the above recollections, and that her first menstruation began at eleven years and was accompanied by a lot of abdominal pain and by much staying in bed.

Other girls had pain with their first intercourse. I never did. My husband said he felt only tightness. There was no blood on the sheets on my wedding night. Mother made a big fuss over that. She had put a lock on my bedroom door and bars on the bedroom closet.

Zelda again reported pains in her left breast as she told of being in her bedroom closet with her oldest brother. I suggested a light trance during which she offered further revelations. She recalled playing hide and seek.

Very dark, I wanted to get out. He wouldn't let me. There were a lot of shoes on the floor. My brother, Sam. He was sixteen and very handsome. He was my mother's favorite, and he knew it. But he was good to us. I was scared but he told me to lie down on the floor. Hot. Uncomfortable. I can feel the shoes sticking into me. He finally opened the door. We struggled over taking off my pants. Then I did. I must have, because I remember I couldn't find them afterwards. I got panicky.

Q. But you didn't tell your parents?

A. No. Coz I wished that he would try it again. I don't remember that he did. He's living in —. Now it really hurts there Doc. (She rubs her left breast.)

I remember the side of the store, and my parents'
bedroom in back. And a small hallway to the kitchen—
I keep seeing that hallway—so narrow, two people
would bump against each other when they tried to get
by—Oh! My mother's younger brother! He was a great
teaser—He was another one wanted me to take off my
pants—but that was under the porch. I guess we had
a rendezvous. I was twelve. My bosom was growing—
I had a broomstick skirt, full, blue, with prints—I lay
on top of him. He was always going to mother for money
or whenever he got into trouble. I asked him about
having a baby. He said he wouldn't let that happen to
me. But I didn't menstruate for four months after that,
I was scared out of my wits!

If these pains and lumps are warnings I haven't been
heeding them because I've been going strong (cohabitation for pay). It seems as though I have to do it. I get
depressed if I have no action. And I'm too busy to
practice music. But I dislike repeats. I prefer new men
every time.

At this appointment, two weeks following the first session, Zelda
reported that both pains (breast and abdomen) had disappeared
within two or three days following her first visit and that she had
noticed the lump in her right breast was getting smaller. "It even
disappeared for a few days, I thought."

Examination showed that the lump was actually about one third
of its previous size and was receding from the nipple area, toward
the lower outer quadrant. Normal mammary glandular tissue was
palpable where the rest of the lump had been. The *left* breast and
the abdomen continued to be negative, and she still refuses biopsy.
It is as though she would rather be dead with cancer than alive with
a scarred or disfigured bosom.

With difficulty Zelda recalled the first two associations at her
previous visit two weeks earlier: "number two" (bowel movement)
and "Fred" (father's name), but she had no recollection of the
third association (fornicate). However, she again volunteered the
recollection that the customer who had been abusive had also been
drunk and had refused to pay her because he had been unable to
respond to her caressing. Instead, he had to resort to self-help in
order to achieve orgasm. "He may have reminded me a little of my
father, I'm not sure . . ."

No trance was suggested at this second session, but she was
automatically in and out of a very light trance from the moment
she sat in the same chair. Consequently, it was a simple matter

to review the possibility that she had not only been attempting to recapture and complete her childhood adventures but also to rationalize her adult behavior. In her call girl profession, every customer was a father substitute; but now she was making him pay for the privilege. This serves as a fitting punishment for having not only started to seduce her but also for letting her take the blame along with mother's rebuke and scolding. Her first conscious recall of the incident had been that it was father who had played with her and that mother had scolded Zelda and not father. This brought up another problem:

> I can't bring myself to resume my music with any confidence. My coach says I'm ready, but I think I'd be better off if I practiced piano.

Associations were then invited to music, in general, and to piano in particular.

> We were too poor to have a piano until I was seventeen. Mother got one, and she paid for the lessons. Once I got angry at something and I tore up my music. She made me paste it together and take my lesson anyway. I remember crying and doing the scales and exercises at the same time. After that she stopped the lessons because I'd refused to practice.

When I asked her how she would have handled a similar situation with her own daughter, she smiled and said, "I guess I'd have done the same thing." This identification was the first evidence of weakening of her alleged hostility to mother. The first remembered major cause of that hostility had been the (unjust?) accusation and scolding at four when she was discovered sitting on her father's knee. The next one, mentioned earlier in the session, had been mother's insistence that Zelda give up music as a career because she just was not good enough and, anyway, she belonged with her family instead of touring in show business—implying her disapproval of the divorce.

I inquired whether mother may have been projecting her own musical incapabilities and added that mother may also have been trying to prevent disillusionment, in view of Zelda's many past failures and increasing competition from younger theatrical aspirants. Zelda was busy in reflection and made no comment.

I then reminded Zelda that this would not have been the first time that mother had tried to protect her from dangerous or frustrating entanglements (father's knees and hands, her brothers, bars on the closet and the lock on her bedroom door), and I wondered what Zelda might do if she were to find her own daughter in a similar situation.

By this time Zelda was back in trance (auto-induced, or possibly brought on by my voice), and I asked her rather casually and as though talking to myself, whether mother had ever bought Zelda a new dress, had ever shown her off to friends and family, had ever indicated that she was proud that she had nursed and bathed her, taught her to walk and talk, sent her to school, and so forth.

Zelda's nonverbal body language consisted of barely perceptible nods of acquiescence. These nonverbal responses guided my remarks and the feedback resume just before arousal from trance.

I summarized the ABC's of Z's lifelong struggle to win over mother's approval by overemphasis of her apparent need for men. I did not hint at an Electra or Oedipus competition with mother for father's affection. Instead, I pointed out that mother's concern for Z's childhood morals, her clothing and appearance, and her adult musical aspirations did not seem to fit in with Zelda's conscious image of a rejecting mother.

I ended with the suggestion that I would not be surprised that from now on Z. would be more than ever glad to be a woman, to possess normal, healthy and attractive breasts and well-functioning internal reproductive organs, to comtemplate her husband as her daughter's father, and to think of her husband as an individual with problems of his own rather than as a convenient scapegoat for the shortcomings of her father, uncle, or brothers. I also suggested that whatever had attracted her to music in the first place could still be valid and could still serve as an important motivation for her to enjoy expressing herself, no matter who might be listening.

It is highly probable that Zelda will eventually be needing her surgeon again when her cyst fills up, as often happens. The case is not presented to indicate that surgery is old-fashioned nor that hypnotherapy is a panacea. The case does show advantages of hypnoanalysis for speedy uncovering of emotional repressions and also illustrates some of the dynamics in a psychosomatic conversion phenomena.

The mechanisms of her pain and cystic tumor constitute, in effect, psychosomatic and psychovisceral displacement of tension, a defense against her incessant search for sexual pleasure as a symbol of acceptance by males, denial of the desire to control father and brothers vicariously through her clients, and a penance or self-punishment for her misconduct and resentment against mother. Z. still deceives herself by rationalizing that it is only a minor "sin" and that she is not a religious person, anyway.

To the discerning clinician, there are ample signs of psychopathology, for her defenses are obviously breaking down from sheer inadequacy. The breasts and right tube or ovary are only the first of the target organs for her multiple conflicts. Yet this is how many a case begins, when it appears to have all the earmarks of a strictly organic or surgical problem. Intensive follow-up and cooperation from her family are essential for her recovery.*

OTHER DISGUISES FOR SEX CONFLICTS

Sex conflicts may be disguised by obesity and other compulsions. Feeding problems and digestive complaints commonly mask sexual conflicts. Here is one case of an obese girl who said she wanted to reduce.

Aimy

Aimy was an otherwise well-adjusted and attractive college student but felt that she was too fat and asked for hypnosis in order to reduce her weight. Resistance appeared quite early, resulting in my abandonment of formal attempts to induce a trance. Instead, she spent the session with a few cigarettes but was invited to lean back, to relax, and to imagine figures or outlines in the smoke.

Aimy was soon in a light-to-medium trance from which she aroused herself, sponstaneously and frequently, to report fragments of an important childhood experience.

> We were in the hayloft. I was about seven—my girl friend was about the same age, but I guess she was bolder than I . . . There was this boy—a cousin about fifteen, I think. And they were doing something . . . I thought at first he was attacking her or wrestling, and I called her to come away. But she didn't say anything . . . I knew I should have left, but I didn't . . . I don't know if it happened again, but—now I wonder!

At this point the session ended with some reassurance from me that she would retain as much as she needed to remember for the present and that the rest would come back later whenever she was ready for it. One week later she was delightedly "embarrassed" to report that now she realized that what she had witnessed was a scene of willing seduction.

---

* For several years she was treated in a local clinic nearer her home, but recently she returned for further help. Her body was still intact except for a chronic and nondisabling lowgrade generalized cystic mastitis.

There was less resistance to hypnotic relaxation. She was encouraged to verbalize freely, but she concentrated mostly on the remembered scene. During a pause, I suggested that she consider the possibility that she may have envied the other girl in the hayloft. She was way ahead of me and promptly roused herself to set me straight.

Of course I envied her! I still do. I was such a ninny.
But I was a hypocrite, too. All those years of feeling
"Holier than thou" and all that jazz. But what's all
this got to do with my failure to lose weight?

I suggested that she "relax" again. This was the signal which we had agreed upon for her to reenter trance. I then mentioned several possible explanations for retention of her weight.

One of these suggestions, of course, was the possibility that losing weight might make her more attractive to boys and, therefore, more vulnerable to her suppressed desire to "perform" with one of them as her bolder girl playmate had performed in the hayloft a decade earlier. I also offered the suggestion that she could permit her own common sense and her own unconscious mind to select from these possibilities that which she considered to be the most appropriate reason.

She again aroused herself halfway from trance, smiled and blushed as she nodded her confirmation. Then she ruefully remarked

It isn't the boys who reject me. They like my figure
just as it is. It's I who push *them* away—but I'm not
always as successful or diligent as I ought to be. But I
can still take care of myself . . . Now you take this professor . . .

At this point Aimy stopped talking and blushed more deeply as she suddenly realized that the example she was about to give would have proved the very point she was attempting to deny.

At a later session she admitted that she would marry the professor if he were eligible; and during the following two years she was convinced that she was pregnant at least half a dozen times— and by several different bed partners. Shortly after graduation, this girl who, like most college girls, was sure she could "take care of herself" married the father of her expected baby (not the professor).

She has, thus far, lived an exemplary domestic life, but she has not reduced her weight. Some problems can be lived with, especially when change or symptom-removal may prove to be disastrous.

Chapter 17

MISCELLANEOUS PROBLEMS

THE ABUSED CHILD

Abuse takes many forms. Work is no stranger to women, but about half of the women in this country are employed outside of the home. Parents are often threatened by their own changing status as well as by the arrival of children. They too have a great need to be loved and will seek affection outside the home if necessary; but babies and small children are obviously handicapped. When the child is restless and overstimulated, or in distress, the parent becomes impatient. He misinterprets this as a direct rejection of himself, and he takes out his frustrations on the disobedience which inevitably follows his demands for quiet.

Hostile or indifferent and undemonstrative parents force their children into drugs, homosexuality, running away, and other delinquencies. Harsh and abusive parents may also produce schizophrenic withdrawal. Physically abusive parents produce malnourished and battered bodies which often end in premature death.

When physical neglect or abuse is apparent, the counselor should be on guard. He needs to investigate claims of "he's always falling" or "she bruises easily." An accident-prone child may be one who is frequently beaten. He may also be emotionally depressed to the point where he no longer cares. *Newsweek* carried photographs of a four-year-old girl weighing only seventen pounds. "Her skull was fractured, one arm and both hands were broken." The same child, after five weeks of successful hospital care was unrecognizable as she happily rode a tricycle.[19]

According to researches, seven out of ten battered children are under five. Many have fractured skulls and blood clots, internal injuries and limb fractures as well as malnutrition. Personality disorders are also common findings. These children are usually seen in hospital emergency wards. Indigent parents are the usual abusers; but laborers, farmers and even professional people are also among the offenders.

THE ABUSED STOMACH

Homemade cooking is not always successful. A happy stomach can digest almost anything that the average wife can concoct, but when other sources of friction are unresolved, the digestive tract often takes a beating. Halitosis, nausea, vomiting, diarrhea and constipation usually straighten themselves out after a few days, but ulcers are a more serious problem. The psychosomatic aspects of digestive and other common disorders have been discussed in a previous volume.[53] The following brief report on recent observations over stress in certain animals will serve as a reminder for the conscientious counselor.

Stress Factors in Ulcers

In swine, overcrowding and competition for space at the feeders and at watering troughs has resulted in an increase in stomach ulcers. When swine are placed in pastures with plenty of space, they show a smaller incidence of ulcers than animals that are confined in pens, yet fed the same rations. Another report described an outbreak of ulcers when the gentle herd manager was replaced by a more aggressive man.[14]

Wives are not always to blame. Husbands often put up with unsuitable meals because they do not want to offend their wives. Wives have to economize to keep within their budget. They may try to please, yet harbor resentments that show up in mistakes such as overseasoning or undercooking. Husbands are often tardy for meals, and wives are not the only ones who can provoke an argument at mealtime. Dishes are often allowed to pile up just to prove how hard one has to work. Childhood memories of certain foods, odors, dishes and other chores can upset the best of appetites. Counselors should inquire into specific details. Children are not the only spoilers.

ABC's OF FAMILY BUDGETING

Financial problems are usually ahead of sexual problems as precipitating causes of marital discord, although personality conflicts actually top the list. The marriage counselor may need to consult local social service experts or annual yearbook almanacs on the relative proportions of one's income that should be allocated for rent, food, transportation, insurance, education, charitable contributions and recreation.

For instance, consider a wage earner who grosses $100.00 a week. His take-home pay is only $91.25. If he restricts his rent to $25.00 a week (one fourth of his salary), food to $30.00 and transportation to $10.00, he has the magnificent balance of $26.25 to cover his family's clothing, insurance, education, church and charitable contributions, installment buying, newspapers, magazines, haircuts, toys, Christmas presents, tobacco, alcohol, and returning social obligations.[4]

Statistical studies change so rapidly that it is difficult to keep up with them.*

In the mid-sixties it is estimated that four out of every five families in the United States now own at least one automobile, or have an equity in a car. Also, one family in every five has two or more cars. Three cars to a family and several television sets and an extra summer home or camp and boat are additional financial drains that are by no means uncommon. Extra jobs are obviously needed and extra liabilities are involved in terms of less time and energy available for the business of marriage.

It has been observed repeatedly by sage philosophers that income determines our expenditures and that we generally adjust our expenditures to meet the funds that are available. In other words, *we spend more when we have more.* It is also the experience of every housewife that *work can be expanded or contracted according to the time available for its completion.* In other words, when one is too busy, a "lick and a promise" has to suffice, but when one has plenty of time, new projects can always be found, at least for one's spouse, if not for oneself.

A third "parkinsonian law," well known in history and government as well as in industry, is that when the business of the home expands because of more people, more rooms, more appliances, etc., then more complications can be expected. Com-

---

* About half of the women in the U.S. are gainfully employed. They also hold title to a large share of the property and control much of the spending. Some estimates give them the lion's share of the latter.

plications mean trouble, more mistakes and failures. Expansion means complications and the beginning of decay.

In other words, the larger the project the less individual attention is possible. The old saw of doing things for yourself if you want them done well still applies. Consequently, when responsibilities have to be delegated to someone else, one may expect weaknesses and shortcomings to show up because good workers, like good leaders, are hard to find. These factors help to explain some of the nostalgia for the good old glamorous days of courtship and the first years of marriage when the home was small, and the family was limited in size, when there were fewer mouths to feed and bodies to clothe, and the responsibilities and complications were relatively simple.

Recreational Outlets May Need Overhauling

Active recreation is preferable whenever possible. Joint and separate activities are available in multiple areas. Encouragement to pursue individual as well as mutual interests prevents boredom. It also prevents the development of frustrations and restricting compulsions which are so often the mark of incompatability.

Couples may need to be reminded that there is more than movies, TV sports, fishing and Bingo or an occasional dance or outing sponsored by the church sisterhood or brotherhood. Counselors are inclined to ride their own hobbies and should therefore exercise restraint; but keeping an open mind usually pays off. For instance, while bowling is not one of my hobbies, I was surprised and impressed with the following data recently supplied by one of my patients.

"Ginny" was referred for hypnotic relaxation because of an aversion to wearing a dental plate; but that did not seem to interfere with her bowling enthusiasm.

However, after we had uncovered some unfinished emotional business in her life, two changes occurred almost simultaneously: (1) her bowling scores improved to the point where "I can almost beat my husband, now," and (2) she also resumed wearing her partial denture for increasingly longer periods of time. From her I also learned the following enlightening facts:

There are nearly three million sanctioned women bowlers and over five million men bowlers in the United States, Canada, Hawaii, Alaska and U.S. military bases overseas. Age is no barrier, some of them continue bowling well into the nineties.

Nuns in their long professional habits play with equal enthusiasm, their full skirts offering no appreciable obstacle to their bowling efficiency.

There are bowling leagues for paraplegics who bowl from wheelchairs; and there are also leagues for the blind who use a horizontal guide bar to approach the foul line from the starting line, fifteen feet back. Sighted observers keep them informed on which pins are still standing.

There are nearly half a million junior bowlers from under six years to nineteen years of age. There are even recreational bowling programs for the mentally retarded who do not care at all about scores, nor whether they win or lose. They just have a whale of a time bowling and hitting the ten-pins, while their supervisors keep score.*

Investment Counseling Services

Older counselors think of investments as something for the wealthy and older clients, but banks, insurance companies and investment counseling firms are discovering that a large proportion of young people are much more responsible than newspaper headlines would lead us to believe. They think differently, and they think big! During the depression of the thirties a ten thousand dollar policy was quite respectable. Today, instead of five and ten thousand dollar policies, more and more young folks are buying fifty to one hundred thousand dollar policies. This represents a jump of 1000 per cent during the past fifteen years, compared to an increase of earnings of about 100 per cent during the same period.

The simple fact is that "term insurance" costs less than "whole life" insurance. Life insurance is a cash-building program that pays annuities after a given number of years. One can also *borrow* on whole life policies in proportion to payments.

---

* *The Woman Bowler*: 31(5), April 1967; and 132:12, July-Aug. 1968, 1225 Dublin Rd., Columbus, Ohio 43212. *Bowling*: 34(12), July 1968, Amer. Bowling Congress, 1572 E. Capital Drive, Milwaukee, Wis. 53211.

Term insurance affords protection only and has no cash value until death. It does, however, give maximum protection for minimal investment. Later, when one's income rises, even if he is incapacitated, it can be converted to a savings and investment policy. Conversion can be made *without further physical examination* regardless of the health of the policyholder at the time of the conversion. The younger the policyholder when he first takes out the policy, the lower his premium.

As an example, a recent graduate from a local college, aged twenty-three, with a degree of B.S. in business administration stepped right into a job in the experimental lab of a large defense plant. His starting salary is $9,000 a year plus fringe benefits. He purchased a $50,000 policy for commercial term insurance at an annual premium of $125.00. In addition he entered a mutual funds investment program at $50.00 per month. In fifteen years he will have paid $9,000 into the fund which pays back compound interest at 12 per cent and projects to about $18,000 (cash value) by the end of the fifteen years. Meanwhile his family is protected by the $50,000 policy which costs him $1,875 for the same fifteen years. Total premiums for both insurance and investment is about $63.00 a month or $750.00 a year.*

The average college graduate today, without experience, starts with a salary of about $6,000 plus fringe benefits of close to $1500. Many counselors are not earning very much more than that, yet some of them have several degrees and considerable experience.

Consultations with experts on mutual funds, real estate, reputable stock brokers, bank executives and attorneys for estate planning should be encouraged. Haphazard choices based on friendly "tips" or personal "intuition" frequently end up in disaster for clients who try to be their own specialist. The same rules apply in business and legal matters as in health where the best is none too good.

---

* John Potter, Personal Communication, July 1968.

MARRIAGE COUNSELING PROCEDURES

The Intake Interview

The intake interview is usually more productive when each spouse is seen separately, but at least one conjoined conference in indicated. This usually furnishes more information. It also tests the reliability of the informer and may be more explosive. Thereafter, periodic joint conferences, at intervals of four to six weeks, may prove advantageous while each spouse is seen separately on alternate weeks or several times a week, when indicated.

Most couples are embarrassed to discuss sex when they are together with the therapist; but when it arises, tactful objectivity and neutrality is indicated. For instance many are surprised to learn that one satisfactory intercourse, occurring once or twice a month during middle age, is preferable to attempting to maintain the much greater frequency of the honeymoon. Some men are ashamed to admit that they require sex several times a day during the first few years of marriage. Some women feel that they have never had any climax—nor expected one. Many are still amazed to learn that they, too, can enjoy sexual intercourse. Others recognize sex as a powerful tranquilizer. Occasionally a woman reaches the first stages of labor without even knowing that she is pregnant, although this is comparatively rare.

One may start a conference by inquiring into how the couple met. Was it a civil or religious marriage ceremony? And who was present? What are the couple's feelings about having children and their attitudes toward family planning?

Inquiry should also be made about their church affiliations, attendance at services and observance of customs. For Catholics, a revealing answer may be forthcoming when you ask how long it has been since their last Communion. Neglect to observe religious customs often indicates resentments against God and also against the family that indoctrinated them.

Another important area is the relationship with their in-laws. It is especially important to know *how well each spouse was accepted by the other's family.* This usually affects their attitudes toward children as well as their feelings about each other.

A wife can hardly feel kindly toward the in-laws who boy-cotted her wedding, nor can she be enthusiastically responsive to her mother-in-law's favorite son, especially when that son hap-pens to be her own husband. When a wife says of her own family, *"Oh, they adore him!"* there is liable to be ample ground for jealousy.

Next there is the matter of birth control, an area which is very much out in the open, yet is still avoided by too many physicians and other old-time marriage counselors. Moral and religious restraints are still at war with contemporary liberal and practical attitudes, but it is not only the younger generation that rebels. Older couples also have mixed feelings; and religion is not the only objection. Fears of childbirth still exist in many couples. They need adequate discussion.

As already stated, techniques for contraception are rarely entirely satisfactory because most techniques are seldom com-pletely safe from human error. Religious scruples, once learned during childhood, cannot be lightly put aside. When other church rules have been violated, sex is liable to be a convenient scape-goat. Fears of childbirth and of competition from one's own children are usually denied and repressed. They are best inquired into at subsequent private conferences when each spouse is in-terviewed separately.

Unfortunately, the recommendation to make peace with one's conscience via confession, penance and communion runs into such complications as *de facto* divorce and remarriage. For the Catholic, this means living in sin or deserting the new spouse, a dilemma which most people are unable to resolve without emotional and domestic turmoil. Yet even here, there is a deeper obstacle that has its roots of origin in family ties and constella-tions.

For instance, in-laws may use the breach of religious regula-tions as an excuse to criticize, whereas the real sources of their rejections lie elsewhere. Parents who have absented themselves from the marriage of their children are likely to be the same parents who failed to prepare their daughters for menstruation or their sons for the responsibilities of dating. Each spouse continues to carry on the parental feud and takes out his resentment on his mate.

When such unpleasant background material is elicited by appropriate questioning, the counseling therapist may be met with stout denials from the man and a flood of tears from the woman. But whatever the response, most of these questions actually require no verbalized answer. Merely voicing them is enough to set the couple to thinking about important aspects of their relationships, other than sex, especially in the area of sibling rivalry and parental rejection. Unconsciously most couples know that these and other aspects of unfinished emotional business are liable to be the main roots of most of their sexual maladjustments. They have their earliest premarital and honeymoon privacy for comparison.

Incidentally, according to Mace, a recent study of 839 women showed that the average woman who is on oral contraceptives reports shorter lengths of menstrual flow and shorter cycles. She also reports more regularity, less pain, less hostility and resentment, and fewer premenstrual tensions.[30]

The Family Album

A perusal of the family album and scrapbook, especially of the wedding and honeymoon pictures, when available, frequently furnishes a wealth of information in a brief period of time. Unsuspected good looks or tensions and family resemblances often stand out clearly as sources of identifications. Similarly, the photos that are *absent* from a collection, especially in one's personal wallet, may be more significant than those which are included.

Newspaper clippings may not always be accurate records, yet they too furnish valuable clues to important events and memories that need ventilation, analysis and reorientation.

Role Playing

Role Playing for marital problems is one of the fastest and most effective procedures, even though many husbands and a few wives refuse to attend group conferences. Role playing in my office often starts with my pretending that I am the patient while the patient portrays his spouse. Then we reverse roles. Sometimes one of my nurses is invited to come in and play out a brief scene. She takes her orientation from me with the consent of the patient, but her cues are picked up from what the patient actually says or does, or fails to say or do.

Later in the week, the follow-up is made easier in a session of group psychotherapy.[52] Surprisingly enough, much can often be accomplished in as little as two or three minutes. The method is especially useful when a spouse is unable, or unwilling, to take his partner's role. Here is a simple example.

> An anxious mother at the end of a conference has just con-fided that her unmarried teen-aged daughter is pregnant and will have to marry her (willing) boyfriend, "I don't know how I'm going to tell my husband. He'll never . . ."
>
> Knowing her well, I did not hesitate to break in with unfeigned enthusiasm and *show her how to tell him,* "Congratulations, Grandma. That's the best news I've heard today!"
>
> Mother was startled by my unexpected response. She slowly broke into a broad smile and hastened to add, "It'll really be his *first* grandchild because the other one didn't . . ."
>
> She dissolved into tears of relief as she realized that she had been avoiding the inevitable by emphasizing the negative aspects of the situation instead of accentuating the positive. Her daughter was of age and was also following an ancient social custom to prove fertility. She trusted her boyfriend who stood by ready to marry her—which he did a few weeks later as soon as arrangements were completed.

When role playing is used in my evening group conferences, an indirect approach is often desirable. A hypothetical situation is suggested to one of the regulars who is then invited to select a spouse or other pertinent player. When the occasion warrants, one of the real spouses is then slipped in as a substitute or "double." Presently, the other spouse, if present, is invited to step in as double for the other partner and before long, the real principles are engaged in an active exchange with each other.

The counselor is responsible at all times for preventing vitu-perative insults in public, but this is not always possible. He has the same responsibility in the privacy of his office. He should not permit the couple to force him into the role of judge and jury. He should remember that much is accomplished by merely encouraging a verbalization of the problem. Many questions can be put without requiring an answer. They provide material for provocative contemplation and sober reflection.

The counselor can, however, lay down some useful rules of procedure. He can insist on each partner's hearing the other out. The couple will usually cooperate and soon learn to take their cues from his attitude, his courtesy and his objective impartiality.

When one partner is obviously way off base, the counselor can interject a hypothetical question which assumes a much greater exaggeration and usually catches them off guard. It may even provoke amusement. Once you can get them laughing at themselves, as well as at each other, the ice is broken, and the rest is comparatively easy. For example, I said to one suspicious and nearly paranoid husband, "Well then, assuming that your wife is now pregnant from this repairman who's been hanging around, and assuming that your husband has two mistresses whom he, of course, has to support, why not see your attorneys and break it off clean? You can fly to Mexico and be free in twenty-four hours."

Since he knows that she has just finished menstruating, and since she knows how much he earns and where he spends his time, the deliberate exaggeration promptly reduced their tensions. They were suddenly confronted with possibilities that would be more disturbing than the problems which actually bother them. They were then much more willing to explore the probabilities that other causes than alleged sexual wrongs are at the bottom of their difficulties.

Another example of this occurred recently during a demonstration group at a medical meeting. A doctor's wife had reported "headaches" beginning several months earlier. Onset coincided with her daughter's keeping company with an older man whom mother considered as undesirable. One of the audience, as a volunteer "daughter," asked the real mother what she had against her suitor, mother protested that he was "just a little too old." She denied insinuations that she had constantly objected to every one of her daughter's previous boyfriends.

Finally, the substitute daughter remarked, "Well, it doesn't matter what you say. I'm gonna marry him anyway coz I'm three months' pregnant."

The real daughter was not pregnant, but the psychodramatic substitute daughter (wife of another doctor in the audience) was indeed very conspicuously pregnant. Her remark brought out a generalized laugh in which the lady with the headache joined— but nothing more needed to be said. The message was received, loud and clear, that there were factors in her daughter's life over which she definitely had no control.

Each of the real parents were then given a role-playing opportunity to respond to the substitute daughter's announcement and to their credit each parent accepted the situation as graciously as possible, congratulated her, and exchanged meaningful glances.

Mother's headache had vanished by the end of the demonstration, some fifteen minutes later. She was duly praised for her cooperation in the teaching demonstration, but the issues were not pursued. She now *knew* what it was that she had been dreading.

Whenever possible, full credit for analysis, understanding, changes and results should be transferred to each of the participants. Patients should also avoid reminding each other by quoting what the counselor or therapist said or thinks. This renders him *personna non grata* and weakens his influence over the spouse who has to listen. Spacing the visits to keep costs down is essential. Long-range planning for new horizons and joint ventures is also in order. Accentuate the positive features of their assets.

Occasionally an inept partner has to be taught how to interpret his wife's language as well as her behavior as in the following case of Aubrey.

Aubrey had given up his organizational activities in order to please his wife. One evening, while laboring on some home projects in his work clothes, his wife put the children to bed early and called to him. "Honey, why don't you stop working for tonight. You've been at it all afternoon. Why not take a shower and get into your pajamas and come watch the nine o'clock movie with me?"

"It had been five weeks since we'd had our last intercourse, but

I guess I was pretty stupid. I didn't get the message until just now when I was telling you about it."

Another husband was upset because of his wife's use of the word "no."

"We'll have a wonderful relationship and a perfect build-up. Then, just as I enter, she says "No," and keeps on repeating "No" until we've finished. She enjoys her sex and shows her pleasure in all kinds of ways. But when she says that "no" it all but freezes me up and I feel I've failed her in some way."

I asked him about her thighs. Were they kept close together, and did he have to pry them apart before consummating the sex-play? He said that was no problem. She was all spread, ready and eager. I then told him that, in my opinion, the "no" did not mean what it said; that it could mean that she still felt the influence of some of her premarital training. For instance, it could mean,

No, I mustn't let you . . . No, I shouldn't enjoy it . . . No, I don't deserve such happiness . . . No, the ecstasy is too exquisite, and too good to last . . . or No, you mustn't. There, I've said it; and now my conscience is clear, so I can enjoy it.

He promptly stopped worrying about it as the rest of their difficulties became resolved.

THERAPEUTIC ABORTION

Help in obtaining a legalized therapeutic abortion is a common request that eventually reaches the psychiatrist. Other than in cases of rape, or a very young teen-ager, or a grossly unstable wife, the most common threat by the reluctant mother-to-be is suicide. The counselor and other non-psychiatric specialist is usually the first court of appeal. His first procedure is referral to an obstetrician for confirmation of pregnancy and to maintain objective calmness to neutralize the patient's panic. The obstetrician, in most states, then secures the opinions of two psychiatrists who examine the pregnant patient independently. A second obstetrician or the chief of staff gives the final okay; but when there is no unanimity of opinions, the problem is dumped right back in the counselor's lap, and he is often grossly intimidated by the threat of suicide or resort to an illegal abortion.

Yet, in a study of two million women who were in the childbearing age there were 207 suicides, but only three of them were pregnant. The study covered three years, and the actual number of pregnant suicides was only a sixth of what had been predicted on the basis of previous statistical projections.[47]

The authors, Rosenberg and Silver, concluded that pregnancy may serve a protective function and that most such mothers managed well enough without serious mental or emotional illness that could be attributed to their pregnancy.

On the other hand I have known such mothers to attempt suicide even after the therapeutic abortion and to require extensive treatment not for guilt but for depression and desertion by the father who was responsible for the pregnancy in the first place.

Other factors than suicide are naturally involved, and the problem bedevils every counselor and therapist at one time or another. Dr. Erickson's strategy includes the use of negative psychology by urging the parents not to even consider giving a name to the unborn baby lest it be the wrong sex for the name. Another is to suggest projection into the future, with no other pregnancy for the rest of her life.

I frequently remind my patients that whole families of children have been known to be wiped out by accidental drownings, fires and disease; that too many women are unable to conceive at all; but, that after all, one can always *adopt* someone else's baby. . . .

As for families and what people will say, it never ceases to surprise and delight me to find that the vast majority of many hundreds of unmarried mothers, whom I have counseled during the last forty years, have families that can take it in stride. They accept. They forgive and forget. And they learn to live with the status quo.

Similar strategies for displacement of interest can be cited by all therapists, but direct confrontation of the couple with their moral and legal responsibilities still has its merits.

DIRECT CONFRONTATION WITH RESPONSIBILITY

This is especially valuable in the marriage counseling of dependent people. When the patient is obligated to work out the problem with a parent or spouse or in-law, the therapeutic benefits are both psychological and physiological.

Numerous studies have shown that important neurochemical changes occur during a challenging psychological encounter. For instance. Sachar reports that corticosteroid excretions can be used as an index of emotional stress in certain types of depression. It increases when the patient is confronted with his problem and decreases when he has resolved whatever it was that caused his depression in the first place.[48]

It is also important to remember that excess of epinephrine (adrenalin) is produced by tension whether or not one vents his feelings and that exposure to challenging learning situations is essential for normal growth and development. The greater the challenge, the more work the brain and body is required to perform. The result is earlier maturity and, in some experiments, a brain with a thicker cortex. For instance, when rats were exposed to light, sound, playthings and litter mates, they developed a slightly thicker cerebral cortex than litter mates which were raised in an impoverished environment with nothing but food, water and cleaning.

This confirms the anthropological observation that the growth of man's brain and head coincides with the usage of tools and implements. Yet, regardless of which came first, the larger brain or the enforced use of tools and hands, there is no question that children who have no problems to solve are less stimulated and less energetic and resourceful than those who do.

The same is true for adults who try to escape reality. Consequently, in marriage and family counseling, firmness and confrontation with their own responsibilities to meet their challenges are usually more effective than coddling and too much assistance. In the case of Olaf, below, hypnoanalysis was effective only after direct confrontation with his habitual evasions.

Here are two brief heart cases where confrontation was used, but with opposite results. The first turned out well; the second did not.

> Jimmy, a youth of twenty-five, consulted me for a "nervous heart." The physical heart was perfectly normal, but the "nervous heart" was a lovely girl two years his junior. The chief difficulty

appeared to have been his fear that his mother would not approve of his proposed marriage. Jimmy's own good judgment told him that he must disregard his mother's tantrums and strike out for himself; but his long-established habit of depending on mother for approval made him unwilling to risk her threatened nervous breakdown.

Treatment consisted of four counseling interviews. One of them included his fiancée, who proved to be as wise and mature as she was lovely. During the interview after her visit I remarked that, in the opinion of an outside and hopefully impersonal observer (myself), the young lady not only reached but actually exceeded *his* highest standards. He was also assured that it appeared fairly evident that his mother's threatened "breakdown" would not likely prove to be a serious detriment to her usually well-guarded "ill health."

The couple were married away from home, as advised, and returned after a month's absence to find mother doing quite nicely. While not waiting with open arms for her new daughter-in-law, she was willing enough to accept her son's decision to live in a separate apartment. Few mother-in-laws can really love their daughter-in-laws wholeheartedly. Therefore, as long as neither party insists upon trying to compel mother to love the young bride and are willing to make their own way in life, they may be expected to get along perfectly well. They did and no further guidance was needed.

Dora, twenty-two, consulted me because of the apparent cooling off in the ardor of her fiance. The young man was his mother's first-born child. He was also having personal difficulties with an organic heart disease. Dora chose to ignore my advice to leave the city in order to accept a better job and to await the crystalization of her fiance's conflicting emotions. Instead, she continued to press him for a wedding date. Once the date had been set and despite several tragedies in his family, she insisted upon going through with the ceremony.

He, too, consulted me on his own. He admitted all my contentions that the two were ill-suited temperamentally and that his own heart ailment did not deserve so heavy an emotional strain. Ignoring my advice to wait a year, he went on with the experiment.

Within two weeks after the marriage it became apparent that his bride's former attachment to a younger girlfriend was too strong to permit a breaking off. Seeking to please his discontented wife, and against my advice, Dora's girlfriend was invited to live at their home; but despite all efforts on the friend's part to be tactful and considerate, the husband's jealousy proved to be too much. The marriage survived just ten weeks, after which the bride and her girlfriend left the pathetic groom alone in the first and only love nest which he had attempted to establish outside of his mother's home.

He later sued for divorce which Dora did not contest. It was granted some months later on the grounds of cruelty. She continued in her old job, still living with her girlfriend. He returned to his mother. Both appeared to be healthier and happier than before, and neither ever remarried. Twenty years later he died of his cardiac condition. The whereabouts of the girlfriend are unknown, but the wife is now a successful executive.

HYPNOANALYSIS

Qualified therapists can often speed up marriage and personal counseling with some variety of hypnoanalysis. Early erotic impressions may linger or return to plague adults at unexpected times. The impression may have been incomplete, or fantasied, and the occasion for its recurrence may be obscure. Nevertheless, some fleeting odors, sounds or colors, a chance phrase, a new restaurant, an old poem, a letter from an old friend, a scene in a movie or telecast, or a vivid dream may revive "forgotten" childhood anxiety concerning some aspects of sex.

Such was the situation with Olaf, an industrial research specialist who found himself in danger of losing his job. As a result, he began turning more and more to books on dreams and self-analysis, seeking some answers to his sudden lack of self-confidence. The following brief abstract from one of his hypnoanalytic sessions shows how he tracked down an elusive screen memory (possible witnessing of parental coitus) and finally got rid of the anxiety which threatened to disable him.

Olaf had already been "treated" elsewhere by a professional hypnotist. He came, self-referred, requesting deeper analysis and hinting at some great secret which he felt was being repressed. Week after week for several months, he would open the conference with the same request, and then proceed to evade all efforts to pursue his alleged objective. The time was therefore used on other therapeutic aspects of his personality problem. The following session, however, finally bore fruit when I confronted him with his repeated evasions and pointedly ignored his plea for sympathy "I had a bad week . . .") as another attempt to sidetrack me.

He relaxed reluctantly on signal but promptly visualized a suggested blackboard. From then on he was merely encouraged to associate freely. Here are the highlights of his perceptions.

Blackboard—green apple—wisps of clouds—galaxy of milky way space moon (full) alone in space quite yellow—looks like a lemon now. Sort of a staircase—curving oak—going up like in big houses.

Dr. suggests a calendar, and Olaf "reads" 1898, December 10. Dr. then suggests a screen or mirror.

I see a mirror—I see what looks like a witch with conical black hat and golden star on top . . . like my mother—very young, brown hair.

Q. What is she doing?

A. Nothing—just looking—somebody else with vicious eyes.

Dr. Keep watching.

Olaf rubs right eye which now shows a quivering upper lid. The mirror has disappeared.

Three taps are now given as the signal for a new response.

Many things flash by quickly. Large mahogany mirror we used to have at home. It has a black and gold frame—flashes of room—suddenly I am in a hospital—operated for tonsils—I see a nurse coming out of some vaporous steam. I see only the eye—briefly—someone sleeping—the right eye.

Dr. again suggests a blackboard. Olaf visualizes the smudge from erased circle but rejects the suggestion for contrasting flowers (introduction of color).

There are books over it (the hallucinated table)—black binding—desk (is) brown—no bright colors, like an old chemistry book I had. I saw a funny book and (another) book—brown—thick with many pages. Father used (it) for formulas.

There is another pause so Dr. again suggested that he visualize a calendar.

Q. What's the date?

A. January 19 or 14, with the 4 being backward [mirror image].

Q. The year?

A. 1923.

Q. Can you now see the mirror?

A. No (cough) maybe it was just a mistake.

He becomes semi-aroused. I think I'm too conscientious (conscious) of the present.

Dr. makes no comment. Olaf's trance deepens spontaneously and Dr. then suggests a scene in the country, walking.

Olaf. Yes, along a river—flat country—high trees.

Q. Do you see a church?

A. Yes. A cathedral—very large.

Q. And a theater?

A. I saw something which started out like a flower —orchid—conch shell—like female genital organ—very pink flesh. Opera in Stockholm— red plush curtain—someone in white. Sick embroidery. He cues my uncle (father's brother).

Q. What's he doing?

A. Just studying, alone. Haughty expression changes to—I can't see him anymore.

Dr. invites Olaf to change to another theater.

Olaf, now in the second theater:

I see a skull—greenish—before that I saw a scene of operetta Marie San Jeane (story of young woman who goes to a cloistered school. (Olaf clears his throat) —a nun's school. The nun thinks she's a demure young girl, but there is a regiment nearby and she plays in the orchestra and does all sorts of things. It's a fine story. Skull to left, keeping in the air—sort of looking— like Oedipus Rex—blind—his eyes were gouged out.

Q. So he wouldn't see?

A. That's right.

Q. What?

A. See a sort of a big penis painted in like Seurat.

Q. What's the penis doing?

A. Nothing—hanging down in the middle of the air. Head is uncovered plus the patch—scrotum —quite hairy—unreal greyish color except the head is pink or red. It's disappeared.

The time was almost up so I suggested a dream on signal (three taps) that would serve to integrate his hallucination. Olaf consciously rejects the suggestion and shakes his head. Instead, he continues to describe a series of brief, but significant memory flashes:

White and green and grey shifting surfaces, X. Flacher! Big brass bed we had in our house—big sheet curved like a half a tunnel and a man having intercourse with a woman standing on her knees in front of a sofa.

At this point he was silent for fifteen seconds, after which he came out of trance spontaneously.

Ostensibly, he had rejected my suggestion for a hallucinated dream to clarify the various clues. But part of his mind had heard the five-minute warning signal (a very soft gong beneath my desk, connected with a button in the receptionist's office). He had chosen to continue his psychological exploration and did, in fact, finally uncover as much as he needed to remember in order to allay his anxiety.

After the last revelation, which may have been fact or fantasy, or a combination of both, no further reference was ever made to his associations or to his repeated belief that some deep sexual trauma had occurred during his childhood. He never again requested deep hypnosis, discontinued self-deprecations, turned his attention to current business problems, and reported spontaneous improvement in his family and personal life.

RECIPES FOR SUCCESSFUL MARRIAGE

Recipes are like clothes. They work best when tailored to meet the needs of the particular couple. Here are a few general suggestions that can be fitted into any marriage program. Most of them have already been used during courtship; but there is novelty in recalling them to daily practice. Women are generally advised to look like a woman and act like a lady. Men are reminded that women may not always show their appreciation of chivalry, but they usually like it anyway. Strength, firmness and consistency should be tempered with tolerance and kindness. Both partners have a lifelong job; and they should continue to work at it.

Temporary separations, if only for a few hours or a night or a weekend, help to restore privacy and appreciation for each other's company. Short vacations together are even better, because they help both partners to relax.

Private dates, made by prearrangement, should include a whole evening and preferably extend to a whole weekend, at least once a month; away from family, children and friends. It does not have to be expensive. Even a bus ride to a neighboring town, and a sleep-out in sleeping bags and a pup tent offers a change of scenery and a chance to appreciate home all the more.

Remembering anniversaries, especially birthdays, and with no more than a scribbled note, if funds are low, represents an inexpensive substitute for status symbols and gifts that one cannot well afford.

Reciprocal courtesies and the use of clean language is an excellent preventive. So, too, are kind words, an indulgent smile, a turning away of the head when food is spilled or a dent made in the car, and forebearing to remind each other of well-known shortcomings or comparisons with unpopular members of either family.

Overhaul of budget should be a weekly affair, participated in by both partners. Weekly audits are none too frequent. They may save countless thousands of dollars. Good work habits are also part of the time-budget. Too many people squander more time and energy on recreation and amusement of a passive nature, as well as on tobacco and alcohol, instead of activities that can maintain their health, their peace of mind and mutual emotional growth.

Enlarge social circulation. Make several new friends each year. Keep the best of the old ones, but get out of the rut of socializing with the same people week after week. Make sure to return invitations and occasionally extend new ones to the sort of people you would like to associate with.

Keep the nest shipshape. Occasional changes in home furnishings, paint, and arrangements help to avoid monotony. When items are too costly to throw away, try giving them to Goodwill or Salvation Army, a charitable rummage sale, or to someone who will appreciate them, or swapping at a white elephant sale.

When clothes closets need overhaul, and new garments are required, buy for quality as well as style. Most wives will be thrifty and may even do some of their own dressmaking when their husbands are appreciative and do their share of economizing.

Husbands will not have to be told to do necessary repairs when their wives sing their praises in public as well as in private.

Home is for family and friends. It should be well lit, adequately heated, utilitarian and uncluttered; but it is not a place for busybodies, critical relatives, and unappreciative guests, no matter whose best friend or favoriate aunt is involved. This includes the children, too. If they are stuck with sponging playmates, put them to work learning skills and assets that will attract playmates you can approve of.

Authority must be shared and it must be consistent. Parents who permit unruly behavior, habitual indolence and neglect, and hangers-on who will not carry their fair share of the family's obligations and household responsibilities, usually deserve exactly what they get. Discipline must be worked at. It must be fair. When overdone one should be as prompt in correcting his own mistakes as in "straightening out" others.

Acceptance of married partners for what they are, rather than rejection for what they are not sounds simple and is effective. Yet it is precisely what they did when they agreed to marry. This does not mean that no change should be expected nor attempted; but each partner must do his share. Change should be done gradually and together. Acceptance of children and the rest of the families—if possible—is also essential. Mistakes and delays should be allowed for. Emphasis should be on achievements, successes, and the blessings that one has, rather than the comforts and luxuries that one has not.

Success in marriage is like success in life. It depends upon what one does with his natural assets. Despite the gamble with uncertainties of environment, sickness, and other human frailties, one should enter marriage with the firm resolve to make of it a fulfilling career and a grand adventure.

REFERENCES AND READINGS

1. ARDREY, R.: *African Genesis,* New York, Dell, 1961.
2. AMAROSE, A. P.; WALLINGFORD, A. J., and PLOTZ, E. J.: Prediction of fetal sex from cytological examinations of amniotic fluid. *New Eng J Med,* 275:715-717, 1966.
3. BARUCH, D., and MILLER, H.: *Sex in Marriage: New Understandings.* New York, Hoeber, 1965.
4. *How Budgets Work and What They Do.* New York Women's Div. Inst. of Life Ins., 488 Mad. Ave., N.Y. 22, Jan. 1963.
5. CAPRIO, F. S.: *The Art of Sexual Lovemaking: A guide to a Happier Sex-Love Life for Married Couples,* New York, Fairview Book Co., 1967.
6. DALTON, K.: *The Premenstrual Syndrome.* Springfield, Thomas, 1964.
7. DAVIS, KATHARINE B.: *Sex Life of 2,200 American Women.* New York, Harper, 1929.

8. DENGROVE, E.: Behavior therapy of sexual disorders. *J Sex Res,* 3:49-61, 1967.

9. DICKINSON, R. L.: *A Thousand Marriages.* Baltimore, Williams & Wilkins, 1931.

10. DUVAL, E. M.: *Facts of Life and Love for Teen-agers.* New York, Assn Pr., 1956.

11. DUVAL, E. M.: *Why Wait Till Marriage,* New York, Assn. Pr., 1965.

12. ECKERT, R. G.: *So You Think It's Love.* New York, Public Affairs Pamphlets, No. 161, 1967.

13. ELLIS, H.: Sex in relation to society. *History of Marriage. Studies on the Psychology of Sex.* New York, Modern Lib., 1936, Vol. IV.

14. FULLER, D. E., and BOENKER, D. E.: Gastric ulcers in swine. *JAMA,* 204:168-170, 1968.

15. GRAVES, E., and NILSSON, L.: Woman en route to a miracle. *Life Mag,* 61:48-62, July 22, 1966.

16. GRAY, MADELINE: *The Normal Woman.* New York, Scribner, 1967.

17. GOLDSTEIN, A. S.: The magnetic attraction of mixed mating. *J Centr Conf of Amer Rabbis,* April 1964, pp. 14-35.

18. GREENBLATT, B. R.: *A Doctor's Marital Guide for Patients.* Chicago, Budlong, 1967.

19. HELPER, R. E., and KEMPE, C. H.: *The Battered Child.* Chicago, U. of Chicago, 1968. (Reported in *Newsweek,* June 3, 1968, p. 68).

20. JACOBS, R. I.: *Hypnosis in the Treatment of Sexual Problems.* Paris, Congress Intl. D'Hypnosis et Med. Psychosomatique, April 28-30, 1965.

21. KELLEY, G. L.: *Sex Manual* (marriage counselors' edition). Fishbein, M., and Kennedy, R. I. R. (Eds.), New York, Oxford U. P., 1959.

22. KEYSERLING, H. (Ed.): *The Book of Marriage.* New York, Harcourt, 1926.

23. KINSEY, A. C.; POMEROY, W. B.; MARTIN, C. E., and GEBHARD, P. H.: *Sexual Behaviour in the Human Female.* Philadelphia and London, Saunders, 1953.

24. KINSEY, A. C.; POMEROY, W. B., and MARTIN, C. E.: *Sexual Behaviour in the Human Male.* Philadelphia and London, Saunders, 1948.

25. KUBIE, L. S.: Dr. Kinsey and the medical profession. *Psychosom Med,* XIII:172-184, 1955.

26. KUBIE, L. S.: Psychiatric implications of the Kinsey report. *Psychosom Med,* X:95, 1948.

27. LEVENSON, S.: *Everything But Money.* New York, S. and S., 1966.

28. LEVIN, M.: The physician and the sexual revolution. *New Eng J Med,* 273:1366-69, 1965.

29. LEWIN, S. A., and GILMORE, J.: *Sex Without Fear.* New York, Med. Research Press, 1966.

30. MACE, D. R.: *What Makes A Marriage Happy?* New York, Public Affairs Pamphlet No. 290, 1967.

31. MALINOWSKI, B.: *Crime and Custom in Savage Society.* London, Kegan Paul, 1926.
32. MASSERMAN, J. H. (Ed.): *Current Psychiatric Therapies.* New York and London, Grune, 1966, vol. 6.
33. MASSERMAN, J. H. (Ed.): *Current Psychiatric Therapies.* New York and London, Grune, 1967, vol. 7.
34. MASTERS, W., and JOHNSON, V.: *Human Sexual Response.* Boston, Little, 1966.
35. MEAD, M.: *Coming of Age in Samoa.* New York, New Am. Lib., 1949.
36. MEAD, M.: *Male and Female.* New York, Mentor, 1955.
37. MENNINGER, K. A.: *Love Against Hate.* New York, Harcourt, 1942.
38. MISHLER, K.: Family therapy in the home. *Psychiat Rep 13*:10-12, March-April 1964.
39. MORRIS, D.: *The Naked Ape.* New York, McGraw, 1967.
40. MOSS, R. H.: Psychological aspects of oral contraceptives. *Arch Gen Psychiat, 19*:87-94, 1968.
41. NASH, E. M.; JESSNER, L., and ABSE, D. W. (Ed.): *Marriage Counseling in Medical Practice.* Chapel Hill, U. of N.C., 1965.
42. NILSSON, L.: Drama of life before birth. *Life Mag,* April 30, 1965.
43. PATERSON, A. M.: *Manual of Embryology.* London, Oxford U. P., 1915, pp. 328-329.
44. RAY, M. B.: *Doctors of the Mind.* Boston, Little, 1946.
45. RICHARDSON, G. S.: Ovarian physiology. *New Eng J Med, 274*:1183-1194, 1966.
46. ROBITSCHER, J. B.: Marriage, divorce and mental disability from "pursuit of agreement". In *Psychiatry and the Law.* Philadelphia, Lippincott, 1966. (Abstr. in *Med Sci,* June 1966, pp. 37-42.
47. ROSENBERG, A. J., and SILVER, E.: Suicide, psychiatrists and therapeutic abortions. *Calif Med, 102*:407-411, 1935.
48. SACHAR, E. J., *et al.*: Psychoendocrine responses. *Roche Clinical Frontiers, 3*:6, July 15, 1966.
49. SANGER, M.: *Happiness in Marriage.* New York, Blue Ribbon, 1931.
50. SOUTHERN, A. L.: Intrauterine devices. *J Clin Obstet Gynec, VII*:814, 1964.
51. STEARNS, A. W.: Does failure run in families? (A study of 1000 unsuccessful careers). *Amer J Psychiat, 105*:801, 1951.
52. STEIN, C.: *Practical Psychotherapeutic Techniques.* Springfield, Thomas, 1968.
53. STEIN, C.: *Practical Psychotherapy in Nonpsychiatric Specialties.* Springfield, Thomas, 1969.
54. *Today's Health Guide.* (Multiple authors), Chicago, Amer. Med. Assoc., 1966.
55. TAYLOR, A.: *Love Is A Four Letter Word.* New York, Beechurst, 1948.
56. VAN DE VELDE, T. H.: *Ideal Marriage, Its Physiology and Techniques.* Browne, S. (trans.), New York, Covici-Friede, 1930.

57. WESTERMARCK, E. A.: *History of Marriage.* New York, Macmillan, 1930.
58. WESTERMARCK, E. A.: *Future of Marriage in Western Civilization,* New York, Macmillan, 1936.
59. WILLIAMS, W. W.: *Sterility—The Diagnostic Survey of the Infertile Couple Including Therapy,* 3rd ed., Springfield, Williams, Walter, 1964.
60. WOLLMAN, L.: The role of hypnosis in the treatment of infertility. *Brit J Med Hypn, 11*:3-11, 1960.

INDEX